D1125579

The Prevalence of Nonsense

The Prevalence of
NONSENSE

Ashley Montagu
and
Edward Darling

A DELTA BOOK

A DELTA BOOK

Published by DELL PUBLISHING CO., INC.
750 Third Avenue, New York, N.Y. 10017

Delta ® TM 755118, Dell Publishing Co., Inc.
Reprinted by arrangement with Harper & Row,
Publishers, Incorporated, New York
Manufactured in the United States of America

Third Printing

To the memory of
ROSE AND BEN COWAN

Contents

Foreword

Permanent possession of the gold-encrusted blue ribbon for arrant nonsense is conferred, of course, upon the belief that truth is unchanging and that what this book presents as fact will never be regarded as nonsense in its own right.

During the past three centuries something like six million scientific articles have been published. Today such scientific reports are being produced at the rate of half a million a year, while the number of scientists and articles have been doubling every fifteen years. Each year some 60,000 scientific and technological journals are published. Facts are accumulating so swiftly and furiously that nobody can keep abreast of them all, and it would be silly to try.

It used to be that a charging bull thundering in at full speed to annihilate the matador would complete his charge before he turned around and came back. In all the history of bullfighting there had been no case showing the contrary action until Dr. José M. R. Delgado of Yale University School of Medicine stood swordless, waving a heavy red cape, before such an animal in full charge and pressed a button on a small radio transmitter in his hand as the bull came within a few feet of him. Observers held their breath to see the bull stop short, braking to a halt with all four feet a yard or two from the scientist. Dr. Delgado pressed another button, and the bull "obediently turned to the right and trotted away." The event was photographed in brilliant detail and reported to the *New York Times*, May 17, 1965, by John A. Osmundsen, who explained that the trick was this: "The bull was obeying commands from his brain that were called forth by electrical stimulation—by the radio signals—of certain regions in which fine wire electrodes had been painlessly implanted the day before." Dr. Delgado's experiments on the biological basis for emotional behavior had shown that such functions as friendliness and animosity can be modified or inhibited by electrical stimulation of the appropriate part of the brain. The morning's demonstration was the most spectacular proof of the effectiveness of the theory, and the doctor wagered his life on its success; he thought it was worth it to shock people into a realization that human behavior may in turn be modified for intelligent control of the megatons of destructive power now at man's disposal. . . . There is a great deal more to the story, but those are the salient facts and they illustrate how truth can change. We make no apologies for the truths which shed light on nonsense in the pages of this book: they were true when they were reported. But if some bright observant mind discovers one which has since become outdated, please don't write to your congressman: write to the authors—they'll be grateful for the correction. Especially if you can document it.

Above all, this book is not written in the expectation that a simple statement of fact demonstrating that a particular belief is a piece of nonsense will discourage people from continuing to cherish such a belief; for the simple fact is that facts do not speak for themselves—facts, like Scripture, are at the mercy of any clever manipulator. Hence, when confronted by a challenge to one's beliefs, the proper response is not a readiness to believe or disbelieve, but action designed to verify the facts for oneself. All of human history illuminates the experience that men are much more ready to die for the preservation of the myths they believe in than for the support of truths that demonstrate those myths to be chimerical.

Even among the literate and learned an act which has become habitual is not easily changed by a simple statement of fact. In Milwaukee, in January, 1966, a *lighted* sign—not just any old sign like FRESH PAINT or something equally unimpressive—was attached to the top of a disabled elevator in the county courthouse. The sign screamed NOT IN SERVICE. And it was lighted. Yet within just a few hours, workmen were called from their job of repair work to free passengers who were trapped in the elevator. Among them were a county judge, the court chaplain, a bailiff with two prisoners, a bondsman, and three women clerks. They had been concentrating on their own special problems; they had always taken this elevator; they took it now. Why bother about signs?

So this volume does not expect the reader to stop believing in whatever absurdity has become habitual with him, however impressive the signs. But it does hope that it will perhaps shake him enough to raise doubts in his own mind about some of his most cherished confusions.

The alleged wisdom of the folk is so packed with erroneous ideas that it is difficult to understand how some of us have survived from cave to forest to farm to factory. This granulated sagacity offers in sugar-tit form misconceptions which run the diapason between what it is darkly suggested will invite bad luck, or will lubricate the ways for the launching of good fortune, to misinformation about the world around us and its inhabitants, vegetable, animal, and mineral. Almost all of it is fallible.

Which makes it something of a miracle, when one stops to think about it, that the average man actually succeeds—most of the time— in getting safely out of bed in the morning, getting safely washed and shaved, and traveling unscathed from home to office, where he moves pieces of paper from one place to another, attends meetings, answers telephones, and thus handles what is laughingly referred to as a day's work, and then makes the return trip to bed without showing so much as a wound on his person.

He has faced and escaped so many perils, unarmed as he is, in the course of this diurnal pilgrimage that the miraculous nature of his adventure begins to assume a faintly incredible aspect—except that we see it happen and must therefore believe it. But the greatest danger he has faced all this time is the hazard contained in his own misconceptions.

For instance, if the reader swept over the phrase, "the average man," employed a few lines earlier, without visibly wincing or knitting the brows, we have all the evidence required to prove how readily we accept the popular errors to which we are heirs: for there *is* no such creature as the average man. The phrase is meaningless. It is as empty as "the typical American." It is a lazy man's cliché by which the speaker makes a weak attempt—not a thoughtful attempt, but a feeble one—to refer to a basic type that does not in fact exist. The trouble is that this man picked at random is presupposed to exhibit certain qualities shared by most of the citizens around him: in our own use of the "average man" a moment ago we assumed that he arises every morning, washes, shaves, travels to an office, and so forth. Lots of people do. But lots of people don't. Consider the three and a half billion-odd inhabitants of this globe and ask yourself how you are going to add them all up and divide by the proper number to come out with an "average" on *anything*—length of fingernails, preference for peanuts over Brazil nuts, ability to hold his breath—obviously we have no idea what the average man is. Perhaps when you use the phrase you mean somebody much like yourself, only not quite so bright. Maybe that's what we meant, too. Instead, we used the meaningless term.

Thus it is with *Homo sapiens*—another misnomer if there ever was one. This potentially brilliant creature will accept some old wives' tale—such as the proverbial saying that the man who works hardest gets the greatest rewards—and will go off actually believing it. You can tell him anything—as the television commercials illustrate from dawn to dusk and far into the helpless night; and if he doesn't actually believe what he is told, he'll act as if he did. Such and such a remedy will cure postnasal drip, whip a cold in jig time, and have you dancing like a jackanapes by midnight. You try it, and it does nothing at all. Absolutely nothing at all. You have to carry a box of blowing tissues wherever you go and your cold gets worse. So what happens the next time you have a cold and dripping nose? Clearly you invest in another package of the same remedy, because you keep hearing all the time that it will make you well. And if you say you don't act this way at all, we merely point out that your cousin does if you don't. The generalization stands.

Despite the fact that man is an animal who can read and write and keep historical records, we continue to pass along from father to son the most incredible misconceptions and build them into the folklore to the point where they become gospel. To take only one example:

Is it not general knowledge that ours is an age of the dirty novel, the sex-ridden movie, and of obscene literature in general? Is it not true that when we were boys things were different? Surely this much is self-evident. You'll hear it said at any serious cocktail party.

The fact is that the first American novel was a story of illicit love, incest, and suicide (*The Power of Sympathy* by William Hill Brown, published in Boston, 1789).

The purpose of the present book is to expose to public view some of the most outrageous nonsense of our day—but we do so without entertaining the alluring whimsy that to expose it will end it. In a way it would be almost a shame to do that, because some of it is pretty droll.

The Prevalence of Nonsense

I believe that our Heavenly Father invented man because he was disappointed in the monkey. I believe that whenever a human being, of even the highest intelligence and culture, delivers an opinion upon a matter apart from his particular and especial line of interest, training and experience, it will always be an opinion of so foolish and so valueless a sort that it can be depended upon to suggest to our Heavenly Father that the human being is another disappointment and that he is no considerable improvement upon the monkey.

—From *The Autobiography of Mark Twain*

I

❦

Humans and Human Customs

Everybody seems to have his own favorite mark of the difference between mankind and our cousins of the meadows, forests, waters, and skies: man is an animal that laughs; man is an animal that uses tools; man is a creature who manipulates symbols; man is conscious clay. We leave it to the reader to make his own selection; but it would be entirely true and appropriate to say that man is the only animal who makes organized war on his own species.

Indeed, one cannot produce a single instance from the animal kingdom to show that within any species a form of behavior resembling organized war is found, waged by group against group within the species. And this includes the ants. So many stout virtues are associated with the ants that it seems almost a gratuitous insult even to *wonder* about them. Un-American, it seems, in a dirty sort of way. However, the critical mind sees that ants[1] do not line up, count off, shoulder arms, or in any way visible to the human eye "conduct" organized warfare.

War, indeed, is the most unnatural, the most artificial, of all *human* activities, for it originates in artificial causes, is waged by artificial entities (states), is fought from artificial motives, with artificial weapons, for artificial ends.

Yet there have been important spokesmen, some of them princes of the Christian Church and others, speaking from their own point of

1

2   THE PREVALENCE OF NONSENSE

view in the name of science, who have held that warfare can be morally justified under certain circumstances, or that war is natural and helps keep the population in check and aids the process of natural selection and the survival of the fittest.

Some of these spokesmen will point to "savage" tribes and ask us to notice that these are almost constantly at war with one another. They should look at the tribes themselves, for the sober fact is that they are not persistently warlike. Havelock Ellis put it very well, in the light of what has been discovered by anthropologists since 1919, when he wrote:

Savages are on the whole not warlike, although they often try to make out that they are terribly bloodthirsty fellows; it is only with difficulty that they work themselves up to fighting pitch and even then all sorts of religious beliefs and magical practices restrain warfare and limit its effects. Even among the fiercest peoples of East Africa the bloodshed is usually small.

Speke mentions a war that lasted three years: the total losses were three men on each side. In all parts of the world there are people who rarely or never fight; and if, indeed, the old notion that primitive people are in chronic warfare of the most ferocious character were really correct, humanity could not have survived. Primitive man's struggle was not against enemies of any kind; it was a struggle to survive; and it rendered cooperation more necessary than ever.[2]

The Very Rev. Francis J. Connell, on "When May a Nation Go to War?", a nationwide broadcast on the Catholic Hour, September 12, 1954, said:

There can be occasions when even a war of conquest will be justifiable, a war waged for the purpose of acquiring more territory. The case would be this: A nation has increased in population to such an extent that there is not sufficient land to provide a decent livelihood for the citizens, so that they are reduced to the direst poverty and starvation. In such circumstances the first duty of the government is to attempt to remedy the situation by peaceful measures, such as purchasing more territory from another nation, or sending some of the people abroad as emigrants who will become loyal and dutiful citizens of the land of their adoption. But it may happen that no other country will sell land, or admit the people of this overcrowded nation into their borders. In that event, when the situation has grown desperate, the nation that is put in this situation of extreme need may lawfully go to war in order to seize a portion of territory that is not needed by another country.[3]

But the War-Is-Natural School dies hard, and we find learned gentlemen pointing out—perhaps less frequently today than previously—that mankind is biologically impelled to make war and indeed that war is, as Sir Arthur Keith put it, "Nature's pruning hook" to keep her orchard healthy.[4] There might be some faint trace of a parallel if the farmer pruned out the best trees and left the diseased ones to produce seed for the new crop—which is what war does: the most physically and mentally fit get into uniform, and the less healthy physically and mentally carry on at home. A much better case for the pruning hook metaphor could have been made in the days when wars were fought hand to hand, as in the days when Sir Arthur's Lowland ancestors fought the Highland foe; but the concept certainly descends into the category of folly under modern conditions of total war. Natural selection certainly cannot be involved when a stray shell lobbed from miles away happens to kill someone.

We have made the point that man may be differentiated from other animals in that he makes war on his own species; and we hope we have also made the point that to do so is not "Natural," it is not nature's way, it is something man invented as human society grew more complex. Nevertheless, we use this example of prevailing nonsensical belief to lead all the rest because it is the most destructive form of nonsense in which our species indulges.

Dominion Is as Dominion Does

It is perhaps nothing to wonder at that the idea of man as the master of everything on earth is a notion that has become widely popular—at least among the human species. We have Scripture to support it: God said to Adam and Eve, "Be fruitful, and multiply, and replenish the earth, and subdue it; and have dominion over the fish of the sea, and over the fowl of the air, and over every living thing that moveth upon the earth" (Gen. 1:28). As far as the record goes, there was no admonition about using a certain amount of care and judgment in applying this sovereignty; possibly it was assumed. In any event, man has been ruthless in subjecting all nature to his wishes, and the myth that he can do so and get away with it forever is just beginning to be questioned. The greed of certain individuals meanwhile has rendered some species extinct—such as the carrier pigeons which used to darken the skies as they passed in infinite numbers. The bison, which blackened the plains, would be extinct if he had not at the last moment been protected by law; and the whooping crane is all but gone. In great danger, according to conservationists, are the orangutan of Borneo and Sumatra, the fallow deer of Persia, the Mexican ridley turtle, the aye-aye, Madagascar's rarest lemur, and others. The Survival Service Commission of the Union for Conservation of Nature, meeting at Lucerne in midsummer of 1966, was told that there are nearly 800 animals around the world in danger of extinction: 277 kinds of mammals and 521 birds.

Man has the dominion, all right. That much is no myth.

But every coin has two sides, and we are happy to report that occasionally there is news that a creature which was believed to have been extinct survives after all. The coelacanth fish, long thought to be extinct, was caught in a fisherman's net in South Africa in 1938; and on July 22, 1966, *Life* magazine had two color pages on the same species showing photographs taken by the French photographer Jacques Stevens 130 feet below the surface of the Indian Ocean off the Comoro Islands. The *Life* piece was entitled, "After 60 million years: Portrait of a Living Fossil," and accompanying the text was a 1½-page-size portrait of a very fishlike fish with blue phosphorescent eyes and a ragged tooth formation, looking like something picked up on Skid Row: tattered but ready for more. Our hero was four feet long and described as the "oldest known living vertebrate." It was the first of the species ever to be photographed alive.

Then there was the Burramys possum, a pigmy type, which was found alive in the University Ski Club hut on Mt. Hotham in the Victorian Alps, Australia, by Dr. K. D. Shortman, a biochemist, and D. Jamieson an associate. Heretofore it was believed that this possum was extinct; the creature was known only from fossil remains of skull and jawbones found in the Wombeyan Caves of New South Wales and in Buchan Caves of Victoria. They dated from the Pleistocene period, about a million years ago.

Dr. Shortman found the little fellow remarkably friendly and addicted, once introduced to them, to cheese and apples. He was ten inches long, from his nose to his rear, including six inches of tail.

Sophisticated Man Is Not Superstitious?

Those who speak of the various "ages" of man, such as the Age of Belief, the Age of Discovery, the Age of Reason, the Atomic Age, and so forth, may be responsible for the nonsensical belief, widely held today, that mankind has become sophisticated, that we are less superstitious than the species used to be, less susceptible to hoaxes and irrational fears; that our minds, in short, are far from the primitive.

Perhaps the matter can never be fully resolved, since a scientific poll cannot be taken of the human being of other ages to learn just how superstitious he was. Certainly some of his superstitions have been exploded by modern science, and certainly there are hundreds of thousands of people today, able to read, who can be aware of such exposés. But we accept new superstitions as we discard old ones; intellectual development does not necessarily reform our mental behavior and habits even when we know better. A scientist may develop a most complicated computer, and still toss some salt over his left shoulder if he spills it at the table, or walk around a black cat, or refuse the third light on a match, or whatever it is he harbors in the way of superstitious hangover. For, no matter how far advanced our intellectual development, we still have no control over the autonomic nervous system: we cannot prevent the hair from "standing on end" when we are suddenly frightened in the dark.

So, while we have every right to point out the nonsense which man accepts, and indeed by which he directs his life, we would do well to temper our merriment with the realization that at bottom our own thinking is just as solidly based upon the primitive mentality as was that of the serf, the ancient Roman, or the tribesman in awe of the Umbundu chant. As the French philosopher Lévy-Bruhl put it: "Dans tout esprit humain, quel qu'en soît le développement intellectuel, subsiste un fond indéracinable de mentalité primitive." (In all human kind, whatever its intellectual attainments, an ineradicable basis exists of primitive mentality.) And Nilsson said: "Primitive mentality is a fairly good description of the mental behavior of most people today except in their technical or consciously intellectual activities."[5]

Is Man More Than an Animal?

Something in the rooted prejudices of the folk objects to hearing that human beings are really animals. The negation covers the diapason from complete rejection of the idea to tentative acceptance—with reservations: man is the only animal who weeps; man is the only animal able to laugh; man is the only animal who can think; he is the only one with consciousness of self; the only one who worships; the only one who uses tools; and of course, in Mark Twain's famous comment, "Man is the only animal who blushes—or needs to."

Perhaps one could say that man is the only animal who can leave a written record, who develops language capable of abstractions, who uses fire, who makes gods and devils. We have pointed out that *civilized* man is the only animal who wages organized war on his own species. Not that other animals do not kill to eat and to defend themselves or their young. But, as Konrad Lorenz urges in his volume *On Aggression*, once the need for food or for defense is satisfied, an animal has no interest in killing; and therefore in the course of evolution, killing for any other purpose is the exception rather than the rule. This author holds that it is the very fact that modern nations *are* civilized that makes them wage organized war on each other. Where the other animals have a sort of automatic control that prevents unnecessary killing, humankind in the course of becoming groups and states (civilized) lost that control. No animals in the world would have planned and committed the famous massacre of the Macdonalds at Glencoe near Loch Leven which the Campbells carried out on the morning of February 13, 1692 ("The Campbells are comin', yo-ho, yo-ho . . ."). Perhaps it is in recognition of mankind's social, not biological, development as a war-waging animal that such scientists as Dr. Hermann J. Muller, winner of the Nobel Prize for his work in genetics, have urged the development of sperm banks to help in artificial insemination in a program which he calls "genetic surgery" for the development of human attributes of intelligence and cooperation through alteration of the heredity-controlling genes.[6] He appears to feel that if these measures are undertaken soon enough they may prevent us from becoming so civilized that we wipe out all life on this planet.

The Swami and the Sacred Cow

The superstitions and ritual observances of others become increasingly ludicrous to us in direct proportion to the distance between ourselves and the ritualists; thus we note with only passing amusement the alarm of the hostess in the neighborhood who is distraught at setting thirteen places at table; but that a twentieth-century civilized modern city like New Delhi should permit traffic to be brought to a halt by wandering cows, which must not be disturbed because they are sacred animals, brings forth guffaws. The situation is incredible.

Oh, no, you say; the sacred cow bit applied only to the old days before the enlightenment of rapid transit and modern plumbing. Yet recently Swami Rameshwaranand, saffron-robed Hindu priest of the right-wing Jan Sangh party, blocked all legislative business in the lower house of Parliament for over an hour while an estimated five thousand demonstrators outside chanted a demand for an official ban, a political, governmental ban, on the slaughter of cows. "Glory to mother cow," shouted the swami, "and destruction to the government that kills the cow." To the legislators, the feeding of millions of useless cows, at a time when the lives of millions of human beings are threatened with death from starvation, had seemed hardly the modern approach to the problem; but when a point of view is seen as a religious dogma, it suddenly becomes an irrationality with a deadly serious aspect.

HUMAN LIFE IS SACRED?

Here it is necessary to tread with the utmost wariness and retain the nicest control of language, because we have made use of "is" as a predication, employing it to connect a noun and an adjective; and when we do this "we invariably express a false-to-fact relationship,"[7] as the experts in semantics delight to point out. But before we gather on this tightrope it is essential to understand what we intend by *sacred,* although of course every reader of these words already believes he knows what the word means. It has associations through the Latin *sacer* with words like sacrament, sacristy, and sacrifice and all the way to desecrate, execrable, and sanctimonious. In fact, in its French form, *sacré,* it has the double meaning of holy and accursed—since "that which violates the sacred is accursed."[8]

Actually, *sacred* is the past participle of *sacre,* to consecrate, and in the sense of "something secured against violation by religious sentiment" has been traced to 1530; it has continued to mean "set apart" or hallowed as being especially dear to a deity or as something entitled to the reverence reserved for holy things.

So when we say "human life is sacred" we mean it is holy, hallowed, to be secured against violation, consecrated.

Yet, as Korzybski would be the first to point out, our statement is contrary to fact in that the quality of being sacred is not discoverable in the objective reality called "human life," any more than greenness is in the leaf when we say "the leaf is green" or blue is in the eyes when we say "the eyes are blue." Rays from some light source impinge upon the leaf; some are absorbed and are picked up by the retina to produce an inside-the-person sensation which we have been taught to call green. We all know that. The "green" is a projection from us to the leaf; and the *sacred* is a projection from us into the *human life*. We could descend from the tightrope by exchanging "is" for "appears to be" or "should be." But we should remember that "the events outside our skin are neither cold nor warm . . . but these characteristics are manufactured by our nervous systems."

Now: the nonsense about "human life is sacred" is that, while we all stand staunchly with church, school, and Rotary in repeating the *words* and perhaps even believing that we mean them, our species throughout its history has not produced the fruit by which we shall know the words to have anything more than ritualistic significance.

The slogan is of very recent origin anyhow. Throughout the centuries the Church that considered the human *soul* vastly important had no concern for the human body. It is only in the slow evolution toward greater social responsibility that the literate and educated among mankind have even gone so far as to adopt the *verbal* shibboleth. The ethical teachings of the Bible may have attempted to convince us that we are our brother's keeper and should be "neighbors" to each other; the ethical teachings of all the great religions have done the same thing, and the Golden Rule appears as a basic idea in religions around the world. But when we covet, even our most illustrious leaders see to it that Uriah the Hittite leads the van in battle so that David may appropriate the voluptuous Bathsheba.

In fact, the ideas of social Darwinism as expressed by Herbert Spencer's phrase, "the survival of the fittest,"[10] which strongly supported laissez-faire capitalism, were supposed to be an expression of nature's way of improving the race: the weak must die out, "and it is best they should die," as Spencer saw it. Human life, in short, was not only *not* sacred; it was perpetually on trial and if found wanting must perish; and the state ought not to do a single thing to prevent such a "natural" outcome, not in terms of free public education, housing, sanitation, or any other social action. Social Darwinism was in vogue well into the twentieth century, and still finds scores of well-heeled adherents. It was not, perhaps, until the market crash of 1929 and then the disastrous collapse of the New Deal in the Recession of 1937-38 that there was a concerted revolt against social Darwinism. In 1939 Harry Hopkins said: "This country cannot continue as a democracy with ten or twelve million people unemployed. It just can't be done. We have got to find a way of living in America in which every person in it shares in the national income in such a way that poverty in America is abolished."[11]

It was not that mankind had not been *exhorted* to treat the neighbors with love, from the earliest thinkers to the present; but perhaps it was that there was little or no biological necessity to do so until recently. And so, instead of acting as if human life were sacred, men treated human life as if it were the most easily expendable of goods, something that could be irresponsibly proliferated at will and as irresponsibly discarded. In cold-blooded genocide, in needless wars, in massacres motivated by religion, in executions by the state, in sacrifices to the gods—and in plain thuggery for the loot's sake—men have been ripping each other's throats. The historic process continues. And "history is little else," said Voltaire, "than a picture of human crime and misfortunes."[12]

We do not intend to give the impression that social man has revolted against the bloodshed and now is beginning to act as if human life *were* sacred—although there is evidence that some progress is being made in that direction[13] and much more is *said* publicly about equal rights and the sanctity of the individual person and freedom from want and the Peace Corps and the war on poverty and international economic assistance: the idea is perhaps rising to the top more often than in previous ages. Meanwhile we are able to laugh at ourselves a little about our pretensions, as in Thomas R. Ybarra's justly famous quatrain about a Christian:

> A Christian is a man who feels
> Repentance on a Sunday
> For what he did on Saturday
> And is going to do on Monday.[14]

Yet we must face another symptom of our times—the disengagement, the alienation, the indifference to the welfare of our fellows which was so incredibly exemplified in New York when Miss Kitty

Genovese was repeatedly attacked in full view of neighbors watching from apartment windows, and finally murdered, while not one hand went to a telephone to call for aid. Human life did not appear to be very sacred that night. . . .

Even so, it is impossible to follow the news closely for very long without a growing realization that the creature we laughingly refer to as "civilized man" is beginning to adopt the ideal that human life *is*, or *should* be, sacred. We can hope that a day will come when there will not be so much nonsense surrounding the statement. But a new threat to that ideal has been pointed out by scientists increasingly in the past few decades: overpopulation.

What will become of the ideal of the sanctity of human life when every new birth is a tragedy? At the very time when Thomas Robert Malthus was composing his first draft of the *Essay on the Principle of Population*, a song was current in England about "a little old woman, and she liv'd in a shoe,/She had so many children, she didn't know what to do." In the early versions of this cheerful rhyme the old woman "knocked 'em all o' the head" and killed them.[15] In later versions she returns with a coffin and finds them all laughing; but that was not the first thrust of the verse.

What was apparent to Malthus in 1798—that the population tends to increase geometrically while the food supply increases arithmetically, and that hence misery and poverty have been and will be the lot of man—stirred very few echoes in the New World, where the bounty of nature was utterly unlimited and more hands were badly needed. But with medicine's growing ability to make birth safe and to fight disease and thus make life last longer, the population explosion suddenly becomes a paramount issue throughout the world.

The irresponsible, feckless proliferation of human beings, usually the products of those least able to discharge their obligations to the children they have heedlessly brought into the world, represents the most devastating human destruction on our planet. Large numbers of these offspring are doomed to die of deficiencies, disease, and famine. So it has really happened: the world is now overpopulated.

In 1967 there were 3.5 billion humans on earth. By the year 2000 it is estimated that there will be 7.4 billion—more than double the 1967 figure. Within 33 years!

The world food supply has been increasing at an average rate of 1 percent per year; and world population by 1.8 percent. With each hungry mouth requiring 1,900 to 2,000 calories per day (in the view of medical and nutrition specialists, starvation begins for everyone at 1,350 calories per day), the necessary food supply in 1965 was about 7 trillion calories daily; and at the rate of population and food increase mentioned, by A.D. 2000 the total world consumption would be 9,916 billion calories—or 1,340 calories per day per person: starvation. Now of course there is not going to be any "average" consumption of 1,340 calories—some people are going to have a great deal more and some are going to have a great deal less and are going to perish from undernourishment. The Agriculture Organization of the United Nations reported in January, 1967, that in the year just past, between 1 and 1.5 billion persons were suffering "from varying degrees of malnutrition, from chronic hunger to starvation." Could any facts indicate more grimly even to the most disengaged and alienated that, if the present figures for population and food are projected into the actuality of life thirty years hence on this planet, it is inevitable that millions will perish in the slow death of starvation? The Fourth Horseman, one recalls, he on the pale horse, was given power over "the fourth part of the earth, to kill . . . with hunger" (Rev. 6:8).

Surely there is no nonsense more bitter than to have a chorus in the wings chanting a litany of the holiness of human life while on stage at front center 25 percent of the babies die before they reach six months of age, as in villages of Egypt—where the birth rate is a frenzied 4 percent per year. Even at the rate of 2.8 percent per year, as in Latin America, the population more than doubles every twenty years. This is "God's will"—that children be produced mercilessly to starve to death? This is reverence for life? It is, in the most literal sense of our word, nonsense. Especially when a nation like Japan can prove that by legalizing birth control and abortion the population can be restrained to stay within livable limitations.

Nor should Americans feel too smug when today, in this affluent society, more than 12 million children live in degrading and grinding poverty.

Human life *is* sacred. It's an ideal worth fighting for.

Man the Tool Worshiper?

Man the maker of tools can create electronic apparatus so accurate that their creator begins to believe they are superior to himself and worthy of what amounts to worship. He begins to credit the machine with infallibility.

In the sense of deliberately prevaricating for the purpose of deceiving, probably nobody in his right mind would accuse a computer of telling a lie. The machine is not going to go into a sulking fit if the operator forgets to kiss it good night, and then revenge itself upon its human master by fabricating incorrect answers the next day. And yet the computer can make mistakes—some of them built into the mechanism by human agencies in the first place. Take the case of Denmark's oldest citizen, Mrs. Sofie Madsen, veteran of 104 Danish winters. She received an order to prepare to start going to school at the next term, along with the rest of the kids. The error was made because the automatic punch-card machine that issued the list can count no further than 99 and therefore had no alternative to indicating Mrs. Madsen's age as 4.

That automated machinery can be in error is really a great comfort in an age when, as some wit remarked, the computer is beginning to usurp the position as man's final arbiter formerly occupied by the dog. The computers can make more mistakes in a single morning than a whole kennel of dogs could straighten out in a year. Consider the case of the state government at Salem, Oregon, where electronic devices were installed to keep up with the mountainous paper work that kept increasing. Officials responsible for the installations—and the bills that accompanied them—reassured the voters by promising the elimination of hundreds of jobs formerly done, to the accompaniment of human error, by human hand. And, lo, the people listened to the voices of their rulers and awaited the miracles.

Then in January, 1965, a man who has never owned a boat and never had any intention of buying one received a renewal blank for his boat license. Boat license? He'd never *had* a boat license. Why should he renew it? He wrote an indignant letter.

A routine check was begun which unveiled a technological disaster. A computer suffering from what, in a human, might have been indigestion, had run amuck, mixing up names, addresses, license fees—all in one beautiful omelet. Finally, in a mad and hopeless gesture, the machine wiped clean whole reels of tapes carrying the agency's records. One can almost hear the computer saying, "Oh, the hell with it."

The director of the Marine Board, Robert Rittenhouse, who had to face the newspaper reporters, explained that it would take weeks of examining the old-fashioned paper files to rebuild the records for the machines.

It then became the turn of the Department of Education and the Public Utility Commission. In something like a blizzard, the computer spewed forth checks carrying incorrect withholdings and inaccurate retirement amounts.

Then came a special session of the legislature to draw up new boundaries for Congressional districts. The secretary of state, Tom McCall, decided to get an analysis of the various plans—and of course he turned to the computers. Results were actually being printed when an accountant—a human one—chanced by and glanced at one of the sheets being piled up by the press. He cheerfully pointed out that the figures did not add up correctly. Members of the data processing staff, aghast at this new development, checked with manually operated adding machines and found that the accountant—the human one—was absolutely right. This called for a reprograming of the computers. The statistics began to roll again. But after a few days it was noticed by some bright-eyed human observer that the district populations had been shifted. The legislature finally went ahead on its own, leaving brokenhearted computers sobbing in their grease.

This brings us up to July. We started in January, if you recall. In July the Department of Motor Vehicles ran off license renewals—you'd think they'd *learn;* but perhaps they don't talk to the Marine Board people—for about 68,000 passenger cars and 3,500 house trailers. The department mailed them out. Then they began getting calls: and you can believe it or not, but the computers had substituted June or January as the renewal date instead of July. But motor vehicle officials are hard to baffle. They simply announced that everyone who got a notice in July should renew in July, no matter what the slip said.

The computer may become the boss someday, as the prophets of disaster are so happily foreseeing; but it won't happen before we have one or two laughs at the expense of the electronic geniuses.

It is not that we believe automation is not here to stay. It certainly is. And the machines are so wonderful and can perform such miracles that we are in some danger of imputing to them omnipotence and infallibility. It is this popular error against which we inveigh—not against electronic devices as such. Errors on the part of the computers are reported frequently enough so that we can refresh ourselves with a draught of caution, however.

There was the delightful case of Mrs. Evelyn Brokenshire of Cardiff, for instance. She got a bill from the Wales Gas Board for $974 when it should have been $11.20. When she complained, the case was investigated and Mr. T. Marvin Jones, Chairman of the Board, went over to her home to apologize in person. As United Press International reported it: "Mr. Jones explained that the mistake was made by the new $420,000 computer installed to save time and manpower."

And then there was the beer fiasco at Burton on Trent. Computers were assigned the job of estimating how much beer the Christmas and New Year's trade would demand, so that the breweries could control their output accordingly and not produce either too much, which might get too old and have to be poured out, or too little, which would cool the hearts of the citizens, especially during a festival period. The machines simply got everything confused; some slip in the programing produced figures wildly at variance with the facts, and half the pubs in town ran dry at the same time that the city's "biggest breweries were busily pouring barrels of beer by the thousand into the public drains," and ended up by dumping about $700,000 worth before the mistake was discovered.

In any case, the computers can do one thing that the dog cannot do; and it may be that this alone seals the fate of man's favorite mentor. A dog cannot write a book. But a computer has done so. Pratt and Whitney published it under the title, *Angular Indexing Tables*. It weighs four and a half pounds and was written by an electronic brain in 112 hours. Human mathematicians estimated that it would have taken "two crackerjack mathematicians two years" to do the job.

"Thumbs Down"—the Signal for Death?

In 1873, when the French painter Jean Léon Gérôme exhibited his picture of some of the action at the old Roman Coliseum showing the blood-hungry spectators savagely demanding the death of a gladiator and leaning forward with their thumbs all pointing down, he called it "Pollice Verso." At which point he made more history than he realized, because he clearly gave the meaning of "thumbs down" to "pollice verso," although *verso* really means *turned*, and could mean *extended* or even *rotated*. However, the picture is extremely graphic and is widely known through frequent reproductions—and it is not at all hard to understand why anyone who had seen it would take up the idea: it carries great conviction. We believe that today's meaning of "thumbs down"—which is unquestionably a gesture of rejection—owes its content to Gérôme. For it was not always so. "Latin scholars have advanced almost every other conceivable gesture except that shown by Gérôme. . . . The Latin phrase has been translated 'with thumbs turned inward' and 'with thumbs turned outward,' in either case using the thumb as if it were a dagger pointing at oneself or thrusting into an opponent, much as we 'thumb a ride.' "[16]

The Oxford English Dictionary, however—that vast edifice in thirteen huge volumes, than which there is no thanner—points out that in 1600 Holland translated *Pliny* (XXVIII.ii. 297): "To bend or bow downe the thumbes when wee give assent unto a thing, or doe favour any person." Assuming it's a favor to be allowed to live, "thumbs down" meant "let him live." A 1693 translation of Juvenal's *Satires* (iii. 68) by Dryden renders the Latin "Where . . . with thumbs bent back, they popularly kill." So "thumbs up" was the death gesture. Even after Gérôme there were some stiff-necked scholars who stuck to the original meaning; and the OED lists them in due order. But there is nothing that can dam the flow of meaning from a certain direction when enough people begin to use a word for a certain purpose, and it is impossible for scholars to foist neologisms upon the people just because they are "fit." Thus we find even the Britannica (11th edition) giving the negative meaning to "thumbs down" first: "If the spectators were in favor of mercy, they waved their handkerchiefs; if they desired the death of the conquered gladiator they turned their thumbs downwards." And then the article adds: "A different account is given by Mayor on *Juvenal* iii. 36, who says: 'Those who wished the death of the conquered gladiator turned their thumbs towards their breasts, as a signal to his opponents to stab him; those who wished him to be spared, turned their thumbs downwards, as a signal for dropping the sword'."

"Thumbs down" is not the only expression to change or reverse its meaning—the process is going on in every living language all the time. *Undertaker* formerly meant *entrepreneur,* one who undertakes a project, as a manufacturer; now, of course, it means one who undertakes to bury the dead, and the associations are unpleasant so that today's entrepreneurs in the burial business call themselves morticians or funeral directors. A *hussy* was first a simple "housewife," modest and virtuous, just as *wench* was entirely respectable and meant "pupil" or "daughter" or even "orphan" (it derives from Anglo-Saxon *wencel*, "weak" and needing protection). *Catiff* simply meant "captive" from the Old French, and it was applied in pity, since a captive is miserable; but it came to have an indication of odium and took on the meaning of "coward." And so forth.

In connection with the remark a moment ago that the scholars cannot foist a new word upon the language—it won't be used unless the folk pick it up—perhaps some readers will remember that there was a contest during the Prohibition days for some word which would convey scorn, contempt, and general rejection for a person breaking the law; and someone came up with "scofflaw." But you seldom hear it, and scarcely ever see it in print. In short, it carries no emotional weight of any kind. If you call me a scofflaw, I am not insulted, hurt, or even annoyed; instead, I am more likely to laugh.

Once the trend had begun to swing toward "thumbs down" to mean "death to him," nothing could stop it; and that's what we have today.

It is Immoral to Prevaricate?

Nice people don't lie. Thou shalt not bear false witness. Father, I cannot tell a lie. It is for slaves to lie, and for free men to speak the truth. The lip of truth shall be established forever: but a lying tongue is but for a moment. A lie stands on one leg and truth on two. One could fill pages with similiar sentiments from the literature of all peoples, and at least one man has done so.[17] The nonsense in this case lies not in the apothegm but in mankind's hypocritical and solemn adherence to the verbal expression as compared with the faulty living application of it in daily life. A French realist remarked that, since society is an edifice built with blocks of egoism, the keystone of the arch—that one stone that holds the thing up—must be hypocrisy. This sounds rather cynical, but we have to admit there is at least an echo of truth in it. *The* question of telling a lie, then, begins to take on shadings and become more a relative matter: How *big* a lie is it ethical to employ "for good purposes"? Can one tell a little white lie to keep one's guest happy? "Your new hat is lovely (but I really think it's a horror)"?

One of the best examples in literature which gives the full treatment to this paradox (one must not lie; one cannot live socially without lying) is the dramatic comedy by James Montgomery, *Nothing But the Truth*—a play which is deserving of revival, but which, for some reason, continues to be forgotten. It had its first appearance at the Longacre Theatre in New York City on September 14, 1916; and for any graybeards who may brighten at the mention of their names, such persons as young William Collier and young Ned Sparks were in the original cast. The comedy revolves around the fact that one of the partners in a hard-boiled and very successful stockbroking firm—a young fellow whose eyes are glazed with idealism and also with love for the boss's daughter—tries to defend absolute honesty as a business ethic, especially in connection with selling shares of stock in outfits whose worth is still unproved. The senior partner, E. M. Ralston, openly laughs at him. "A lie is just as good as truth if the result is all right. Profit is the only thing in business. . . . There are certain necessary business lies." The lover can't accept that. Ralston tells him he couldn't tell the absolute truth for twenty-four hours and keep "any friends or do any business."[18] They bet $10,000 on the proposition, and then for two full acts the comedy shows how much trouble an honest man can make for himself in the course of an ordinary day of social and business living. He is on the point of losing his sweetheart, his partnership, and everything he values in life, as the clocks marks 4 P.M., the end of the twenty-four hours, and permits him to lie his way back to love and financial and social security.

We Grow More Neurotic as Society Becomes More Complex?

Back on the farm, if a man has intelligence enough to round up the cows—they do it by themselves, of course, because they want to come in for a spot of chow and also to get milked—all he has to do is let down the pasture bars and fasten the stanchions when the cows take their places in the barn—handle the milking, turn the animals out again, feed the hens, cut a little wood, and tend to the crops, he could count on nature for the rest. He could go to bed at dark, tired, well exercised, and healthy; and he could snore until dawn, with nothing to make him toss in the night or dream of nerve-driven terrors. Ripe apples, new-mown hay, unpolluted air, the sun on his shoulders, and the corn ripening sweetly on the hillside. And on Sundays, Black

Tom and Brown Nellie pulling the light buckboard to the little white church in the valley, where God smiled at his children and blessed them.

That's the picture. Carefree, in nature's lap; honey on the fresh-baked bread and a chicken in the pot.

Then the road came through, the sons followed it to the towns and worked in the mills and drank in the taverns and struck for higher wages and went to the movies and learned evil ways; and they had to learn to jump quick or an automobile would run them down; they had to learn to fight to protect themselves from thugs. Life became complicated and the sons became neurotic. The "strain of modern life" was cracking them. Families broke up. Crime increased. Peace of mind disappeared.

Such is the summary of the drama of city vs. country in the life of man. It's very familiar; and it has long been accepted as true. The city mouse and the country mouse. The uncontrolled madness of our own days compared with the golden days that are past. This is what Way-land Young calls "the myth of the Golden Age," the feeling most of us have that "somewhere, at some time, things must have been better."[19] "In Christianity," he adds, "it is institutionalized in the story of the Fall."

At first you may doubt it; but the fact is that in terms of percentages fatalities among those who drove horses were higher than for drivers of motor vehicles—60 percent higher in England and Wales in the years 1921-1923, for instance.[20] When they asked G. B. Shaw on his seventy-fifth birthday (1931) what the greatest single improvement was which he had seen in a long and observant life, he replied without hesitation that it was the betterment of traffic conditions in the cities with the removal of horses.

If one wanted to carry the problem of personal tension back far enough, one would come to a troglodyte ancestor whose life was more filled with the necessity for split-second decisions than normal civilian life today ever demands except in the rarest emergencies. Later, when he lived in primitive societies, he was surrounded with such a complex of taboos, fears, and superstitions that his life, far from being simple and calm, was filled with tensions. He had no lights at night; no knowledge of preventive medicine or of anything but the simplest therapy; no dentistry—when a tooth split, it was a goner. And his life expectancy, as we know, was vastly less than ours. By comparison, we have little to worry about. A bad mistake today may cost us prestige and even money; but a bad mistake in a state of nature might cost our lives.

In short, a very good case could be made for the proposition that we are considerably less neurotic—although we talk more about neurosis and probably know more about it than did those of the Golden Age—than any civilized groups have ever been. When someone remarks that there are more neurotics than ever before it should be borne in mind that there are more people than ever before—millions more—millions who were saved from infant deaths and have been kept alive through formerly lethal diseases, meanwhile cheerfully reproducing their kind.

The Manufactured "Popular Error"

Every public figure naturally wants the people to accept and, if possible, to applaud him, because the rewards of popularity eventually pay off in terms of power. The man who commands public interest by what he says and does—he also commands the headlines and the microphones and the motion-picture and television cameras. In short, he becomes highly visible, as they say on Madison Avenue; and following his high degree of visibility he attracts a certain number of people. Of course he may repel others; but he is placing his bets upon the proposition that he can attract more than he repels—and if he wins that bet he becomes a wielder of power because his adherents will follow his wishes.

Thus some propagandist for Mussolini invented the phrase, "He made the trains run on time." Mussolini may have done many brutal and tyrannical things; he may have destroyed human freedom in Italy; he may have murdered and tortured citizens whose only crime was to oppose Mussolini; but "one had to admit" one thing about the Dictator: he "made the trains run on time." When a large enough number of people became convinced of the truth of the shibboleth, the saying grew to have the power of a popular belief.

There was little or no truth in it: people who lived in Italy between the March on Rome (October 28, 1922) and the execution at Como (1945) will bear testimony to the fact that Italian railroads remained as insouciant as ever with regard to timetables and actual schedules. It made no difference to the myth; it never makes any difference, once a popular error has become a folkway: one can show proof of the falsity until the cows arrive at the south pasture gate: he made the trains run on time. At least he did that much.

The manufacture of desired folk belief has become a major industry in our own century, and the modern witch doctors who supervise the art are among our most highly paid professional advisers. From the public relations expert to the plain, ordinary press agent, they are intent on impressing the proper image of their sponsor or client upon the public. Of course this entails achieving the public acceptance of popular errors by the score. The tradition is ancient; but to go no further back than the past hundred years, we see the myth taking root of Andrew Carnegie as the most famous donor of free libraries. It is no myth that he gave the libraries. But it is a myth that his interest was in literature. By 1880 he and his partners were rolling out profits of more than $2 million a year from their steel mill; and he advised Frank Doubleday to get out of publishing because there was so little money in it.[21] He frankly exploited labor in every possible way, regarded it as good business to cheat on supplies for the Navy, and was the essence of the hardboiled capitalist to whom nothing counted as much as profits. His fellow industrialist and contemporary, John Davison Rockefeller, was furiously assailed by Henry Demarest Lloyd (*Wealth Against Commonwealth*, 1934) and thoroughly exposed by Ida M. Tarbell (*History of the Standard Oil Company*, 1904). Experts were hired to make the Rockefeller name more pleasantly scented in the public nostril, and we see the old gentleman not only handing out dimes at the crossroads but, more significantly, putting up $500 million dollars to found the Rockefeller Institute for Medical Research. His son carried the philanthropy further, with the building of Riverside Church and setting up the Rockefeller Foundation. Who now associates the name of Rockefeller with secret mergers, special privilege, hidden agreements with competitors, the crushing of infant industries, under-the-table arrangements with railroads and pipelines, monopoly practices, labor brutality, and all that? John Davison Rockefeller is identified in the reference books as "American industrialist and philanthropist." And it's true, true, true. One is not attacking old J.D. or his memory, but merely pointing to him as a perfect example of the public figure who wanted to project a favorable image into the folklore and succeeded in doing so in a scientific manner.

The synthetic product in such a case is every whit as effective as the natural cloth, and perhaps more so. All we ask is that nobody should try to convince us, if you please, that the picture of J.D. patting kids on the head and passing out dimes reflects the essential character of that king of the robber barons—a phrase which we hasten to add is borrowed and not invented for the occasion. (Webster III on "robber baron": "An American capitalist of the latter part of the 19th century grown wealthy through exploitation of natural resources, governmental influence, or low wage scales.")

We've seen the same process at work on all sides. Little curly-haired Shirley Temple, the princess of the moppets—remember her? Can you imagine her slapping her mother? Or kicking and screaming on the floor saying, "I don't *want* my hair curled!"? The mythmakers are no amateurs.

THERE ARE NO ATHEISTS IN FOXHOLES?

Taken literally, the statement that there do not exist, in any of the one-man or two-man temporary shelters dug in the ground by soldiers under fire, any members of the armed forces who hold that there is no god, "no matter in what sense 'god' be defined,"[22] is obviously nonsense, since nobody knows whether there are any or not. Any scientific poll of active foxholes today would be out of date tomorrow—or at least at the end of the next week—since the shelters dug for protection against shelling are temporary; and the idea of polling troops under fire on the subject of their religious beliefs, and specifically on their theology, when every man of them is doing his best to avoid being killed the next minute, is on the face of it ridiculous.

But the metaphor should not be taken literally, of course—no metaphor should be taken literally. What the phrase *means* is that men at crucial life-or-death moments when they are not able to control events around them tend to accept the faiths of their childhood again for the comfort those faiths give, and do not stop to argue the rationality or the irrationality of those beliefs. Supposedly this is a moment of truth when all the superficial bull-session, smoke-filled debates become inconsequential; and at such a moment a man accepts his place in the universe according to the religious teachings learned at his mother's knee: the faith of his fathers. To this proposition one can only say that some men apparently do this, and some do not, and in any event no man can foretell how he will behave at the final moment when he faces death. Innumerable men have testified that even in the moment of truth there was nothing of a religious character that occurred to him. The deathbed recantations of atheism attributed to Voltaire, Ingersoll, Paine, and a host of others, may be taken for what they are worth—which is not very much.

On the other hand, some 35 percent of the population of the United States is unchurched in the first part of the third quarter of the twentieth century. But of these unchurched people not all are atheists. We simply have no idea how many—churched or unchurched—consider themselves atheists. Many just lose interest in organized religion and drop out. Atheism, on the other hand, is a very specific religious position: that there is no god of any kind, personal, as a supreme force, as nature, or in any other meaning.

Hence the proposition that there are no atheists in foxholes is nonsense, but its purpose is to suggest to wavering citizens that a belief in God is characteristic of men in extremities and therefore should be accepted by wavering citizens. You'll notice it is the clergy who emphasize the apothegm.

Clergymen's Children Are Usually Black Sheep?

We laymen appear to have a stereotype of the clergyman, the man of God, the priest, the comforter, the healer which presents that representative of omnipotence in two quite different lights: in the first, he is the stern implement of the Almighty, righteous, firm, unbending, learned, multiloquious, and dressed in unrelieved black; in the second, his accouterments merely disguise a voluptuary, a rapacious, greedy, oversexed profligate preying on helpless virgins and widows the minute he gets a chance. Perhaps this is because, having once agreed that the clergyman is in close touch with the supernatural, we find it easy to switch from the prince of light to the prince of darkness, depending on how we happen to feel about the clergyman in question. But the range is all the way from the Mathers to Elmer Gantry, or, indeed, Satan himself. Whatever else he is, the clergyman is conspicuous and visible. And that goes for his children as well.

If a stern and rockbound minister upbraided you by name in the public meeting, let's say for drunkenness, and you had to bear the scornful glances of your neighbors as the verbal lashing continued, would you not be glad and delighted to find that same minister's son at the tavern on the following night? Would you not buy the lad a few drinks? And when he passed out, would you not point to him and say, "That's the minister's son—dead drunk!"? Behind the role of clergyman are the witch doctors and medicine men of our dark past: and we fear them and we need them, all at the same time. Since we would prefer not to fear them, we tell each other privily that the clergyman's offspring are more susceptible to temptation than our own offspring. And this we find very comforting, especially when we find an example to prove the point.

However, it seems that Havelock Ellis made a special study of this matter, comparing children of clergymen with those of lawyers, doctors, and army officers. His investigations showed that "eminent children of the clergy considerably outnumber those of lawyers, doctors and army officers put together." Other studies have been made by students of heredity basing their investigations on parents listed in *Who's Who*, and the theory that children of the clergy are more sinful than other groups simply does not hold up, despite certain illustrious exceptions.

It's Not Nice to Paint the Face?

Societies have looked upon makeup in many different ways; it was definitely *comme il faut* to use cosmetics in Cleopatra's day; it was just as definitely sinful in the Puritan days, and at no time more so than during the height of the witchcraft hysteria of the seventeenth century. In fact, as late as the reign of Queen Anne (died 1714) an act was passed declaring that anyone who "seduced any one of Her Majesty's subjects" by means of face paint and false hair was guilty of witchcraft.[23]

The nonsense in this case—to paint or not to paint—as with so many popular ideas, is not in the use or avoidance of the makeup but in the absolute conviction that to do one or the other is in itself evil. It was nonsense for the Puritan to repress all sense of fun, all the joy of play, and to focus dourly upon hell, hard work, and probable damnation, scaring the young kids every Sunday into hysteria. The nubile young ladies knew enough to pinch their cheeks before entering the room, to bring up the color, even if the actual rouge was sinful.

Yet one can understand why cosmetics were considered wrong in Puritan cultures. The Bible, which they read so dutifully and to which their attention was called whenever a moral question was at issue, associated face painting with such characters as Jezebel, Aholah, and Aholibah, and prostitutes in general; the practice was abominated by Jeremiah, Ezekiel, and the author of Kings. (See Ezek. 23:40, II Kings 9:30, and Jer. 4:30.) "And the assembly shall stone them . . . and burn up their houses with fire."

Also the association between skin painting and magic is very old; ancient Britons used woad; many primitives still paint themselves; and the Devil was accustomed to paint his own face so as to disguise himself. This, of course, is one source of the condemnation of cosmetics by the Church. Shakespeare himself speaks of face paint only in pejorative terms, reserving his most mordant satire on the subject for the scene at the grave in *Hamlet,* where the prince holds Yorick's skull in his hands and tells the skull, "Now get you to my lady's chamber, and tell her, let her paint an inch thick, to this favor she must come; make her laugh at that."

Cotton Mather must be turning over in his grave on Copp's Hill as the pubescent young females from Grade Seven or earlier pass by the old burying ground with their Theda Bara eyes these days. And yet they are not all prostitutes. They can't be.

The Puritans in New England Burned Witches?

Persons believed to be witches were burned by the thousands in Europe, especially during the great persecution of 1434-1447 and for three hundred years thereafter; some were hanged, some decapitated, and some pressed to death. But none were burned in New England, by the Puritans or by anyone else. The movie *I Married a Witch,* starring Veronica Lake and Frederic March, opened with a scene of witch burning in seventeenth-century New England—but either the research department was sloppy or the director decided to transfer a European execution to these shores for dramatic purposes. In any case, the easy acceptance of witch burning in New England by popular belief is based on something other than history.

Before we go any further we ought to know what we mean by "witch," and we should not confuse witchcraft with sorcery or primitive religion or the craft of healing—although something of all these remains in our understanding of witchcraft, by association or because of language. Old English *wig* signified "idol" and was the basis for *wigle* (divination), thus leading to *wicce*, witch, or sorceress: one who practices the black arts; thus an ugly old woman, a crone or hag; and to go one step further, one who has made a compact with the Devil and in consequence possesses supernatural powers.

Douglas and Williams ingeniously suggest a differentiation not mentioned by other etymologists: that witchcraft is Christian, following the bull of Pope Innocent VIII in 1484 which equated witchcraft with heresy; a witch serves the Devil, in his repudiation of Christ. But sorcery is pagan; and the sorcerer serves himself.[24]

Contemporary usage is clear about *witch*: it refers, first, to a crone in league with her master the Devil; and, second, to a young and extremely attractive woman—quite the opposite sort of sexual imagery.

In periods of terribly low public morale throughout history—during a scourging plague, in a season of famine, or at any other time when it seems as if things could not get worse without bringing on the end of the world—utopian groups have sprung up crying that the last days are imminent, that men should repent and prepare; and hysteria has gripped the populace as scapegoats have been sought. When it was realized that witches served the Devil, then obviously a rich source of scapegoats had been found; and conservative estimates indicate that by the seventeenth century more than 200,000 witches had been discovered and slain—at least half that number in Germany alone.[25]

England hanged her witches instead of burning them alive. The last witch to be convicted in that country was Jane Wenham in 1712: she was convicted but not executed.

The Salem hysteria occurred after one of the worst winters on record. "One calamity after another had been heaped on the Bay Colony—smallpox, Indian raids . . . and the growing certainty that New England had lost forever the near-independence it had enjoyed under the charter. God had manifestly turned his countenance from a people unworthy. . . . There were many who believed seriously that Doomsday was imminent. All signs pointed to its coming."[26] It was the bleak winter of 1691-92. The refusal to accept Governor Andros had caused the revocation of the charter, one remembers; and added to the bleakness of the weather was the bleakness of the religion of Calvinist predestination, with its emphasis on eternal hell and the sin of sex working on young and old, but especially on ten young women ranging from the minister's daughter, Betty Parris, age 9, to Sarah Churchill and Mary Warren, both 20. These adolescents, with dark fantasies of sin and hideously repressed, through the agency of the maid Tituba from the Barbadoes who told fearful tales of native magic and built up girlish imaginings to the point of actual explosion, suddenly began misbehaving at family prayers—and the terrible witch hunt was on. When it was all over, thirteen witches had been hanged and one pressed to death.

Which was bad enough and horrible enough while it was happening; but it does not make New England either the source of witch hunting nor one of the bloodiest battlefields of witchcraft. In Boston the executions numbered four. No more; and one of those, Mary Parsons, was executed for the admitted murder of her own child rather than for witchcraft.[27]

There is not the slightest doubt that our forefathers really *knew* that there were witches on earth; they *saw* them. On September 22, 1692, "seven witches and one lone wizard were packed into a cart and hauled the long mile to Gallows Hill" in Salem—an ascent which was very steep, and hard pulling for even the strongest animal. Somehow the cart got stuck in the road where the pitch was sharpest; and "the accusers, riding close behind, plainly saw the Devil hold it back."[28] The records also show that witches believed in *themselves*—at least some of them did.

It is also true that most of the witches were women. After all, demonic possession is a form of hysteria; and the language itself is a giveaway here, since *hysteria* derives from *hystera*, uterus. Witches were able to make up love potions; they were able to create impotence; and they had carnal intercourse with demons. The association with sex is terribly clear.

If we were to assume a posture of superiority because we are no longer superstitious, no longer believe in witches, we would accomplish another popular error. There is an English group of witches centered in New Forest, and their head, Mrs. Sybil Leek, told the London *Daily Express* in 1964: "I am a white witch, and come from a long line of white witches, who exist only to do good."[29] Witches today are not—or at least they claim they are not—in league with Satan. They have become do-gooders and appear to be inordinately proud of themselves. *Punch* in September, 1958, mentioned "a witch who cured men and beasts and made faulty cars go when garages were baffled."[30] The self-styled "Queen of the Witches" is Mrs. Monique Wilson, a disciple of the famous Gerald Gardner, and she recently posed for photographers without embarrassment.[31]

ALL MEDICAL MEN HAVE TO KNOW LATIN?

No doubt all medical men do know *some* Latin; they know, for instance, that the list of drugs for curing diseases is called *Materia Medica*. It's true enough that in the old days when Latin was the international language and medical treatises were copied out by hand in Latin, all doctors *should* have known Latin rather well; and it is true that until recent decades a premedical student had to offer Latin as one of the entrance requirements. Today this is no longer the case; but any doctor intending to do significant research in the history of medicine would be at a loss without a working knowledge of the language, but not otherwise.

Before Gutenberg and the use of movable type in the middle of the fifteenth century, only the clergy and a few so-called scholars could read—it will be remembered that one could plead "privilege of clergy" and be immune to arrest if one could prove the ability to read. Every craft had its secrets, and with the medical craft these date back to Hippocrates (460-370 B.C.). Doctors still take the "Hippocratic Oath" to serve their patients well and keep their patients' secrets as safely as the confessional. But there was of necessity a vast amount of mumbo-jumbo: actual medical *knowledge* was scant indeed. One could advise a patient suffering from asthma to take foxes' lungs for a cure—but this was not based on knowledge; nor, of course, did it cure anything. Up until very recent years, until the era of the specialist indeed, most of the doctors in Europe and America had six basic treatments: bleeding; Dover's powder (for gout); Peruvian bark (quinine); calomel (mercury chloride for curing intestinal worms); purging; and antimony (tartar emetic). More advanced practitioners might be familiar with the herbal of Dioscorides, a doctor with Nero's armies in the first century A.D., which contained some 600 plants (of which 100 are still retained in the *materia medica*). But most of the curing was guesswork, and the doctor combined his best guess with a soothing manner, a psychological pep talk, and a sympathetic ear, and sometimes the patient got better. But doubts of the doctor were reasonable and fearsome; and it is well known that Molière was convinced that the doctors had killed his only son with antimony (*antimoine*, monk's-bane, so-called because it caused the deaths of some monks who had been fasting) and carried his feud with the medical profession into five of his comedies, with vicious satirizing of the doctors' pretensions and their actual ignorance.

In fact, as Richard Calder points out, "Up to 1935, the physicians were merely witch doctors. They treated symptoms, not causes, of disease. They gave sedatives or stimulants, as the case might be. The doctors had about five specifics [remedies with a recognizable curative effect on a particular illness]—quinine for malaria; ipecacuanha . . . for amoebic dysentery; and Paracelsus' mercury or Ehrlich's 'salvarsan' to attack the spirochaete of syphilis. . . . Most were ancient."[32]

So of course the profession came in for a good deal of sometimes scabrous kidding, one of the gentlest remarks being that "natural immunity" means "Being able to catch a disease without the aid of a physician."[33]

With or without Latin and Greek, however, members of the medical profession are under the public obligation to maintain the conventions which set the doctor apart from hoi polloi and all penny stinkards, as the Elizabethans called the crowd in the inexpensive seats. This extends to costume and speech as well as to manner, and it inevitably involves a certain amount of pretense, because we would not support a doctor who didn't *seem* to know. As Calder points out, the frock coat and tall hat are as necessary to Dr. Oliver Wendell Holmes as are the buffalo skin and horns to the Pawnee witch doctor: this is the convention of costume.[34] The convention of language tends toward the *deliramenta doctrinae*—the mad delusion of learning, a phrase which dates back to 1377 at least and which can be applied to any art, craft, or specialty with curious effect, as Shakespeare showed in that hilariously mad scene (Act V, scene iv, line 95) in *As You Like It* where Touchstone explains the language conventions of polite dueling and shows how "we quarrel by the book" and gives the degrees of the lie from the Retort Courteous to the seventh degree, the Lie Direct. So if one calls as simple a thing as an eyeglass an *oculus berellinus*, as did Bernard de Gordon the Scotsman,[35] it is only because the doctor could preserve his guild rights as well as his ignorance behind such gobbledygook and impress the patient. One must always remember, as Goethe said, where an idea is wanting a word can always be found to take its place—especially a technical word.

THE "BRITANNICA" IS THE BIGGEST AND MOST COMPLETE?

An aggressive, long-continued promotion and advertising policy combined with one of the earliest (1898) installment sales programs which allows one to own the whole set with a down payment and remit the rest later, is perhaps responsible for the fact that to many people the Encyclopaedia Britannica is incomparably the biggest and most complete summary of human knowledge the world has ever seen. Without the slightest derogation of that great—but often mistaken— human literary effort, it cannot make any claim to such status. An early fifteenth-century Chinese encyclopedia was more than fifteen times larger:

The Ming emperor Young Lo, who reigned A.D. 1403-1425, by decree caused the compilation and publication of the Young Lo Ta Tien, the aim of which was to collect everything on Confucius, history, philosophy, and general literature. Two thousand scholars were on the job for five years, and when it was finished the work contained 20,000 separate sections which required more than 900,000 pages. It printed 367 million characters, which is the equivalent of about 500 million words.[36]

SODA POP IS AN AMERICAN INVENTION?

It has been said that Coca-Cola, along with apple pie and the hot dog, is the only serious rival to the Stars and Stripes as a symbol of the United States; and it is not hard to understand why the various bottled products of the soft-drink stands, generically known as tonic—supposedly because they buck you up in a non-alcoholic manner—are believed to be American in origin. Carbonated-water beverages were certainly *adopted* by America and developed here while the elder societies clung to their beers and wines; but it is nevertheless a popular error to say that they are American in their origin, or that they are recent—meaning new within the past century.

The inventor of carbonated water was the great English scientist and theologian, Joseph Priestley. He was given international honors for his discovery of oxygen; and burned out of house, home, laboratory, and meetinghouse for his theology by a Birmingham mob which would have lynched him if he had not made a hairsbreadth escape.

After 1767, when he was called as the minister of the Mill chapel at

Leeds, he gave all his spare time to experiments with electricity and in the chemistry of the air. It was the latter which led to the discovery of oxygen (which earned him the title of "the father of modern chemistry") but as a by-product, as pure serendipity, he discovered carbonated water.[37]

Perhaps it is only fair, having mentioned the Birmingham mob, to explain. Priestley had taken a Birmingham church; and he preached a Unitarian doctrine which held that Jesus had the same relation to divinity that all men have, and no more; and that to worship him was pure idolatry. Of course the High Churchmen sought to destroy him. But the actual witch hunt was built up on the basis of his sympathy for the French Revolution. Englishmen had not forgotten the horror which accompanied the beheading of an English king in the last century; and now the French had seized their own runaway king when he had tried to flee (at Varennes, June, 1791). This Priestley, it was charged, sought to bring the violence and bloodshed of the French Revolution to England. There was to be a supper in Birmingham to celebrate the assault on the Bastille on July 14, 1791. What a time to nip the radical, the traitor, the subversive. So the crowd burned Priestley's church and his house and raged unchecked for three days, seeking freethinkers and treasonists.

Priestley never heard of Coca-Cola, however. The formula for that was developed by Major John S. Pemberton, formerly of Wheeler's Cavalry, C.S.A., in 1886, and the first batch was cooked in a three-legged pot over a wood fire in the back yard.[38] Two of the ingredients were the dried leaves of a South American shrub, coca, and an extract of the kola nut; and the inventor's friend, F. M. Robinson, suggested the name from these ingredients. "More money has been spent advertising Coca-Cola than any other single product in advertising history," Campbell says (p. 64).

But the inventor of carbonated water never made a cent out of it.

CHRISTIAN DOCTRINE LESSENS ANTI-SEMITISM?

Central to all Christian teaching is the doctrine of love; and it has roots in the Old Testament: "Thou shalt love thy neighbor as thyself" (Lev. 19:18.) Western culture owes a debt to the ancient Jews for that writing. Jesus repeated the idea many times and in many ways.

Paul summed it up in his famous précis: "And now abideth faith, hope, charity, these three; but the greatest of these is charity" (I Cor. 13:13). John quoted Jesus as saying to the disciples, "This is my commandment, That ye love one another" (John 15:12). But Matthew takes the exhortation further: "But I say unto you, Love your enemies, bless them that curse you" (Matt. 5:44).

Therefore, on the face of it, one has the documentation necessary to prove that Christian doctrine does indeed oppose such a hatred as that which goes by the name of anti-Semitism. The nonsense appears in the redoubtable and often demonstrated fact that Christian teaching does not have this effect. Jesus, a Jew himself and well versed in Jewish literature and law, but of an independent cast of mind which permitted him to think for himself when it came to hairsplitting technicalities of the law, taught his followers that love of man is second only to love of God and that one follows the other. This word was given to Jewish followers: he spoke to his own people. When Paul took the gospel to the Gentiles, it spread through the Greek and Roman world and through the East. Within about twenty years after the crucifixion, Paul wrote I Corinthians, which we have just cited. Previous to about A.D. 50, the story had been passed along in the oral tradition only; and it was another twenty years after Paul before the other Gospels began to be written, the first being Mark, supposedly based on Peter's verbal accounts as an eyewitness. But all the Gospels were written by A.D. 100, and although of course they could not be printed, each copy got maximum circulation. Hence the teachings of Jesus have been available in writing for close to two millennia.[39] And there has been no dearth of translations. According to the American Bible Society there were renditions into 1,250 languages at the end of March, 1966.

In short, the doctrines of Jesus are sharp and clear; they have been in written form for centuries; and they are available in every major tongue and many rare languages. None of us therefore can plead ignorance, since if we didn't read the words ourselves, we had them read to us or recited.

Yet it is demonstrably true that members of Christian churches are more anti-Semitic than the citizens at large; the general population is less prejudiced not only toward the Jews but toward other minority groups.[40] Allport's own explanation is that people with "high ethnic prejudice tend, on the whole, to have what I have called an extrinsic religious orientation. . . . For many people, religion is a dull habit . . . to be used for family convenience, or for personal comfort. It is something to *use* but not to *live*."

Other studies have pointed more specifically to orthodox Christian indoctrination as a definite *source* and *cause* of anti-Semitism.[41]

For example, the Bible tells us that the excited mob, inspired by "the chief priests and elders"—that is, by the Jewish Establishment—after the events at the house of Caiaphas where Jesus was finally accused of blasphemy, gathered with increasing bloodthirstiness in the courtyard of Pilate, the Roman governor. This was after a whole night of accusation, hearing of false witnesses, and mounting blood lust. The crowd had the scent of blood in its nostrils, and when Pilate acknowledged that he saw no treason in Jesus, and the mob saw their victim slipping out of their fingers, they made such an inspired howl ("Pilate saw . . . that a tumult was arising") that in some desperation he told them to choose between Barabbas and Jesus, and thus avoided, perhaps, another "incident" which might make Rome say, "Can't that man keep those Jews in line?" Then, dramatically washing his hands in public, he said to the crowd, "See ye to it." And they answered with a traditional Jewish Old Testament saying, "His blood be on us and on our children." Then Barabbas was released, and presumably the mob received him with wild acclaim and went into some sort of snake dance and worked off its explosive emotions in a victory celebration.

Antonio, the Merchant of Venice, was not the first to observe that "The devil can cite Scripture for his purpose." In Matthew, the mob is referred to generally as "the people." In Mark, as "the multitude." But in John it is "the Jews." In Luke it is merely "they."

It seems fairly obvious that if one has been taught from a Holy Book regarded by tens of thousands as the literal Word of God that "the Jews" demanded the death of Jesus and said, "His blood be on us," and so forth, week after week in Sunday school. and if one has been given ribbons of various colors for reward after memorizing certain crucial verses of Scripture, the notion may quite possibly be planted rather permanently in the mind that Jews are a parlous lot, and were once guilty of deicide.

And when it is taken into consideration that almost half the American people are churchgoers, although not all, of course, Christian, it is plain that a very large number of minds are involved.[42]

Historically it was not the Jews who crucified Jesus, but the

Romans. It was against the law for the Jews to execute capital punishment—although they did occasionally stone blasphemers and adulterers, persons of no political interest to Rome. (An angry mob snatched Stephen away from his trial before the Sanhedrin and dragged him outside the gates of Jerusalem, where, as the future Apostle Paul watched, they stoned him to death; and one remembers the story in John where Jesus prevents the stoning of a woman taken in adultery by inviting the person who is without sin to throw the first rock.)

But the fact does remain that, unless the Jewish Establishment had fomented the mob, the Romans would not have crucified Jesus; and therefore it is historically true that *certain* Jews were responsible for his death. Their reasons have been the subject of endless speculation: the Establishment depended on wealth and power for its status, but Jesus taught that God sees the worth of a man in the man's own character. This was revolutionary doctrine, dangerous if widely believed: especially the notion that the possession of wealth is actually a hindrance to godliness. The temple priests, after the whipping of the money-changers, were dedicated to removing this terrorist in protection of their business rights. The established instructors in the law, the scribes and Pharisees, were publicly insulted by this nobody from a hick town in one of the bitterest polemics in literature. He broke the sanctity of the Sabbath (among some of the more fanatically religious, one might not even answer the call of nature on the Sabbath, to say nothing of gathering food on such a day). He repudiated the rules of proper behavior as given in the *Halachah*, which to the Pharisees was the true key to expressing God's will. To Albert Schweitzer it was clear that Jesus was killed "because two of his disciples had broken his command of silence: Peter when he made known the secret of the Messiahship to the twelve at Caesarea Philippi; Judas Iscariot by communicating it to the High Priest."[43]

Jesus preached the love of God to man, to the individual man, in an age when life was held cheap and those in authority treated the poor with contemptuous cruelty. He was rejected by the Zealots, who wanted to fight Rome, because he would not lead an armed rebellion. The Temple treasury was sort of a state bank which received tithes on produce, the half-shekel tax expected from every Jew, plus the free-will gifts of the rich, in addition to fees for pronouncing a sacrificial animal "without blemish" and for changing pieces of money with pagan images (illegal within the sacred precincts of the Temple) into proper currency. It was pitting his lone arm against City Hall, as it were, to threaten this powerful organization, with its well-paying concessions. Therefore when Jesus did not follow up his dramatic and explosive action against the money-changers with an array of armed angelic hosts from heaven or something equally startling, but merely sat quietly in the Temple the next day, teaching, many of his hopeful supporters faded away. Here was no hero after all.

These are among the reasons given. That he was fomenting rebellion against the civil government was, of course, merely a technicality invented to give Pilate an excuse; and even he saw no threat in this gentle—and very likely slightly lunatic—prophet from the hills.

We have persecuted good men in our own time for reasons less obvious than these, accusing them of sedition, of treason by association, and of being secret agents of the world Communist network. The pattern is not unfamiliar.

But when it comes to matters involving religion, our hopes of heaven and our fears of hell, the emotions sometimes get out of control: our torture of the heretic becomes holy work. But in our reasonable moments we know that an unruly mob of demonstrators cannot commit the future of a whole people to the blame for an act the mob undertakes. "His blood be on us and our children." "A new commandment I give unto you, That ye love one another."

MAN BY NATURE SEEKS THE TRUTH?

If the hand holding this book is already shaking with laughter as you read our headline, we can only say that some of you as young people must have had experiences which are supposed to be reserved for adult life. You are supposed to go through youth believing that the answer to the question in our heading is affirmative.

But you're right: we might as well admit it at the outset. What man seeks by nature is the satisfaction of security, not truth; therefore he spends his effort in a quest for certainty, an action which is a reflection of his fear of insecurity. Men want definite answers, not weasely Talking Oak stuff such as threw old Macbeth for a loss. Let's have it in black and white. And if it cannot be had in black and white because it's gray, then let's have it in black and white just the same. Let the answers be satisfactory and we will not bother about how true they are. In fact, given the choice of a familiar lie and a strange truth, most men will select the familiar lie. This characteristic was commented upon by Lord Chesterfield in connection with the salons of eighteenth-century London; by Mark Twain among the frontiersmen of nineteenth-century America; and by Stefansson among the Copper River Eskimos of the twentieth century. The trait is universal.

Perhaps two of Stefansson's anecdotes will serve to illustrate:

On one occasion he was present at an Eskimo séance at which a shaman performed who was supposedly gifted with tongues. He rattled off something which he asserted was "white man's language." Stefansson said he could not understand a single word of the gibberish. Ordinarily one might have expected that such a remark from a visiting white man would cause some slight doubts as to the shaman's accent, at least. No such thing. It was the status of the visitor that was thus brought into question. Stefansson could not possibly be a true white man. Must be some mixture. Or else he was pretending to be a white man. . . .

Another time he was trying to explain to the Eskimos the known facts about the surface of the moon. Stefansson found his audience incredulous, and since they had no instruments for viewing the moon themselves, he asked why they didn't believe him. It seems that the Eskimo shamans reported the moon's surface quite differently. And they professed to have been there, personally, many times. When pressed, the explorer had to admit with a shrug that he had never had that experience himself. Which, of course, settled the matter.[44]

One could pick up additional instances almost as rapidly as the mind will work, and probably a great deal closer to home. Do you not have some special gesture, or ritual remark, or good-luck piece, or something else which tends to reinforce your own security on the basis of no documentation, even in the face of reason—like the ballplayer's rabbit's foot, or the traveler's St. Christopher medal, or knocking on wood?

2

Persistent Notions About Food

As one of the earliest classifications under which to examine the misconceptions of folk wisdom, we choose food. We are very fond of food and want to keep it coming in our direction; but if the reader has already dined and is in no mood to consider so gross an act as feeding, he may start out with another chapter—sex, for instance—and we will not be annoyed. It's your book. At least we hope it is. If it isn't, then return it—unmarked. With the jacket intact.

The subject of food has a gripping fascination for most people (note the huge sales of all kinds of cookbooks, where-to-eat books, and books by epicures) not only because we are always ready for a snack, but also because 90 percent of the population through the centuries spent the waking hours producing and distributing food, right up to the Industrial Revolution. Today only about 20 percent are so engaged in the United States; but the rest of us are vastly interested in what that fifth of the population is doing; and America's largest business is still the production and marketing of food. We have more than 50,000 companies in this country processing a variety of edibles, and many, like General Foods, with nearly 30,000 workers on the payroll and hundreds of food products issuing under its 30 top brand names, are giant corporations. Incidentally, this behemoth among corporations traces its beginnings to 1895 when C. W. Post marketed a health food called Postum Cereal Food Coffee and a couple of years later Grape-

Nuts, another health food, and then, in 1904, a kind of corn flakes which Post called "Elijah's Manna." The preachers called down the wrath of heaven on him for daring to associate his commercial product with God's gift to the children of Israel in the Wilderness, and the government of Britain flatly refused to register the blasphemous trademark. Mr. Post hurriedly renamed his product Post Toasties, and all was well.[1] (Elijah, however, as perhaps Mr. Post would have known if he'd paid closer attention in Sunday School, was fed "bread and meat" [I Kings 17:6] by his ravens, *not* manna, which was "white, and the taste of it was like wafers—made with honey" [Exod. 16:31] a product which the children of Israel found a poor substitute, day in, day out, for the meat, fish, cucumbers, melons, leeks, onions, and garlic of Egypt).

SALT: DANGEROUS?

One of the most insidious pieces of folk wisdom is the "knowledge" that salt must be avoided in the diet. Some people profess this with an almost religious fervor, and believe absolutely that adding salt at the table is one of the chief causes of cancer. Salt lovers will be comforted to know that there is no evidence, experimental or clinical, of any kind, to support such a belief. The charge is one of those wise-sounding assertions which, because of its simplicity and specificity, appears to have the ring of truth when, as a matter of fact, it is the completest nonsense. Certainly one can eat too much salt; one can eat too much of anything. But a reasonable seasoning with salt improves both the flavor and the nutritive value of foods.

CANNED FOODS: POISONED BY THE CANS WHEN OPENED?

There are those who will tell you, with enormous assurance and an expression intended to carry absolute conviction, that if you open a can of food you should take the contents out at once, because the reaction between food and can and air makes the food poisonous. Anybody attempting suicide by this method, however, is headed for disappointment and probably isolation in the mental wards: food doesn't become poisonous in an opened tin can any faster than it does in an opened bottle or in an open dish. Airborne bacteria will cause food to rot in time, as everybody should be aware; and rotted food is indeed poisonous. But the tin can has nothing to do with it. It is true that acid foods, left in tins, may take on an undesirable taste—but it is not the taste of poison. You could open a can of beef stew, use half, leave the rest in the tin, put the tin in the refrigerator, and eat it several days later as safely as if it had been wrapped in oil paper on a China plate.

Incidentally, there is another folly associated with tin cans, and that is the error of calling them tin cans. Tin is much too expensive and rare a metal to make cans of, which will be thrown away as soon as emptied. Instead, thin sheets of rolled steel are dipped in molten tin, and the best tinned cans in the world don't have a coat of tin thicker than one-five-thousandth of an inch.[2] The Americans learned the process from Welshmen, since England had a practical monopoly on the process until the McKinley Tariff of 1890. Before that, the process was a monopoly in the control of Bohemia, where tinning sheet iron (mentioned by Agricola, "the father of mineralogy" half a century earlier) was practiced as early as 1620. However, a process for making tinplate canisters, an improvement over the Bohemian method, was patented in 1810 by Peter Durand, who is also credited with introducing the tin can into America in 1818.[3] But tin was nothing new in the world in the seventeenth century: as a compound of bronze (but not in its unalloyed state) it had been used in prehistoric times.[4]

High-Class Restaurants Never Serve Frozen Foods?

When he was 26, Clarence ("Bob") Birdseye went to Labrador to join up with Sir Wilfred Grenfell and work on the famous hospital ship. Instead of returning, however, he became a fur trapper and trader. One of the chief deficiencies in his diet, and something he missed terribly, was vegetables. Then he discovered that in the subzero weather vegetables like cabbages, thrown into a barrel of sea water, would freeze so quickly that the flavor seemed not to be injured. Bob would chop out a cabbage, thaw it out, and it seemed to him to be as good as ever. From this experience he began to try other foods—fish and caribou. The quick-freeze technique does not detract from the nutritive value but merely holds up the activity of bacteria; and in the speed of the freezing the larger ice crystals do not get a chance to form—it is they which tend to break down cell walls, harm the texture, and allow the natural juices to escape. Bob could see the commercial possibilities in his discovery. He registered Birdseye Seafoods, Inc., in New York State and advertised that he was ready to ship fresh fish anywhere in the world without using ice or preservatives. Unfortunately he was up against a whispering campaign of folk wisdom: his quick-frozen foods were said to be no different from cold storage or preserved products, and to have fewer vitamins than the fresh food. If the best restaurants used his services, they would not admit it publicly. His first corporation went broke. But Bob knew he had something and he was a persuasive man. The American Medical Association approved his products. Soon he had financial backing and opened again, ready for a long campaign if necessary, in Gloucester. He would take anything the fishermen came to the wharf with—porpoises, sharks, tortoises, octopuses—and freeze the flesh and eat what he had frozen. He knew he was right. So did General Foods, and they paid him about a million dollars for his company and made him head of the Gloucester laboratory of the merged group.

FROZEN FOODS: DO THEY LOSE THEIR ORIGINAL TASTE VALUES?

Possibly some long-forgotten but still vindictive enemy of Mr. Birdseye is responsible for the whispering campaign that the freezing of foods makes them less palatable. There's no truth in it, provided the foods have not been dehydrated. Freezing, indeed, detracts neither in palatability nor in nutritive value, but actually helps to retain the vitamin and mineral content of the foods frozen.

WILL PICKLES AND ICE CREAM AT THE SAME MEAL GIVE ONE A BELLYACHE?

Some years ago Henry Ford was interviewed by the *New York Times Magazine,* and he expressed the opinion that proteins and starches are dangerous to health if consumed at the same meal. This opinion should be placed in a similar category with the same authority's judgment of history. All natural foods contain proteins and starches in one form or another. Cherries and cream won't hurt you one bit—unless you eat too much. You can drink enough *pure water* so that you become dizzy; but we are not talking about excesses. Did apple pie à la mode ever send you to the infirmary? Okay—eat a smaller helping and it won't.

SUGARS AND STARCHES: BAD MEDICINE?

Reasonable amounts of a sugar or starch, even if they are pure sugar and pure starch with nothing else added, are not in the least harmful. Perhaps one reason for the popular nonsense about these matters is that to some people a taste for sweets becomes a craving and the citizen eats excessive amounts. Or the delight in spaghettini gets beyond control and the citizen had too many helpings "just this once." Excess in either case will produce obesity; and of course if you eat so much sweet or so much starch that you have no appetite for other foods containing the necessary vitamins and minerals, you're losing out on a balanced diet. But the generic curse against either sugar or starch eaten moderately has no basis in fact. Enjoy life!

WHITE COLLAR: FEWER PROTEINS?

The word goes around in folk circles that a person of sedentary habits would do well to avoid too many proteins: he does not need, they assert, anything like the protein intake required, let's say, by an active worker with a pickax, if there are any left.

But the biological fact is that a worker who spends his day in a chair, with occasional excursions to the water cooler, needs almost as much protein as does the sweating laborer. He requires fewer carbohydrates and of course less fatty food than the man in overalls; but don't cut down on his proteins.

FOODS THAT GO BOOM IN THE NIGHT

In some parts of the country people will tell you in utter seriousness that there are certain foods (depending on the part of the country) which will react on other edibles in the stomach in such a way as to cause you to explode. We are not referring to a little gas on the stomach: what is meant is an interior bomb that will blow you up—and out. If you hear this legend in your travels, enjoy it as an interesting bit of folklore—but don't believe it. We quote the well-known authority Dr. Jean Bogert: "The substances of which foods are made up are rather inert chemically, so that there is very little chemical reaction taking place between them and *no possibility* of their forming explosive mixtures in the stomach."[5]

THE CANNIBAL ISLANDS?

That there are humans who regularly and by their own preference eat the flesh of other humans whenever it is possible to do so—this is a proposition so long entertained as a fact that it is accepted as the basis for certain stock jokes and cartoons about missionaries and explorers, and can be called an established belief of our culture. We look at the missionaries in the big black pot; we observe the naked aborigines dancing about and working up an appetite (they are almost always black, incidentally); and we smile in anticipation as we drop our eyes to the caption. We don't think this sort of thing can happen to *us*; but we are quite sure that it has happened to others and that it probably still does in the hidden unexplored corners of the globe. We don't even stop to ask ourselves where these simple natives obtained such a large iron pot, and, having obtained it, how they managed to move it from one fire to the next. The whole situation is merely accepted.

In fact, there are no such peoples—cannibals by preference. It is highly improbable that there ever were. Yet the myth is ancient indeed, going back to the anthropophagi (or androphagi), the man-eating men of classical legend. There seems to be something about the flesh-shrinking horror of the idea that has a strong perverted appeal to the imagination, not unlike the powerful pull of any well-told horror story such as Poe, H. G. Wells, John Collier, and others reveled in.

Sometimes the scholars themselves have been responsible for the perpetuation of the cannibal myth. For instance, when the remains of Peking Man were found in the twenties, some anthropologists concluded that he was a member of a cannibal society. The evidence? Some of the long bones in Peking Man showed that they had been cracked longitudinally. Inference: they had been cracked to extract the marrow. Corollary: the eating of the Peking Man had been done by other men; and therefore cannibalism was a way of life with these people. *Quod erat demonstrandum.*

The conclusion is a simple absurdity. Dozens of causes could be invented to account for the fact that some bones were cracked longitudinally. Nothing here leads us firmly to human teeth at work, or clubs wielded by human hands. It's just one of many possibilities.

In prehistoric times populations were relatively small; and if cannibalism had been habitual, such populations would have consumed each other if they had insisted on sticking to the human diet.

The truth is that only under special conditions will men partake of human flesh. Habitual cannibalism, historical or contemporary, is nonsense. Here are the special conditions which make the eating of other humans acceptable to some people:

Famine or starvation. Desperate people in a situation where no food is available and where there is no hope that it will become available have frequently, as a last resort, turned to cannibalism: in the grimmest moments of the Donner Pass, the story of which has never been fully told; in the whaling sagas of boats adrift at sea—our literature can supply many examples, all of them liberally seasoned with chilling horror.

Burial Cannibalism. In some cultures the ceremonial eating of a morsel of the dead member of the group, just before he is buried, in order to acquire a part of his skills or spirit, is customary.

Ceremonial Cannibalism. It is not uncommon among certain warrior tribes to eat part of a slain enemy to transfer his strength to the eater.

Revenge Cannibalism. Eating the flesh of dead enemies as a revenge upon their spirits and as a mark of contempt for them individually has been reported among a number of nonliterate peoples.

Idiosyncratic Cannibalism. Terrible to relate, it is possible to acquire a taste for human flesh, and there are aberrant humans—at least they seem to be bipeds—who have developed it. Such persons have a craving to supplement their ordinary diet with human meat. One of your present authors served as an expert witness in a case in which a 70-year-old man was tried for the murder of a little girl, whom he had allegedly eaten. The murderer confessed to a fondness for human flesh, and it was this confession, written in a letter addressed to the little girl's mother, that led to his arrest and eventual execution. But this sort of thing is individual, *not* found in the population as a whole.[6]

THE NOBLE SAVAGE: FREE OF TOOTH DECAY?

Explorers who return to home ports with stories of unearthly beauty discovered in mysterious and distant lands—islands and other primitive, exotic, and untouched paradises where no sickness strikes, where one picks one's food out of the trees and the girls all think white men must be gods—are probably the originators of the idea that among primitive peoples there is no such thing as tooth decay. So we have current the idea that there must be something native to the blood of primitive man which civilized man does not share—some ethnic genetic factor that is resistant to caries. This is such an attractive idea to the rest of us, who like to keep our dentists in Cadillacs, that the will to believe is very strong.

The truth is that once these natives adopt the artificial diet of civilization, any such factor ceases to be influential. While they lived the uncivilized life, yes—it's true that they suffered much less from tooth decay than civilized man does—with some exceptions such as the natives of Jamaica, for instance, where the use of sugar is widespread and the chewing of the cane is a common habit. Indeed, before they had any contact with the white man, most peoples in their native habitats suffered very little, if any, from tooth decay.

Yet we know that prehistoric man—and he ought to be uncivilized enough for anybody—sometimes suffered from very bad tooth decay. Indeed, some of the teeth of man's earliest ancestors, the Australopithecines, well over a million years ago, were carious.[7] Rhodesian man, a Neanderthaloid type, of about 30,000 years ago, known from the skull without the mandible, had nearly every tooth in the upper jaw, and probably also in the lower, fearfully and painfully decayed— what is more, it is quite possible that the decayed teeth, and the abcesses that some of them led to, resulted in the death of Rhodesian man. Evidence of suppuration in the mastoid region of the skull indicates that Rhodesian man suffered from severe mastoiditis, probably not unrelated to his poor teeth.

However, in most fossil men the teeth are flawless. They may be worn down to the pulp cavities through attrition from particles of sand or other such materials in the food, or from overwork; but no caries.

But you start feeding these people foods rich in carbohydrates and accustom them to the white man's diet, and the teeth start to go.[8]

A contemporary comparison of the teeth of civilized and of uncivilized man by the anthropologist V. Suk, revealed that at the age of eighteen only 10-15 percent of whites in metropolitan areas have perfect teeth; among Zulus it is 85-94 percent.[9]

STUFF A COLD AND STARVE A FEVER?

Popular prescriptions for physical ills equal the number of well people tending to or advising sick people. The sick person will do almost anything to get well, and welcomes any sort of advice; and the well person is sure to have some placebo or specific which he knows will do the job. Just spread the news around your office force that you have a sore throat and see how many varieties of cure you are offered by those who do not have a sore throat. Sometimes it comes to more than one per adviser. Among the most dogged of the folk cures is the insistence that a person with a cold should gorge himself with food, but the person with a fever should go foodless until his body learns to behave itself. We have not been able to trace this proverb or adage to its source; but it is certain that our grandchildren will hear of it. The idea is cognate with the notion that one should never eat unless one has an appetite.

The fact of the matter, as Bogert points out, is that appetite "is often greatest in certain diseases which would be benefited by a short fast or limited food intake, while in illnesses such as fevers the sick person should be fed to prevent loss of weight and strength, due to the disease using up the body tissues when insufficient food is given."[10] We may not care for Bogert's prose style; but his medical facts are eloquent. In short, "stuff a cold and starve a fever" is nonsense as a generalization.

Take a Short Nap Immedately After Meals?

It's a lovely idea, and sure to strike a favorable response in the breast of anyone who is in a position to lie down and snooze after the serious business of refueling; but it is not a sound idea physiologically for the simple reason that digestion, like other bodily functions, is slowed down during sleep. Quite the opposite advice should be taken, except for people with poor digestion: they may benefit from lying down for half an hour after meals.

Mankind has had this knowledge for a long time; but the older generation, falling into slumber easily on a full stomach, must justify the habit, and therefore they support the idea that their tendency is a reflection of a good health habit. But old Dr. Andrew Boorde, who published his *Dyetary of Helth* in the reign of Henry VIII (actually 1542), while allowing certain liberties to the sick about sleeping in the daytime, urged everyone to make an effort to get his rest during the night. "Whole men," he said, "of what age or complexion soever they be of, should take their natural rest and sleep in the night, and to eschew all meridial sleep. But, an need shall compel man to sleep upon his meat, let him make a pause, and then let him stand, and lean and sleep against a cupboard, or else let him sit upright in a chair, and sleep. Sleeping after a full stomach doth engender divers infirmities."

RED MEAT IS NEEDED FOR COURAGE AND STAMINA?

Stop us if you have heard the joke about the Harvard man, the Yale man, and the Dartmouth man, which is a favorite in Hanover. We give it here, for those who need filling in, only in outline form: The three men were giving their order to the waiter. The Harvard man said, in as deep a voice as he could muster, "I want two pounds of red meat, waiter. Make it extremely rare." The Yale man said, "Waiter, I want three pounds of bloody, red, raw meat." And the Dartmouth man said, "Hell, waiter, drive in your cow and I'll cut off my own slice."

Behind the ribaldry is the notion, perhaps a hangover from imitative magic, that one takes on the character of the food eaten: thus if one eats the heart of a lion one becomes brave and fearless. The idea is extremely tenacious and gives birth to a corollary, namely, that vegetarians lack courage and stamina. One would have thought that the single example of 94-year-old Bernard Shaw, testy and vinegary to the last, would have laid this ghost. He was a vegetarian all his life.

In fact, there is no evidence that the kind of food people eat has any influence on the disposition or on the mental or moral traits. The Eskimo, eating almost exclusively animal foods, is, as Bogert was quick to recognize, "very good natured and peaceable," while a Far Eastern ethnic group subsisting almost entirely on vegetable foods is quick-thinking and warlike.[11] Is any animal more ferocious and active for its size than the American red squirrel? Yet his diet is nuts, pine cone cores, seeds, and grasses.

LETTUCE AS A SOPORIFIC?

Among the citizens of certain societies the idea is current that the way to induce sleep is to eat lots of lettuce. The origin of this folk nonsense is hard to determine: maybe someone saw a rabbit sleeping with part of an undevoured lettuce leaf still hanging to his lips. In any event, the notion took root.

There is no truth in it. Lettuce is mostly water, of course; aside from that, it contains protein, carbohydrate, fat, crude fiber, ash, calcium, phosphorus, iron, copper, nicotinic acid, and vitamins A, B_1, C, and B_2. Not one of these has the slightest sleep-producing power. The rabbit just dropped off because he was full and tired of it all.

CARROTS—GOOD FOR THE COMPLEXION?

Actually there is much more legitimate excuse for this folk belief than for many. A deficiency of vitamin A will cause dry skin, and carrots (like many other vegetables) are rich in vitamin A. In fact, one large scraped carrot has 10,000 international units of vitamin A. Since a dry skin is associated with poor complexion, there is reason to believe that eating carrots will help. At least it will supply part of the deficiency and thus help restore the skin to its normal condition and therefore tend to improve the complexion. But there's more to it than *that*. A serious vitamin A deficiency will also cause diarrhea, intestinal disorders, poor teeth and gums, eye troubles, and other equally unpleasant symptoms; and in addition, vitamin A deficiency is only one cause of poor complexion. If a poor complexion is caused by something else, a person could eat carrots until they came out of his ears without improving the appearance of his skin. It's a little like seeing a tree fall in the forest and assuming that a man must be in there with a saw. A man may be in there with a saw; he may be in there with an ax; a beaver could have cut down the tree; maybe the wind did it; possibly it was struck by lightning; maybe it was an old rotten tree anyhow and just couldn't stand any longer.

ONIONS AND GARLIC: CURE COLDS, BUILD STRENGTH?

That onions have curative power against the common cold is a belief deriving straight from homeopathic magic: "Like cures like." With a cold, the nasal passages are restricted and the eyes water; same thing happens when one prepares onions. Obviously, then, onions cure colds. Everybody knows *that!*

Entrepreneurs who have developed the multimillion-dollar business of manufacturing medications for the cold—and their advertising agencies—may, however, rest easy: to date, science has discovered nothing which will cure or arrest a cold; and the onion is not about to replace those tablets or ointments or laxatives or sprays we love so well. At least they make us *smell* better than onions, and that's worth something.

Cognate with the belief in the curative powers of onions is the faith in garlic as a strength builder. It builds strength in the breath, and nowhere else. But as a breath strengthener it has no competition.

FOODS THAT CONSUME BODY FAT?

The belief that by eating something or other one can effect a reduction in one's body fat is by no means confined to the Dark Ages. The idea is so attractive that you'll find it enjoying robust health in our own day: eat this preparation and grow thin. "The tasty new food that consumes your own body fat, painlessly, easily, without risk." What could be more alluring to a nation which is habitually overweight?

The only trouble here is that scientists specializing in nutrition tell us that it is "absolutely impossible for any combination of foods to cause body fats to be consumed, except insofar as a diet high in protein is known to raise basal metabolism slightly."[12] In fact, any food taken in excess of what the body needs tends to be fattening itself. So poor Daddy must go back to counting calories all over again. Sorry!

THE "R" MONTHS AND THE OYSTERS

Thousands of otherwise sophisticated persons in our society are firmly convinced that oysters must not be eaten except in the months that have the letter R in them. They would not even consider eating oysters in July, for example, and they are shocked if you do. And this despite the fact that the original reason for the prohibition disappeared with the discovery of modern methods of refrigeration. Back in the old days it was hard to keep oysters alive in transit to consumers during the hot days of summer. If they died, they spoiled; and when they spoiled—well, your nose knew, and also you could be poisoned. So the rule of the thumb: eat oysters in the R months only.

The truth is that with modern refrigeration and the carbonated shucking methods, "oysters may be eaten in any month of the year."[13] The reference to "carbonated shucking" applies to a method developed by Dr. H. F. Prytherch of the U.S. Fish and Wildlife Service by which the oysters get drunk on carbonated water and relax the muscles which hold the two halves of the shell together. Let that be a lesson to us all.

STOMACH ULCERS FROM ALCOHOL?

Medical research makes it very doubtful that alcohol is ever the sole cause of stomach ulcers, and if you have heard some village prophet solemnly ascribing the ulcers directly to alcohol you have known the oversimplification of folk "wisdom" in action. Popular errors owe their untruth very often to the deeper mistake of attempting to explain complicated matters with a simple formulation. "Prolonged and excessive use of strong alcoholic beverages," as Haggard and Jellinek correctly point out, causes irritation, and this may contribute to the development "of chronic inflammation, gastritis"—which is undoubtedly aggravated by the vitamin deficiency which occurs when a chronic alcoholic tries to substitute booze for food. *In this way* alcohol can be a contributing factor in the development of stomach ulcers. And if an ulcer has already gotten started, the intake of alcohol is unquestionably ill-advised, since it stimulates an increased flow of hydrochloric acid. This is very highly irritating. But to predict that because a person uses alcohol he will sooner or later develop ulcers is as foolish as saying that because you bought a high-powered racing car you will end up in a crash. This is not cause and effect; it just happens that way when other factors are present. *Any* excess in alcohol, or in applying the throttle, can lead to disaster.[14]

CIRRHOSIS OF THE LIVER FROM ALCOHOL?

Nine out of ten literate persons will tell you in sober conviction that cirrhosis of the liver is the terrible price one pays for association with John Barleycorn. What they *should* say is that cirrhosis of the liver occurs more frequently in the inebriate, the habitual boozer, than it does in the moderate user or the non-user. But it is not a common disease, nor is it a common occurrence among the inebriate; and it does occur among young children and among teetotalers. The medical profession has no certain knowledge of what causes cirrhosis of the liver—either in drunks or in nondrinkers. In a recent investigation, the disease was found to be present in 8.7 percent of chronic alcoholics whose cases were noted in autopsy records of several large hospitals, while among moderate drinkers and abstainers cirrhosis was present in 1.0 percent. The best guess among doctors to date is that the disease is not caused by alcohol alone, but by alcohol in association with some other toxin, name unknown. These facts won't affect the drunks—they won't be reading this book; but let others free themselves of a needless fear—if they had one. Just don't become a drunk and you'll probably be all right as far as cirrhosis of the liver is concerned. And that goes for arteriosclerosis, cancer, and kidney disease, too, which have also been ascribed, incorrectly, to the use of alcohol.[15]

PASTEURIZED MILK IS FREE OF BACTERIA?

Our purpose here is not to scare mothers half to death, and before we say anything more we should explain that bacteria are not the enemies of man—not necessarily. In fact, we couldn't live without the "good" ones, and they are in the majority. Bacteria are necessary. It's only the "bad" ones we need to worry about.

Louis Pasteur destroyed microorganisms in milk by boiling it in flasks sealed with cotton. Hours or even days later, after the remaining spores had been allowed to germinate, he boiled it again. This is the same method he used to prevent wine from fermenting.

Pasteurization, while it derives from his name, is not the same method at all, as applied by modern milk producers. What they do today is merely to heat the milk to 55-70° Centigrade or 131-158° Fahrenheit—and while this kills off some bacteria, it certainly does not kill all. The fact is that by the time the milk is delivered on your doorstep the bacterial count is almost as great as it was before pasteurization. That's not the point, however. The point is that most of the "bad" bacteria have been removed from the field of action—if they were ever there at all, as they may have been. Pasteurization, in short, is insurance, not a complete destruction of all bacteria. There ought to be a book entitled, *Our Friends the Bacteria*. Is it the toothpaste people who have made *bacteria* an evil name, or the gargle-and-bad-breath people? Kill off all bacteria and you'll never digest another meal—never!

White Eggs—Superior to Brown Eggs?

Why is it that every attempt is made by poultrymen to make their hens produce white eggs only, and if neither diet nor breeding has eliminated the brown eggs the egg grader does so himself? The answer is that the city markets want white eggs and will pay more for them; and the reason behind *that* is that city housewives want white eggs— but the reason for preferring white ones is hard to pin down. Maybe there is some association of white with general cleanliness in the minds of those busy ladies with their baskets over their arms; we can be sure that unwashed eggs, with small feathers and goo still on them, would be turned down instantly.

Turning to the zoologist, we learn that there is no unvarying relationship at all between the color of the shell and the contents of the egg. Your egg can be white, brown, speckled or red-white-and-blue (the last-named occurs very rarely, even among John Birch hens): the inside is just about the same. As a matter of fact, brown eggs are preferred by housewives in certain societies—on the equally faulty reasoning that they are richer than white ones.

Ground Glass: An Effective Murder Weapon?

Chances are that if you asked the next dozen people you meet tomorrow morning if ground glass is lethal if eaten, those who do not immediately hasten away from you will answer in a strong affirmative. This is one of those things we've always known. *"Of course* ground glass will kill a person if he eats it."

Actually, ground glass is harmless. One does not suggest a diet composed entirely of ground glass; it is said to be singularly tasteless, and is generally eschewed by gourmets. But if you feed it to your rival and wait to see him writhing on the floor, you'll have a long wait. The seventeenth-century physician Sir Thomas Browne experimented with a dog once, and gave the animal "above a dram thereof, subtilly powdered in Butter and Paste, without any visible disturbance."[16]

Splinters of glass, now, provide a different story. Splinters and broken sections of glass may cut the esophagus, the stomach, and the intestines, with most unpleasant consequences, including death. But it is harder to get people to accept glass splinters: they begin to get suspicious.

Honey—A Cure for Bronchial and Pulmonary Troubles?

It is a belief of great antiquity that honey and pine preparations will cure sore throats, head colds, and all kinds of bronchial and respiratory ailments. For example, Sir Thomas Browne reports that the Emperor Julian, who died in the middle of the fourth century, "for his spitting of blood, was cured by Honey and Pine Nuts."[17] And in our own day a sizable industry is built—and flourishes—on the continuation of this faith.

Honey is bland, of course, and feels soothing on a sore throat; a cough caused only by some local irritation may be temporarily relieved by swallowing honey. Besides, it tastes good. But it will *cure* nothing. Pine, of course, has a pungent odor; and possibly people think that this sharpness will cut through a stuffy head cold and create easier breathing. At any rate, it won't hurt anybody. A person with a cold misery, as is well known, will try nearly anything. But there's no cure for it.

"Unclean" Foods: Science Applauds Moses?

Among those who will defend every sentence in the Bible to the last ditch are those who reinterpret the Scriptures for the age of science and explain that the six days of creation in Genesis are to be translated as six geologic epochs; that the "needle's eye" in the metaphor of the rich man getting into heaven really meant a narrow gate in the city walls; that Lazarus had a cataleptic fit and only *seemed* to die; and that Moses, in giving the Jews the dietary laws, was actually speaking with a knowledge of modern hygiene which our laws of science echo. Anything irrational in the original is given this treatment, and suddenly that ancient text gleams with a new luster. Respect for a tradition and for a great and holy book is one thing; but to attribute to it characteristics which it does not possess cannot be respect, but fanaticism.

Yet we find Dr. Charles J. Brim calling the Mosaic Code "a well-defined and complete system of public-health rules and regulations" without which the Jewish nation would have become extinct. "The dietary section of the Mosaic Code," he affirms, "was the result of careful researches by its author."[18]

Dr. Brim had available to him Sir George James Frazer's monumental *Folklore in the Old Testament*[19] where he could have learned what many scholars have pointed out since, that the most fundamental of the laws codified by Moses were much older than the Pentateuch, and that many of the injunctions of the Mosaic Code represent practices which flourished hundreds of years before Moses; and that there is not one of them which is not found today among nonliterate peoples.

The prohibition against eating pig in any shape or form, for example, which is as characteristic of the Mosaic Code as anything could be, is ascribed by Dr. Brim and his followers to a foreknowledge of trichinosis. It would be heroic to ascribe the Mosaic prohibition to this information; but turning to Frazer we find simply that "the pig ranked as a sacred animal among the Syrians. At the great religious metropolis of Hierapolis on the Euphrates pigs were neither sacrificed nor eaten, and if a man touched a pig he was unclean for the rest of the day. Some people said this was because the pigs were unclean; others said it was because the pigs were sacred. This difference of opinion points to a hazy state of religious thought in which the ideas of sanctity and uncleanliness are not yet sharply distinguished, both being blent in a sort of vaporous solution to which we give the name of taboo. . . . The sacramental killing and eating of an animal implies that the animal is sacred, and that, as a general rule, it is spared."

In short, nobody knows whether the pig was saved from the butcher because it was a sacred animal or because it was "unclean." We know that there was an ancient Jewish ceremony in which both the mouse and the pig were venerated as divine; and in fact it is probable that most animals labeled "unclean" were originally sacred. Freud's point, that "an original correspondence existed between what was holy and what was unclean" is important here.

Furthermore, the Old Testament "unclean" represents the idea of "taboo" rather than "foul." The word refers to the sacred and forbidden rather than to the "filthy" or "soiled." These injunctions in Leviticus, equally familiar in primitive cults, have no basis in hygiene —they are purely religious in nature. Examples abound:

When a woman bears a male child, for instance, she is "unclean" for seven days (Lev. 12:2); but if she bears a female child she is "unclean" for fourteen days. (*Ibid.* 12:5). The sense of "unclean" is clearly in the ritual sense here, and has nothing whatever to do with hygiene.

Any contact with utensils or garments touched by a menstruating woman was "unclean," and so was the woman herself (Lev. 15: 19-33). The prohibition was a matter of ritual, based on magico-religious ideas about the evil powers believed to be resident in a woman at such a time—the avoidance of contagion was to be achieved only by complete avoidance of everything with which the "carrier" came in contact. And the purification was a magico-religious measure, not a hygienic one.

No primitive tribe forbids the eating of anything edible on hygienic grounds; but taboos are laid on the basis of magico-religious or totemistic grounds. Animals and plants sacred to certain groups may not be eaten by them—often not even touched. Often enough, certain plants or animals are considered ancestors and must never be harmed in any way.

In such gradual steps most of the dietary prohibitions of the Jews had their origins—sacred and totemistic—which had become hidebound tradition by the time of Moses.

Of one thing we can be completely certain: Moses, in bringing the laws together into one code, did not do any medicinal research: he was not a scientist. This is no derogation of the immense contribution he made: quite the opposite—it makes his contribution all the more magnificently human.

Tuck in Your Napkin and Let's Have Some Creamed Spiders

To the Australian aborigines anything edible is considered food. Their idea of edible is anything that won't poison you. The more civilized peoples use edible to mean something "fit" to be eaten: something "suitable by nature for use as food" especially by humans (Webster III). It is on the interpretation of "suitable" that differences arise, and here also arise roughly a million popular errors on the subject of diet.

That ham and pork and other porcine products are unclean is one of the most obvious. Millions of people in the world today would rather die than eat pig. Some religions—not the Jews alone—have considered pig ritually unclean; and some—the Cretans, for instance—worshiped pigs. Among the Egyptians pigkeepers could not even enter temples or marry the daughters of other men. Even so, they sacrificed a pig once a year to Osiris. A women's organization (the Bulendu) of the Baluba in the Congo must eat pig when they are initiated, but must never eat it again. Christ, it will be remembered, drove certain unclean spirits into a herd of swine. In the Celebes it is believed that pigs hold up the earth and cause earthquakes when they shift about. In the lower Congo a woman who has eaten pork is not allowed to plant (this sounds like a marvelous way of escaping from work, but apparently it was not resorted to for this reason). In some parts of the world drinking pig's blood is supposed to induce the power of prophecy; and among the Caribs there exists the belief that a girl who eats pork will have children with small, piggy eyes.[20] This is merely scratching the surface of pig lore, a subject which is rich in human as well as porcine interest; but our subject for the moment is diet—and the variations in what is considered not only edible but delectable or, on the other hand, unclean.

The wealthy Maecenas, patron of the arts, who could afford whatever he wanted, had a preference for donkey meat. If this makes you shudder, consider this: at the Harvard Faculty Club in this day and year, one of the specialities of the dining room, considered by the congoscenti as a great delicacy and by your correspondents as supremely succulent, is horse meat steak. It's what they *do* to it. And there's no attempt to camouflage the dish with a different name, either. They don't call it Düsseldorf Tenderloin au Jus. No, sir. Horse meat steak. A great brain builder.

The precious Heliogabalus, the somewhat effeminate epicure, was much given to the combs and wattles of cocks—a taste which caused Sir Thomas Browne to wrinkle his patrician nose in disgust.

For Trimalchio, few dishes were more delicious than the dugs of a pregnant sow, unless it was the uterus of a barren one. In certain Roman circles a supreme delicacy was the skin of a womb that had miscarried—"whereunto nevertheless we cannot perswade our stomachs," said the critical Sir Thomas Browne, a lover of English, which is to say plain, cooking.[21]

When Homer smote his bloomin' lyre (see *Odyssey,* Bk. IV) he appeared to consider any form of fish as the last resort of the starving. The English or American fish 'n' chips aficionado, of course, would differ. Bacon was a disgusting food to the fastidious Elizabethan Londoner; it was fit only for the hayseeds and the terribly poor.

Dogs have been considered a delicacy by many people at many different times and places. The great physician Galen recommended them young, fat, and gelded. Testicles are still a prize dish in many areas. Fried worms, as offered by expert Mexican cooks, and even centipedes, can be delicious. We give this on personal testimony, and many another bold traveler will support the claim.

In our culture one of the purest foods imaginable is milk from cows. To most Mongoloid peoples drinking such stuff is disgusting. Even we ourselves may wince a trifle, however, at the idea of drinking milk from any other mammal. Goats' milk for invalids, perhaps. But how about asses' milk? It has long been prescribed for epilepsy. Among the Mongolian nomads mares' milk is one of the chief articles of diet. M. le Comte, the father of Toulouse-Lautrec, used to ride a brood mare into the Bois de Boulogne every morning, dismount at his favorite café, milk his steed into a glass, mix the milk with sherry, and consume it to his own exquisite delight as thousands cheered.

We may squirm at the idea of John the Baptist eating locusts; but what would John the Baptist think if he could read American advertisements aimed at gourmets and offering rattlesnakes as tidbits? Ants, of course, are just the thing for certain palates; we have been told—and we do not take this one on faith without personal verification—that raw ants fresh out of the hill taste like pickled blueberries. Mmmm!

Schools of thought about what is edible can change with the times, of course. Elderberries were called pure poison by Sir Thomas Browne; but we know now that they are the basis of one of the most maidenly of spinster drinks—we learned it in *Arsenic and Old Lace*.

If You Like the Taste—Eat It?

Some of the philosophers of the Noble Savage, advocates of the natural way, are telling us these days that we can trust Old Mother Nature to direct us to a proper diet: all we have to do is eat what we like the taste of. This is our built-in criterion of dietary good and evil, we are told: experimental confirmation is at hand; and besides, we all know that little children, if left to their own devices, will select a properly balanced diet and thrive.

The fact is, as any parent of fast-moving youngsters knows, that little children, left to their own devices, will cram down the little red lane almost anything they can lay hands on, including razor blades, lost buttons, and bird droppings.

Perhaps the enthusiasts of nature are making a parallel between our four-footed cousins of the fields and forests: carnivorous animals eat meat; one can depend upon it. Herbivorous animals eat plants. But that doesn't mean that members of each class will not eat things that cannot be called healthful—the cow to the loco weed, the coyote to the poisoned bait.

Besides, we are not living in a state of nature but in a state of civilization; and very few of the foods of civilization exist in their natural state. Nature is not going to teach us intuitively to recognize the composition of packaged foods: you could make sawdust *taste* good. But don't: the Food and Drug Administration will be cross.

In so-called civilized foods almost every taste is "unnatural" to some extent. Furthermore, the taste buds in some people report deranged or vitiated information. Also, our taste gives us no knowledge of the fact that a lemon, apparently full of acid, will form an alkali in the system, or that many sweet-tasting fruits will form acids once we get them down. And then, too, we can develop cravings that we know perfectly well are *not* good: as for too much alcohol, tobacco, or drugs.

Even so, we are taking bets at the far window to the left that readers of the above paragraphs a year from now will be right back believing again that if you like it it's good for you.

GREEN APPLES—BELLYACHE?

One of America's loveliest and most nostalgic myths, honored in poetry and song, legend and chromo, is that of the Barefoot Boy, the symbol of our lost innocence, plodding along with an apple halfway to the mouth and wearing an old straw hat with the sun slashing across the nose and cheek through a rent in the straw. And accompanied, more likely than not, by a patchwork exemplar of Man's Best Friend.

Part of the myth is the dreadful bellyache the Barefoot Boy gets from eating green apples. Apples which were probably stolen, too.

The fact of the matter is that the stomach makes no differentiation between ripe and green apples. Says Dr. August A. Thomen in *Doctors Don't Believe It*: "If an apple is eaten slowly, and sufficiently chewed, the stomach cannot distinguish between a ripe and an unripe one."

Of course if the Barefoot Boy is going to swipe an *armful* of green apples and eat them all at once and hurriedly, we can't be responsible.

Love Potions—Mythical or Real?

In every narrative there is, however deeply hidden, a wish of the storyteller, according to the psychiatrists. Sometimes the explanations given by latter-day savants are considerably funnier than the originals themselves; and you can take them or leave them, but we don't know how you're ever going to know whether they are true or not. For instance, that Poe was dreadfully afraid of incest and hence wrote *The Black Cat*. Oh, well.

So it is no surprise that we find literature abounding in wish-thinking with respect to aphrodisiacs. After all, how terribly *convenient* if, instead of having to spend all that time, effort, and money in the pursuit of the lady, one could simply give her something to eat or drink that would make her a pushover. Or vice versa—to save the lady all that chasing of the elusive male.

To this day you will find those in the know saying that raw eggs are very effective in this connection. Especially if consumed in beer. Now of course eggs have long been fertility symbols—that's why we have them in the Easter celebrations. But they don't build up sexual passion.

Pliny would have it that the hairs of a hyena pressed to a lady's lips will cause her to become amorous. We cannot trace that one, but we'll wager it won't work.

Onions have been famous as aphrodisiacs for years. They were vouched for by such authorities as Aristophanes and Chaucer. According to today's prophylactic standards, quite the opposite reaction might be expected. Who was that lady I seen you with last night? Oh, she was an oniongrower from down Long Island way. No—it just won't jell.

Potatoes once had the reputation of being powerful aphrodisiacs. It is hard to think of a reason, except that once they were quite rare—and anything that is a luxury, according to Casanova, may be counted upon as an aphrodisiac. For a man of his experience, Casanova could be singularly naïve.

There are no genuine aphrodisiacs. However: alcohol has an effect on the peripheral nerve endings and on the skin which tends to arouse the sexual appetite; and at the same time alcohol dulls the intellectual faculties and thus tends to release inhibition. The combination of these two effects makes alcohol the most available love philter to be had over the counter. There are people who report that the aroma of tobacco does the same thing; but our research indicates that in these cases it is more likely to be the personal associations connected with the aroma than the scent itself which is effective.

Fish—Food for the Brains?

The origin of the belief that fish in the diet increases the power of the intellect is obscure: some have asserted that the idea goes back to an association of fish eating with the clergy in the Dark Ages when only the men of the cloth were educated. Modern supporters of the notion point out that fish is a fine source of phosphorus, and the brain contains phosphorus. But such a line of reasoning would indicate that foods high in calcium are particularly beneficial for people who stand on their feet a good deal, bones containing calcium as they do.

Another reason is held to be the fact that fish is considerably "lighter" than beef and other animal flesh and therefore more suitable for those leading a sedentary life—that is, doing brainwork. Dr. Solomon Strouse points out, however, that the basic proposal about fish as brainfood is simply erroneous and unfounded.[22] Bogert agrees; admitting that fish is rich in phosphorus he adds, "but meat, poultry, eggs and milk are all rich in phosphorus also, and it requires a good many other elements besides phosphorus to build nervous tissue."[23]

It just occurs to us that fish is usually less expensive than meat; maybe that's why they say it builds brainpower—so one won't have to apologize for a cheap meal. Or maybe some jocose observer, seeing how utterly foolish fish look when feeding, cheerfully asserted that eating them would make the feeder intelligent. Anyhow, it won't.

Wine—the Older the Better?

It is well known that fine wines are aged deliberately, and this information has led many people to the belief that wines continually improve with age, and hence the older the better. The alcohol in wine is produced by the fermentation of sugar in the grape, which is caused by a form of vegetable life called yeast. After a certain amount of alcohol has been produced, it kills the yeast and thus ends the process. After that, aging improves the wine only up to a certain point—the fact is that once a wine is sealed in glass bottles, all changes for the better are over. Since the bottles are not always absolutely airtight, wines often spoil after a time. If you have a bottle of wine handed down in the family from your great-grandfather, the chances are it's awful by this time. Get it out and let's see.

A LITTLE OIL OR MILK TO PREVENT DRUNKENNESS?

Very ancient indeed is the belief that if one swallows a bit of olive or mineral oil before taking part in a mild orgy one will be able to "take his liquor like a man" and wake up in the morning without a hangover. Those who have tried it and have waked up with a hangover tell themselves that they are lucky it is not as bad as it would have been without the oil.

Plutarch got this idea from his physician, Claudius. The Romans used oil of bitter almonds. In those days it was believed that drunkenness was caused by the alcoholic fumes rising from the stomach and clouding the brain; but oil, floating on top, would hold down the fumes. It obviously did nothing of the sort, but it was comforting to believe.

Modern adherents of the spread-the-oil school advance the theory that a film of oil spread over the stomach walls prevents the alcohol from passing directly into the tissues. That seems to make a lot of sense at first glance; but consider: the corrugated walls of the stomach are not like a smooth surface; and the stomach glands release hydrochloric acid, which starts immediately to work upon any oil that may have been introduced—indeed, twenty minutes later that oil is not oil any longer but something else which is being processed just as any other food would be.

A parallel to the belief about oil is the faith that milk drunk in advance of the party will be efficacious in the same way. Of course it won't. Nothing will. For it is the law of nature that if you eat your cake it will no longer remain in your lunchbox, and that's all there is to it.

FOR SNAKEBITE—DRINK WHISKEY?

The belief that whiskey is a cure for snakebite is considerably older than the six-shooter but by no means as accurate. In fact, one wonders whether the idea was ever much more than a jocose excuse for having whiskey on the premises. Even in parts of the country where there are no longer any poisonous snakes it is familiar to hear, "Guess I'd better bring home a little bottle of whiskey from the village. Good for snake-bite, you know."

Serious or in jest, the notion is dangerous: whiskey dilates the blood vessels and would therefore facilitate the flow of venom rather than slow it down.

If you could find a whiskey that was at least 70 percent alcohol—meaning about 140 proof (most whiskey being 86 proof)—at least you would have a germicidal liquid to pour into the wound; but the snake's teeth would have deposited the venom well beneath the surface in the first place, so that the germicide would be ineffectual.

A tourniquet above the wound and complete and immediate excision of the venom-filled tissue at the spot where the fangs entered —that's your cure for snakebite. It may not be much fun, but it works.[24]

Incidentally, if you want to dance and sing and give Indian yells after you've had a couple of drinks, one would say you were stimulated; and one would be wrong. Instead, the intellectual watchman who governs your behavior has simply gone off duty. So you do what you feel like doing perhaps instead of behaving with conventional sobriety. You *think* you are being brave and bright and bold and dashing; but the only thing that has really been increased is your inefficiency. Alcohol is an irritant with an effect which is medically sedative. The reason the drinker thinks he is stimulated is that, as Haggard and Jellinek point out, "the immediate irritation from strong alcoholic beverages initiates nervous reflexes which momentarily increase the rate of the heart beat and the depth of breathing. These effects explain the reviving and apparently stimulating effects of brandy or whiskey when given to an individual who is on the verge of fainting."[25]

ALCOHOL—CAUSE OF TUBERCULOSIS?

If we have any point to make on the subject of alcohol, it is the same emphasis that is to be underscored with respect to many another edible or potable product: in moderate quantities it won't hurt most people. To lay the dread disease of tuberculosis at the feet of Bacchus is nothing but a dirty trick born of bluenose absolutism. Nothing causes tuberculosis except the tubercle bacillus. If a person's use of alcohol is excessive to the point where he neglects the laws of hygiene, he is susceptible to many diseases which might otherwise be conquered by the system, and among these is certainly tuberculosis; and another is obviously pneumonia, which is the second highest cause of death among alcoholics as compared with its fifth position in the general population. But here the root cause is not in the alcohol, as such, but in the results of using too much of it.

STYLES AND HABITS IN FOOD

Just as the force of inertia tends to prevent an object from beginning to move, and tends to make it continue in the direction in which it started, so the fear of—or at least the distate for—*change* tends to keep us in the old accustomed ways, to make us want to do things the way grandfather did them, or the way we were taught to do them. One man spits on his palms before grasping the helve of the ax; another rubs his hands in the dirt.

In no field is the ritual and the force of custom more demanding than in the field of diet. Take the potato.

Spanish explorers discovered the potato in Peru and introduced it into Spain, where it created no wild enthusiasm. The rest of Europe eschewed it with vigor. People wouldn't even give it a trial. The rumor promptly spread that the potato poisoned the ground in which it was planted; that it was a sure cause of diarrhea. Some farmers produced potatoes as food for cattle, but for 250 years it was resisted as a food suitable for man. Even when this lowly vegetable received royal acclaim—Louis XVI somehow got to taste a potato, presumably a baked one, and thought it was terrific. So he became a potato fan—even then the rest of Europe would not accept it as a regular part of the diet until the nineteenth century.

Sir Walter Raleigh sent a shipment to Ireland, however, in 1610, and there the potato began to come into its own. In fact, all Europe referred to "Irish potatoes." Little did it matter to the hungry Irish that their neighbors considered them little above the savages for eating this plant; the gentle tuber became a national food: it was hardy, easy to grow, cheap to plant, and the crop was usually abundant. Ireland's debt to the potato has yet to be written: the poets have not written of it, the artists have not made potato motifs, the singers have made it the subject of no song. But the people pay homage to it daily, at almost every meal.

As for the Germans, they wouldn't touch a potato until Benjamin Thompson, head of army ordnance, used his authority to force every soldier under the Duke of Bavaria's banners to plant a patch, care for it and harvest it, and then, God save us, sir, *eat* the tubers! Graubard tells of the innovation in these words: "The duration of military service in those days gave a soldier more than ample time to learn the art of raising potatoes and developing a taste for them. After the men returned to their farms and villages, potato crops appeared all over the country and the food of Europe gained greater security."[26]

Redcliffe Salaman has devoted a magnificent tome to *The History and Social Influence of the Potato,* which the Cambridge University Press nobly published in 1949. No reader whose taste buds have ever delighted in this apple of the earth should do himself the disservice of neglecting to read Salaman's unique book.[27]

Maize, on the other hand, known in America as corn, is still unacceptable to most of Europe, where it is considered cattle food. Some parts of Central Europe and Hungary may be excepted; and perhaps maize is coming into its own gradually; but the resistance has been long-lived and powerful.

But the most nutritious of all foods is still rejected by people of Western cultures: richer in vitamins than meat, easy to prepare, and available everywhere. . . . It is blood. At the thought, we gargle ourselves into horrified and wordless nausea. But the Chinese have long sold dried blood on the open market as an inexpensive food; they look at Americans drinking milk with the same inexpressible disgust with which they would witness the gulping down of urine.

As a matter of fact, many Oriental groups are practically without dairy products of all kinds—for the simple enough reason that where there are more than 2,000 people per square mile the land, under primitive conditions, cannot support both men and animals except those which eat refuse or forage for themselves, like swine and poultry. Which seems to be the cause of a peculiar cultural tradition: lacking cow's milk, babies are nursed by the mother until they are four or five years old.

It should be recognized that in cultures in which certain foods are forbidden, there may be totemistic, magical, religious, or social factors involved, or fear of ritual contamination; or there may be a good logical reason behind it. Unexplained, for instance, is the usage of the Nambikwara Indians of Brazil, who live surrounded by all kinds of domesticated animals that would be edible, yet maintain them merely as pets and won't even eat the eggs their hens lay.[28] Buddha, who died about 500 B.C., specifically forbade the eating of man, elephant, dog, horse, lion, tiger, panther, bear, hyena, and serpent.[29] The Syrians avoid fish; Jews, swine and shellfish; Egyptians, cows; Islam, pork.[30]

Some extraordinarily powerful emotions can be aroused merely by *seeing* the "wrong" food eaten or by realizing after it has been swallowed that what we have dispatched for ingestion down the hatch, as it is jocosely called in nautical circles, is something we would by no means have eaten had we known what it was. An example of the first is the delicate young lady enjoying a picnic with her recently enslaved fiancé. Suddenly a caterpillar fell out of the tree upon her blouse, and she turned white with terror. "Ha, ha, my dear," said her masculine escort, with an excusable display of sangfroid coupled with a tender nonchalance, "have no fear! Why, *that's* nothing but a little old caterpillar," and he swished it off her blouse with one gesture—and ate it. She never spoke to him again. . . . The second case is illustrated by the noble French lady being entertained at a dinner party in South America—her first visit. There was one particular dish which she found irresistibly delicious, but of course we of the nobility do not ask our host direct questions about the food being served. Later in the meal she gathered—quite beyond doubt or question—that the dish she had liked so much had been iguana—a lizard. And she simply threw up, right then and there.

And as far as the taboo goes, history informs us that the Sepoy Rebellion (1857-58) which shook British rule in India was caused by the discovery on the part of the Moslem and Hindu sepoys that the cartridges for the Enfield rifles, which they had to put into their mouths to uncap (not the rifles), were rumored to be greased with fat from cows and pigs. The cows were sacred to the Hindu; the pigs were defiling to the Moslem. Boom!

EAT CEREAL AND BECOME A GREAT HALFBACK?

Nothing in the world could tempt us into making a slighting remark about the advertising industry. Without it, how could a person know what he wanted? No, no—advertising is here to stay, and it would be awful to have to live without it. What would be left for the reader of, say, *Vogue* or *Harper's Bazaar* if the ads were thrown out? Perish the thought.

Besides, you don't have to *believe* everything you read in the ads, do you? Well, do you believe everything you read in comic strips? You do?

Wait a minute, we're getting off the track.

Somewhere or other, we can't remember just where, we have seen ads suggesting that if you eat a certain brand of rather noisy cereal product you will begin to bulge all over with muscles after a while and probably end up on the shoulders of your cheering teammates as your rooters tear down the goalposts.

Milled cereals are almost entirely lacking in body-building materials and vitamins, as it happens. They may explode all over your table when you pour milk on them—this is always good for a laugh, and it is considered a great thing to laugh while you eat as long as you remember to reverse your epiglottis when it's time to swallow—and they certainly save mother lots of time in the morning, but, like sugar, the cereals are not much besides fuel: sources of energy. Not that there's anything wrong with energy; but the body needs mineral salts and vitamins, too.

Cereals won't do you any harm, though, unless you have a tender stomach or fill up so much that you have no room left for the body-building foods you need. By a "tender stomach" we mean one that is easily irritated by bran products or roughage.

THE VITAMIN PILL—THE MODERN PLACEBO?

In the old days, and presumably today as well, the bread pill or sugar pill was, and is, a necessary part of the contents of a doctor's medicine bag. The pill has no therapeutic value of itself—it is nothing but bread, often sugar-coated, and the patient could have gone into her own kitchen and made up twenty of them out of a single slice off the loaf. Yet the pill has a therapeutic value which is not of itself. When the doctor, with many a hmm and clicking of the tongue, completes his diagnosis, pulls a little bottle out of the bag, and says, "You'd better take three of these before every meal for a day or so," the patient begins to feel better, in all probability, after the first dose or two. She feels better, as a matter of fact, as soon as she has the pills in her possession. Somebody cares how she feels; somebody is trying to help her. Every doctor has had the experience: he could find nothing physically wrong with the patient; he prescribed a placebo; the patient improved.

Today our ears—and eyes—are assailed on every side by advertisements warning us against vitamin deficiency and naming half a dozen symptoms to watch for. The symptoms are common to our species and can be recognized if sought in almost everyone at one time or another: weariness, lack of pep, flabbiness of muscle tone, low spirits, loss of aggressiveness. Why did Tom get advancement instead of me? Aha! Tom takes twelve-a-day VP pills! The modern placebo, which can be yours without even calling in the doctor—vitamin pills! The profit in these pills is staggering, and therefore we need not expect the drug industry to cease their manufacture on an immense scale.

The placebo hurt nobody; and the vitamin pills probably don't do any harm, either, unless the taker begins to rely on the pills to fill in the defects of an unbalanced diet. We know that almost every family in the country takes its vitamin pills. Yet there is scarcely a family in the land which *needs* to take any vitamins other than those which are to be found abundantly in the natural foods of a well-balanced diet.

But we appear to be a pill-taking nation, and we do not care what it costs. We like plain white pills; and pills that are half-white and half-brown; pills that fizz in water; pills that divide in half; pills for colds and fatigue and upset stomach and hoarseness and bad breath, and everything but bee stings. And as for the profits! Estes Kefauver showed, to take just one instance, that the dextroamphetamine pills for "chronic fatigue" can be bought for about $2 per thousand if purchased by the generic name; but if a physican prescribes the same thing under a private brand name like Dexedrine, the price is about $40 per thousand.[31]

LIKE IT? EAT IT!

One of the best refutations of the claims of the "Like it? Eat it—it must be good for you if Mother Nature tells you it tastes good" school of dietetics is the example of sugar. We delved briefly into the thought of this school a few pages back but the subject of sugar eating raises the question in a new form.

The human addiction to sugar is very recent, probably for the simple reason that the substance in pure form was hard to come by prior to the days of factory refiners. But there is no tribe anywhere that will not ask for more after the first sweet taste. Apparently our species, along with the bears and certain other animals, have an inborn liking for sugar. It was an expensive taste until recently. Two hundred years ago sugar was selling for about $2.75 per pound, and even in the middle of the nineteenth century it was a rarity on most tables. Today there are candy counters in the subways, on the street corners, and in self-service machines in many business offices, and the consumption of sugar has become more than unnecessary, it has become actually harmful. You like it; but take it easy!

Sugar is a carbohydrate and, as Graubard points out, it can be one of the causes of early fatigue. "After any heavy carbohydrate meal," he says, "the accumulated sugar in the blood tends to drop rather rapidly, leading to blood sugar shortage fairly quickly. A mixed diet has greater staying power, which means that digestion occurs slowly, blood sugar accumulates slowly, and does not disappear as rapidly as it does after a pure carbohydrate diet. Hence fatigue due to rapid sugar removal does not set in as rapidly as it does shortly after a sugar diet."[32]

We used the word "addiction." That is because we do not have the faintest hope that people, including ourselves, even though we know perfectly well that sugar is inadequate, on the one hand, and deficient as a food and is actually harmful to health, on the other hand—we do not believe that people are going to stop using it. Presently, according to one estimate, Americans consume at least 125 pounds of sugar per head annually. Personally, we consider that an underestimate. If you are one of those stern, hawk-eyed, prophetic types which are not in the least tempted by candy, here's a good chance to preen. But you'll preen alone.

One of the reasons why the notion persists that what you have a taste for is naturally good for you—that your appetite for the thing is nature's signal to you that you may indulge the taste—is of course that you *want* to believe it's true. Whether one wishes to go back to Freud's pleasure-pain principle or not, the fact is that we have a psychological "readiness" inclining us to accept what we like and to decline what we don't like, and therefore we are enormously hungry to believe what we want to believe; we are wish-thinkers from the moment the doctor says, "It's a boy," or vice versa—and perhaps before. All right: *certainly* before.

As an example, nothing could be more representative than the proud mother who states with absolute assurance, "My boy could not have thrown the rock that broke the bakery window. He is a good boy." Even if the chocolate from the cream puffs were covering half his face, she's not going to believe what she doesn't want to believe about her boy.

Hence we do not in the least anticipate that a couple of paragraphs in this volume are going to change the popular and idiotic belief that you should eat what you like—or drink.

A somewhat bizarre example that taste can be an inadequate guide to what is good for one comes from a report in the *British Medical Journal*. In this incident an auto mechanic accidently swallowed some gasoline while siphoning a tank. According to Dr. Vinodh Karani, who reports the case, the mechanic thereupon became the world's first gasoline addict. He was seventeen; he now tasted gas for the first time; and he loved it. He craved it. He had to have it. He found he could get along on about a quart per week; but that he required. Dr. Karani said the boy's legs got like rubber as the triorthocresyl phosphate reached him; and it had taken eight months in the hospital to cure him. In short, he had a taste for it; but the gasoline wasn't good for him.

Welsh What?

In English, as is well known, there is a tendency which can be called "popular leveling" or folk etymology or whatever suits you to indicate the process of making the language more consistent or more obedient to the rules of common sense. This is, of course, ridiculous. The English—and also the American—language will have no such rigid laws pronounced upon it, especially the one demanding consistency, that hobgoblin of little minds.

Thus the child will attempt to make the strong verb obey the laws of traditional verbs: "I seed it myself with my own eyes." This is a natural process and nothing but education can correct the trend.

In this tradition, as Greenough and Kittredge pointed out in the first year of this century, we have such excrescences as *Welsh rarebit* "from a whimsical notion that it is compounded of *rare* and *bit*. In fact, however, 'Welsh rabbit' is merely a joke, like 'Cape Cod *turkey*' for *codfish*."[33]

As the years have passed, we must sorrowfully admit that the rarebit bit appears to be gaining popularity, and the rabbit is forgotten almost entirely. In fact, it is hard to remember when we last saw "Welsh Rabbit" on any menu. Maybe you have. But one of the most recent books of usage is now telling the people that "criticisms of *rarebit* are pedantry."[34] If that's the way the ball bounces, then we have to adjust, because our language is living and not dead. But this particular battle is not yet determined. The current revision of Fowler, for example, says "*Welsh rabbit* is amusing and right, and *Welsh rarebit* stupid and wrong."[35]

The new Fowler, however, continues to emphasize this obviously root idea: "What concerns a writer is much less a word's history than its present meaning and idiomatic habits." The trend, then, seems to be toward "Welsh rarebit." Webster III does not acknowledge this: Mencken admits it in none of his volumes on American English; and Evans and Evans have this to say:

The proper name for the melted cheese dish is *Welsh Rabbit*. *Rarebit* is a corruption, due to highbrow folk-etymologizing. Any chef is, of course, free to call any concoction by any name he chooses. But he is not free, among the informed, to overawe others with his own ignorance.[36]

It's a personal prejudice; but we would like to see *Welsh Rabbit* prevail, because it is a term which shows consciousness of origin, which *Welsh Rarebit* has no idea of. But our prediction is that we will lose this argument.

Let it go, then; and with it a dozen other good food jokes which once had meaning and must now be leveled to the common idiom. Life gets more and more complicated as civilization becomes more sophisticated. There is no ducking such a movement. But the smiles resulting therefrom should be increased at the proper proportion also.

This is perhaps too special a field for us to make so much of it in a book intended for the interest of the general literate reader; but there is no checking a committed buff, particularly an amateur.

We therefore continue with joke names of foods, and ask any reader who has something new to let us know about it; so far as we know, the field is virgin: nobody has pioneered it.

Bombay duck. This is a strong-flavored, dried fish intended to accompany curries; and it is famous in India.

Colonial Goose: leg of mutton with savory herbs (Australia).

Deacon Porter's Hat: suet spice pudding.

English monkey: tomatoes and cheese baked on bread.

Fannie Daddies: old Cape Cod for fried clams.

German Duck: half a sheep's head boiled with onions.

Golden Buck: poached eggs with Welsh rabbit and anchovy fillets.

Johnny Cake: corn bread (prev. "journey cake" for lunch on the road).

Mexican rabbit: green peppers, onions, cheese, eggs, and tomatoes.

Scotch Woodcock: scrambled eggs with anchovy.

Poulette Provençale: frogs' legs.

Obviously this is surface scraping, and probably most experienced cooks can make a list ten times as long. Our point is that *Welsh Rabbit* has a tradition, faintly jocose, as many folkways are.

Freezing Will Sterilize?

Because frozen foods will keep more or less forever if the temperature remains low enough, the idea has become prevalent that freezing somehow slays the germs that would cause the food to decay.

Freezing does not sterilize. It does not kill germs. There are many microorganisms which can survive temperatures much lower than those governing the freezing of foods. Freezing inhibits their *growth*, and thus the food remains without decay; but they'd be back at work fast enough if the food were warmed up—even if it were sealed away from any possible access to outside germs—and putrefaction would set in.

That is the scientific fact behind the various warnings about allowing frozen foods to warm up and then putting them back in the freezer. Make up your mind before you remove them and don't take them out of the cold unless you are going to eat them. That's the only safe way.

Three Squares Per Day—Ideal?

Among the customs which, in terms of rational behavior, can only be called nonsense, is the usage based on the notion that three square meals per day are a basic need and that everybody is entitled to this minimum. Where the idea of a *square* meal ever came from is anybody's guess. Evans and Evans think it carries over from the meaning of honest and fair, derived from the carpenter's square and applied to a square shooter, in frontier usage, or a square dealer in cardplaying;[37] and Mathews traces the usage of *square* meaning *square meal* specifically back to 1882 ("I ate a square & talked awhile");[38] in slang, the first meaning given in Wentworth and Flexner is "a full meal" and the only other meaning is the sucker in bop usage. They find a sample in 1894: "I've had my three squares every day."[39] The 1965 revision of Fowler adds another idea: the word *square* may refer to the old-fashioned squaretoed boots, supposedly so healthful in those days and later thought of as stuffy or prim.[40]

To an American it comes with a trailing of clouds of sacrilege to suggest that there can be something irrational about three squares a day; and yet there is good reason to believe that the three-meal regimen is unsatisfactory from the standpoint of the efficient metabolism and output of energy of the organism. Haggard and Greenberg, indeed, have shown that the five-meal regimen—without increase in the total amount of food consumed—is superior. On the three-meal schedule the intervals allow the human furnace to burn down too low, it is alleged. It takes too long to get back to full steam. Adopting shorter intervals between meals keeps the figurative furnace burning at more nearly the same level, and most Americans would do well to consider making the change. Perhaps they are already doing so with the introduction of the coffee break, now practically universal; there is some doubt about the total input not being increased, however. As for the plan of cutting meals still further by going without breakfast or by going without lunch, as certain contemporary sybarites are doing, that is too silly even to discuss, and Andrew Boorde and his *Dyetary of Helth* (1542), to which we have referred before, must put on his dunce cap and stand in the corner for asserting, "Two meals a day is sufficient. . . . A labourer may eat three times a day. . . . He that doth eat often, liveth a beastly life."

We believe Andrew was wrong there; but he had a point later in advising against being sorrowful while eating. "Let every man," sayes he, "beware of care, sorrow, thought, pensifulness, and of inward anger. . . . A merry heart and mind without too much worldly business causeth a man to live long and to look youngly. Care and sorrow bringeth in age and death, wherefore let every man be merry; and if he can not, let him resort to merry company to break off his perplexities." Amen.

3

꧁ꕥ꧂

Beliefs About the Human Body

It is monstrous that we don't, as literate people, know anything
about the human body. As people who are able to read and write, we
are abysmally ignorant about our own bodies. One would think we
would have informed ourselves. That we have not is the nonsense that
heads the list, and becomes the apogee of our stupidity.

One asks, Why? Since the answer has to be theoretical—that is,
since nobody *knows*—the game is open and the number of partici-
pants is not limited. One expert says, "Because we are not motivated
powerfully enough." Meaning that the person with a bad heart may be
willing to study hard to learn all about the human *heart*, but he will
not study the complications of the human eye, nose, throat, foot, or
skin. Another will explain that ever since the Greeks divided man two
ways, body and mind, with mind having the glory and body being
somehow inferior (a notion which flowered under the influence of
Christian theology: let the body suffer if thereby the soul be saved),
their descendants have felt a subtle shame about the body and its
functions, have pretended that what is patently so is not so at all and if
it were we wouldn't admit it—this attitude reaching its fastigium when
sex, however obliquely, enters the picture. Probably Freud would say
that getting the information about the human body is simply too much
work, and we're really not that much interested in any single function

until that function fails to work properly. Honestly, now, you youths with peachbloom skins, how much research are you willing to do on the causes of acne?

There is a complete rollicking chapter on Victorian attitudes toward the body and the language with which such a society was able to survive, given those attitudes. We've all heard how legs became parts of furniture only or, better still, unmentioned except as limbs, and how the artist at the dinner party dared to ask for some of the breast instead of saying "white meat" and was permanently ostracized. Perhaps the best known case is the experience of Peter Simple in Captain Marryat's novel of that name first published in 1834. The incident took place in the Barbados:

> Supper was now announced, and having danced the last country dance with Miss Minerva, I of course had the pleasure of handing her into the supper-room. It was my fate to sit opposite to a fine turkey, and I asked my partner if I should have the pleasure of helping her to a piece of the breast. She looked at me very indignantly, and said, "Curse your impudence, sar, I wonder where you larn manners. Sar, I take a lilly turkey *bosom*, if you please. Talk of breast to a lady, sar; really quite horrid.[1]

There was a story about a finishing school for young ladies which was visited by a distinguished French statesman of the period; when the headmistress guided him upstairs to see the layout of the dormitory facilities, a little group of girls happened to be in the upper hall and, seeing the visitor, ran screaming away, presumably with their skirts over their faces, yelling, "A man! A man!" Indeed, it was not many years ago that the words *naked* and *nude* were judged to have Fescennine implications. One recalls a "Something-or-Other Revisited" article, no doubt by Perelman, in which the writer remembers that as a boy he thought women were solid from shoulders down past hips and thigh to the floor itself and only later learned that the little rascals are the same bifurcated creatures that the rest of us are.

So we denied the existence of the body; and yet somehow the race did not die out. Somebody must have squealed.

If our first thoughts are of sustenance, surely our next thoughts must be about the amusing and endlessly interesting bodies we inhabit for some years. Nowhere is the prevalence of nonsense more dominant than in the innumerable misconceptions about the human body. Brace yourself for some real air pockets.

OH, THOSE BABY-BLUE EYES!

Yes, it is true that all newborn babies, even Negro babies, have blue eyes. The reason for this is that all babies lack pigment of any kind in the layer of specialized tissue of the iris where pigment will later appear. But the idea that the color of a person's eyes is due to the color of the pigment in them—as is generally believed—is totally false. In no eyes of any living soul is there anything approaching a blue-colored pigment.

The truth is that eye color is due to two principal conditions: one, the physical character of the pigment itself; two, the optical phenomenon of interference. There are pigments in the eye, all right—but they are not blue pigments, not ever. The pigments of the eye lie chiefly in the iris; and the iris consists of several layers of specialized tissues, each of which plays its part in determining what color people will say your eyes are. Sometimes the outer layer of the iris is the only one containing pigment cells. But as a rule pigment cells of various kinds are contained in the stromal (basal) layer of the iris. These, together with the nature of the light acting upon them, yield the color effect. Let a bluish light or a reflected blue from a shirt, tie, or dress become active near a blue-eyed person and watch those eyes deepen! How many thrones have toppled because of the interaction of these phenomena.

The blue appearance of the eyes is actually produced by the refraction of light from *brown* pigment particles at the back of the iris. It is very much like the blue veins in your skin—which are really full of dark-red blood; but seen through the skin they do not look that way except in rare and distractingly repulsive instances such as the red nose on the drunk. In blue-eyed people there is an absence of brown pigment in the basal layer—and that is why the babies always are born with blue eyes, as we said.

Thus the color of the eyes is dependent on the refractive capacities of the pigments—the absorptive and reflective qualities—and not on the colors of the pigments themselves.

All this changes, of course, with the use of contact lenses. It used to be that no man, by taking thought, could either add a cubit to his stature nor change the color of his eyes. Those, indeed, were the days.[2]

Hair on the Chest Means Strength?

Let the gentlemen with no hirsute decorations on the chest take comfort from this: Dr. James B. Hamilton of the Yale School of Medicine administered male sex hormones to men who had failed to mature sexually, and they became bald. From this Dr. Hamilton concluded that baldness, and not hairiness, is a sign of mature masculinity. Hence, those persons who associated what they believed to be one of the qualities of the gorilla, a hairy chest, with that other well-known quality of the gorilla, brute strength, were making an erroneous association; but they were doing more than that: they should brush up on their gorillas. These jungle beasts have almost no hair on the chest at all, and though they are preternaturally strong, they are not brutal. They have plenty everywhere else—belly, back, shoulders, arms, and legs—but none on the chest.

"My brother Esau is an hairy man, but I am a smooth man." Yes, and who walked off with the loot?

This myth of the significance of hairiness ties in with another popular mistake: that baldness may be caused by excessive thought—an idea reflected in the contemporary vernacular "egghead" for "professor." Many great thinkers have been bald. Many nonthinkers also have been—and are—bald. The thought processes have nothing whatever to do with the hair-growing processes, of course. However, if we follow Dr. Hamilton's line of thought, it is possible to derive an enchanting explanation for the use of bald men: maturity of masculinity is shown by this very characteristic of baldness. Hence one might say that the bald are mature; and the mature, of course, are thinkers. Harumpf, or words to that effect.

Blondes Get the Best Tan?

The history of advertising will record that in the second half of the twentieth century a certain manufacturer spent millions of dollars to prove that blondes have more fun than brunettes, and that in consequence the brunettes should get themselves a bottle of a certain hair dye and drive all the men crazy. This idealization of the blonde is a great big pain—to us brunettes.

The fact is that tanning in the sun is due to an increase in the spreading of pigment granules in the superficial layers of the skin activated by light rays from the sun. Brunettes have more pigment to put to work in this process than blondes have. Thus they tan more easily and faster than blondes do. Of course the tan shows up with more contrast against those wavy masses of platinum or yellow hair, but brunettes still get the best tan.

If you want to prove you've been on a vacation in the summer—or at least that you spend long weekends at shore or mountain—nothing makes your point more eloquently than a deep tan. During the ski season, the criterion is more likely to be a pair of crutches. But the point is to demonstrate that you're in the class of people who can afford to "enjoy themselves." That you have done so is proved by your tan or your crutches, as the case may be.

The acquisition of a coat of tan as signifying good health—which is what it connotes in contemporary folklore—is actually quite recent. The English beauty, from the Renaissance to the twentieth century, was traditionally white—actually pale. Prior to World War I our ladies went to the beach gingerly, wearing broad-brimmed hats, stockings, something that passed for pantaloons, and long-sleeved blouses. They kept out of the sun as much as they could and suffered torments if they got freckles. They also wished to have 18-inch waists and to have it thought that they grew faint at the very idea of rudeness, roughness, or a touch of honest emotion.

We smile at their attitude; but we should guffaw at our own, since a good tan means nothing except that the skin has increased the pigmentation in order to screen out excess of ultraviolet rays. It does not indicate robustness, good health, muscle, sportsmanship, or ability to steer a boat. It merely means the owner has been exposed to the sun. In the old days the person exposed to the sun was the laborer; now it's more likely to be the sportsman, the golfer, the country-clubber. So now we worship the healthy tan, and make millions selling lotions. In fact there are some preparations among the cosmetics which do much more than protect the skin against burning: they actually put on the "tan" itself.

Tan skin, indeed, has become a status symbol, especially during the off-season and especially to indicate the really successful young executive. If he can show up with a brown skin in February, then all kinds of corollaries are suggested: he had been in the Bahamas for a rest, hence he is not only in the upper brackets financially but must be some sort of irreplaceable man in his shop to be able to take a vacation at such a time of year—and so forth. Basing its appeal on this social fact, one manufacturer bought large sections of advertising space in several big-circulation metropolitan papers just prior to the Christmas season of 1965: it pictured the young successful irreplaceable at his desk in the office, leaning back in his chair and wearing a pair of dark glasses while a lamp shone on him. This lamp, which with a flick of the switch became either a desk light or a sunlamp, was designed to "permit your favorite executive to keep a deep, dark suntan"—and right at his desk. Only $50. Think of it: social status for only $50!

To the extent that a person who spends much time outdoors is in better health than the person who spends most of his time indoors—which has never been demonstrated—a tan may be a partial indication of health; on the other hand, that tan can be an indication that the wearer has subjected himself foolishly to harmful rays of direct sun which are far from health-giving.

The student of human mores may reflect with some amusement on this fad of the brown skin: one of the things it denotes is an acceptance, perhaps even a romantic idealization, of the half-caste; another is a curious reverse snobbery—the maiden with the swarthy skin is no longer the farmer's daughter who must perform menial outdoor tasks in the heat of the noonday sun; she is the island princess alert for the first sound of the soft ukulele and the undulations which naturally accompany those plaintive chords.

Probably it is no longer debatable that in the second half of the twentieth century in most societies of the West a deep tan from the sun does confer status. The day of the pale beauties is gone, despite a last-ditch stand which gave the sun-tan forces a temporary setback that none of them is likely to forget: we refer to the remark of a motion-picture actress by the name of Miss Marilyn Monroe, whose obviously rich endowments in recreational facilities had the lads gasping at one period. Said Miss Monroe in an interview in which she frankly admitted that getting a sun tan was too much agony for one so lightly pigmented as herself, "I like to feel blonde all over." She was instantly surrounded by loyal supporters willing to agree with her slavishly in the most minute detail; but the sun-tan brigade never admitted defeat and are now in full possession of the field.

A final word about acquiring a tan should be added: among the nonsensical ideas in this department is the conviction that one is somehow "taking in" health from the rays of the sun, and that the deeper the tan the more good the sun has done a person. We have seen that tanning is nothing more than a pigmentary response to light; but if it is allowed to become a deep burn, serious injury can be done to the skin and to the deeper tissues. Excessive sunburn—and fifteen minutes under certain conditions could be excessive—causes damage to the vessels of the skin and *may* stimulate the release of too much histamine in addition to the actual burning of the tissues. This *could* produce a condition of shock and make the sun worshiper very sick indeed. What most people do not realize is that it can also contribute to the production of skin cancer and is a major cause of aging and wrinkling of the skin.

BUCKTEETH—CAUSED BY BREATHING THROUGH THE MOUTH?

We breathe through open mouths instead of the nostrils for one main reason, if we do it at all: namely, that we are not getting enough air through the nose. The athlete, whose heart is pumping fast during the action, needs more air than the nostril breathing will provide, so of course he breathes through his mouth too. But ordinarily, in repose, the nostrils convey all that we need. Whatever connection there is between a plugged-up nose and buckteeth, we can be quite certain that the first is not the cause of the second. Not even finger sucking will cause buckteeth unless it is prolonged after the sixth year when the permanent teeth begin to erupt. The principal influence in the development of buckteeth is heredity. But whatever the cause orthodontists can usually straighten the teeth.

CROWDING OF THE TEETH IS A HUMAN DEVELOPMENT?

Every so often one reads that the orthodontist is prospering as never before because the jaws of man are growing smaller and there is not enough room in them for his teeth to erupt properly, and so they become crowded and maloccluded. There is no truth whatsoever in these notions. Man's earliest representatives, the Australopithecines, in several instances exhibited crowded teeth. As our leading authority, Professor Adolph H. Schultz, has stated, "unequivocal crowding of teeth is quite common among recent wild monkeys and apes."[3] "I have never failed to encounter cases with displaced, twisted, or impacted single or several large teeth in collections of primate skulls, and often such manifestations of unmistakable maladjustment in the size of the teeth and the jaws, resulting in crowding, are much more pronounced than in the two or three instances found in the Austroalpithecines."[4] "Crowded premolars are particularly frequent in all manlike apes and comparatively rare in monkeys. Moderate to very marked irregularities in the alignment of the incisors are surprisingly common among baboons and not at all rare in most other species of recent monkeys as well as apes."[5] Such cases seem to result from insufficiently large bony spaces between the incisors and the canines (eyeteeth). Crowding of permanent teeth is frequently associated with delays in the shedding and replacement of milk teeth.[6]

PALE SKIN MEANS ANEMIA?

Persons in perfect health often have pale skins, and this is because the amount of pigment in the epidermis and the supply of blood to the various layers of the outer skin are less than in persons having more coloring. It usually has nothing to do with health if we are pale. The blood supply may be diffuse rather than concentrated—but that's merely an individual difference and is not connected with health one way or the other. In cases of anemia there is a great reduction in the number of red blood cells—and this, too, causes paleness. Ordinarily eating liver readily cures such a condition. Hence the familiar judgment that "she has anemia because she is pale" is likely to be completely wrong. That is not the test.

ROSY CHEEKS MEAN GOOD HEALTH?

Our literature abounds with evidence that bouncing, energetic, barefoot-boy-type good health is characterized by ruddy cheeks and sparkling eyes; and apparently the male of our species has—with rare exceptions—found the vigorous and high-colored female more exciting and attractive than any pale substitute. This may be due to the fact, as some writers have suggested, that blood is the symbol of life (one recalls that in the days of the Four Humors, the sanguine man was an optimist); but perhaps it is more likely to have evolved through experience: the girl with the quick color played a more vivacious game of tag than the anemic and prissy cousin. In any event, history records that the pale ones have always tried to find ways to add a little color—and sometimes quite a lot of color; and they wouldn't go to all that trouble just for fun. (The exceptions have been in occasional cultures where the highborn lady was very delicate and quick to faint if some ruffian exposed his vulgarity by pronouncing the word *leg*, as among the pale Victorians; or among the lovesick in the days of Courtly Love—their pallid skin showed that they were suffering for love's sake and of course this made them irresistibly attractive.)

The high color may or may not be a sign of good health. In the case of a person with a low-grade, continuous fever, caused by some chronic infection, the skin may be beautifully pink and white and the eyes most luminous. Certain forms of tuberculosis and heart disease are associated with high color; and this is true also for some disorders of the circulatory system. Hence one cannot always assume the leaping vitality from the rosiness of the cheek; but what one can assume is that the chromatically meritorious angels will never lack for interesting pursuit, be they healthy or otherwise.

A Brainy Child More Delicate Than the Moron?

Many a protective mother, in order to prevent her little genius from submitting himself—or herself—to the risks of rough-and-tumble play which seems to be native to "normal" children, imagines that the brilliant child is, in fact, physically weaker, and that this is to be expected: she may even develop the alleged delicacy into an indication of superior status. "My little Ermintrude cannot go on those long hikes—she is too delicate. But she gets A's in all her courses, and she is a regular prodigy on the piano."

To which, other things being equal, the proper response is a firm but simple "Balderdash."

Bright children are neither stronger nor weaker than average children. But it is easy to see how the idea takes root. An average child with a weak heart, for instance, could be advised not to play jump rope or tag until the heart strengthens. Meanwhile the child gets a lot of adult attention and spends a good deal of time indoors—with books, musical instruments, or other civilizing playthings. Naturally, then, this child gains proficiency in the cultural fields which the other child, outdoors with the jump rope, does not. But the brilliance has nothing to do with the physical stamina, nor the strength with the brightness.

Handling Toads Produces Warts?

Mankind has long associated filth and dirt and venom with toads and snakes, both of which are surprisingly clean creatures. The old wood-cuts of Antichrist showed the fiend spitting out toads and snakes. The attitude constitutes a dastardly canard which should be vigorously rejected by all toad and snake lovers, if any. Warts are invariably produced by an infectious filterable virus which produces the well-known localized overgrowth of the horny layer of the skin which we call a wart. The virus, as is not generally known, is communicable from person to person by touch. The best removal technique appears to be through X-ray treatment. But neither as a curse of God nor as a result of handling toads are warts produced, and to imagine otherwise is to exchange the scientific method for the ancient imitative magic of the primitive. Yet thousands of people continue to credit the ancient and utterly false association of the bumpy toad with the bumpy human skin. Nothing to it. Toads are delightful comrades, and do not have to be taught not to talk.

Tuberculosis—a Strictly Human Ailment?

While it is true that cold-blooded animals and also the domesticated friends of man, the cat, the dog, the horse, and the sheep, are seldom if ever affected by the tubercle bacillus, those other friends of man— birds and cattle—are very often afflicted by t.b. Human beings do not appear to acquire the disease from birds; but we get it from cattle— especially children, who may be infected by drinking the milk of diseased cows. This is of course one reason for the government inspection of herds. Apparently no other animals outside of the human species and those already mentioned are susceptible; except for anthropoid apes and monkeys, which are readily infected with the human type of tuberculosis.[7]

Feeding the Skin—from the Outside?

In our days at least one entire industry depends upon the belief of the ladies that the skin can be nourished by the application of certain oils and creams to the surface. The same industry is beginning to get a good deal of support from the male section also, according to recent reports.

We hate to be a spoilsport about it, and certainly you are not going to do yourself any harm if you want to put on the oils. But the fact is—in case anybody is interested—that the human skin is nourished from the same sources as is all the rest of the body: through the nutrients carried in the blood stream. The skin is no more benefited, actually, by the surface application of creams and oils than the brain or the heart would be from similar treatment.

If we really wanted to play the Calamity Jane role, we could point out that too much use of creams and oils can be truly dangerous—if their use occludes many of the pores of the skin through which the natural oils of the skin emerge.

No doubt about it, one can satisfy oneself that one has made the skin less dry, at least for the time being, by applying cosmetics of one kind or another; and temporarily one has done so. But for normal people the secretions of the skin glands supply the only lubrication that is needed. Check with the family doctor for details.

WHY DO WOMEN HAVE ONE RIB MORE THAN MEN?

This question was asked seriously by a Sunday-school teacher in a Bible Belt fundamentalist classroom, and it was asked for a perfectly good reason: the teacher wanted to find out if the children had learned their lesson as set forth in Genesis 2:21—"And the Lord God caused a deep sleep to fall upon Adam, and he slept; and he took one of his ribs, and closed up the flesh instead thereof; and the rib, which the Lord God had taken from man, made he a woman, and brought her unto the man." So the gold star for the day went to the little student who explained this event.

We know, of course, that women have precisely the same number of ribs that men do—twelve pairs—and that they are not in the least different from male ribs in any respect. But let's not get smug about it, because it is a fact that the female often has one coccygeal, or "tail," vertebra less than the male.[8] If you ask us, the whole business of tail vertebrae in humans is pretty ridiculous, but there you are.

SEXUAL PROMISCUITY LEADS TO STERILITY?

This is one of those fearsome myths connected with sex which probably originated in the mind of some sexually frustrated mystic who wanted everyone else to be as frigid and abstemious as he was. (Compare the role of Mama in *Oh, Dad, Poor Dad,* of recent fame.) There is no known case of sexual promiscuity leading to sterility. That's the fact. But of course sexual promiscuity, especially in the nonprophylactic days, was likely to lead to repeated venereal infection —and *that* can cause sterility indeed.

Nervousness Means Weak Nerves?

The term *nervousness* refers in a crude (not precise) way to a purely psychological state which has no connection at all with the structure of the nerve fibers. Unless it has been subjected to a partial destruction, there is no such thing as a "weak" nerve. And even if a nerve had suffered partial destruction of its substance, there would usually be no reason to associate this with nervousness. Our "nervousness" is a catchall phrase of popular leveling which really describes nothing specifically. A horse with a sensitive mouth shows its distaste for the bridle and rider by annoying sidestepping. The horse is "nervous." A boy ordered to the principal's office for infraction of school rules is full of fear as to the consequences. He is "nervous." A housewife is tired after a full day of cleaning, cooking, and a meeting of the PTA. She is "nervous." Every one of us is nervous in that we react to nerve stimuli. Weak nerve tissue has nothing to do with it.

Aristocrats Have Blue Blood?

No human being has blood with the faintest tinge of blue in it; all human blood is pure red, from vermilion to alizarin, and darker if the blood is drying out on an abrasion or wound. The illusion that we are blue-blooded was touched upon in the first entry in this chapter, on blue eyes. The further illusion that persons of noble blood or related to royalty have bluer blood than common folk apparently comes from Spain: "blue blood" is a translation of the Spanish *sangre azul.* Here we enter a fascinating chapter of social history. It will be remembered that the Sons of the Prophet set out to destroy the Christian world and to win all men to Islam; and that they swept over northern Africa and crossed over into Spain, only to be stopped at last after hideous slaughter by Charles Martel at Tours. Not in vain was Martel called the Hammer! His victory in 732 stopped the advance of the Moslems in the Western world; but they occupied Spain for about 700 years, established Mohammedan customs and raised Arab and Berber families.

Then came the years of purification, with frightful persecutions of the Jews in Spain, culminating in their "expulsion" in 1492, much to the enrichment of the coffers of Ferdinand and Isabella. The Moslems were expelled a few years later.

Thus over the years it became a matter of social status to be considered a "pure" Castilian; and of course it was true enough that marriages between Moors and Jews were less likely to occur in noble households than among commoners. Thus the Spanish aristocrats tended toward blondness, where the proletariat showed darker pigmentation. Blonds have veins that look bluer than those of darker-skinned persons. Thus we find that blue blood was "claimed by certain families of Castile, as being uncontaminated by Moorish, Jewish, or other admixture" (Oxford English Dictionary). The idea was carried over into English, where by the year 1500 the phrase *true blue* was in use and blue was considered the color of constancy. There were the obvious associations with the sky and with heaven. About a hundred years later we find Shakespeare putting into the mouth of Cleopatra the words, ". . . and here / My bluest veins to kiss—a hand that kings / Have lipped, and trembled kissing" (*Antony & Cleopatra*, Act II, scene 5, line 28).

Blue, in short, continues to be a term of approbation in many connections: a blue chip is worth ten times as much as a white one; a blue ribbon indicates a winner; and to some blue is a symbol of divine eternity. Probably the idea doesn't hurt anybody as long as we remember that factually it's all nonsense: all human blood is of one color and except for abnormal varieties is of one chemical makeup.

My Feet Are Killing Me!

If people are going to insist on walking around on two feet instead of four—and it begins to look as if the habit is here to stay—then they have got to put up with tired feet from time to time, especially if they are overweight, a condition which also seems to be here to stay. But the extremely popular notion that the pain is caused by fallen arches, or even by falling arches, is some miles from the truth. Let's see, now:

The arch of the foot is made up chiefly of the tarsal and metatarsal bones. These are united to one another by numerous ligaments of such noble strength—and the bones are arched by nature in such a way— that the arch itself is never going to collapse. Relax: the arch is there to stay.

If there is any collapse in there—and this could happen—it will be the tendons of the sole of the foot, the plantar aponeurosis. In such a case, the foot tends to flatten out and we recognize the fall of the secondary, or soft-tissue, arch. But this is not the bone-and-ligament foundation, which is what most people mean when they talk of fallen arches.

We must not allow ourselves to be carried away. It is not *impossible* that a complete and hopeless breakdown could occur—one could have faulty bone structure or something. But the condition is all but unknown, as Dr. D. J. Morton, late associate professor of anatomy at Columbia University, made plain; and he was one of America's leading authorities on the feet.[9]

Hair Turns Gray Overnight?

Even medical men have fallen for this one; and of course every close reader of horror stories is aware that "when they forced open the bedroom door the next morning, Lord Cholmondeley's hair had turned pure white." The fallacy is so deeply rooted in our folklore that we find even the hard-bitten editors of *Time* magazine indulging in it. Witness Ernie Pyle's story in the issue of May 31, 1943: "Several weeks before Tunisia fell to the allies, reporter Pyle went into battle with the infantry. . . . He returned to the rear a little grayer." Capping the climax was an eighteenth-century ghost story that we hope was intended satirically: it told of a guest at the old castle, a young man who was totally indifferent to ghosts, who agreed to sleep in the haunted chamber. He placed his brown wig on one of the uprights of the four-poster and left the room to perform his ablutions. Returning, he found that his door had closed and locked. Since it was rather late, he shrugged and settled down for the night outside in the hall. In the morning when they broke open the door for him they found that his wig had turned pure snowy white.

In *The Prisoner of Chillon* (1816) Byron resumes the myth:

> My hair is gray, but not with years,
>   Nor grew it white
>   In a single night,
> As men's have grown from sudden fears.

We were serious when we said "even medical men." Listen to Lee McCarthy, M.D., writing in a textbook: "Sudden and rapid graying of the hair undoubtedly occurs. Even overnight cases are on record. Rapes in young girls have been a common cause—operations, grief due to loss of family, and stark terror have been reported as other causes. . . . Simon describes the curious patient of Duivepart, a healthy male, aged 19 years, who became gray overnight as the result of a terrifying experience in a graveyard. He later had five daughters who were all victims of a precocious canities [graying of the hair]."[10]

Here Dr. McCarthy piles Pelion upon Ossa: not only does he have hair turning gray overnight as the result of a terrifying experience—but he describes the transmission of acquired characteristics to the five offspring. It's enough to make a person's hair turn white.

Graying of the hair, like baldness, is determined by heredity. The age at which a person will become gray, or start getting gray, is determined by certain time genes inherited from one's parents. Almost always it is found that graying begins and is completed in an individual at about the same age in which it occurred in one parent or the other.

Perhaps the best bon mot on the subject is from *The Importance of Being Earnest* when Algernon Moncrieff says to Lady Bracknell, "I hear that her hair has turned quite gold from grief."

SQUARE-JAWED HE-MAN; WEAK-CHINNED SISSY?

It's as dangerous to judge a man by his chin as it is to judge a book by its cover. One naturally associates the face which ends in a great square jaw with power, toughness, strength—especially if there is a five-o'clock shadow, or even a beard, on it. One thinks of the bulldog, certain fearful-looking denizens of the deep, and other prognathous monsters, and one never stops to imagine that there goes a glass jaw which a well-placed right, timed accurately from the shoulder, would probably cause to fold up like a tent. Likewise the person with a chin scarcely visible to the naked eye is deemed a weak character.

An afternoon in the galleries showing portraits of famous persons— or a few hours in the newspaper morgue—is quite enough to set this error straight, for what said Duncan? "There's no art to read the mind's construction in the face." The Spanish Hapsburgs represent a long line of royalty most of whose members were endowed with over-developed lower jaws of great "strength," yet who were personally and individually conspicuously weak characters.

"Who do you think you are—Samson?" a heckler asked Cyrano.

"Precisely," answered our Gascon. "Will you kindly lend me your jawbone?"

IDENTICAL TWINS—EXACTLY ALIKE?

Probably we have all seen so-called identical twins who looked so much alike that "only their mother could tell them apart." But our senses are faulty and our attention wanders: we see but we do not observe. We descend and climb the same flight of stairs every day and cannot report for certain how many steps there are in that flight; we witness an accident and cannot tell what the color of the runaway automobile was; we chew every meal sedulously but cannot say how many teeth we have. When we need to we fill in the blanks with the imagination or from some past experience. Hence, for all practical purposes, these twins are exactly the same: they look the same to us; we cannot tell Harry from James, even if they are standing side by side.

But "identical" has more than one meaning. In one sense, the word shows its parentage (*idem*—the same) and means exactly alike: the wax impression from which the dentist makes your gold inlay (heaven help you) is identical (God willing) with the finished product which is going to be cemented into your tooth. It better be.

In the phrase *identical twins,* however, the meaning is different, as if the "identical" now referred to the ovum from which both twins developed rather than to the twins themselves: and it probably does. Both of the babies developed in the same womb from the same divided egg. Or that the ovum, before it divided, was fertilized by the identical sperm for both twins.

As for the twins themselves, they are never identical, to speak with technical precision. They are so much alike that it is perfectly amazing; and thus folklore and custom focus on the similarity. But the part of the environment within the womb where each baby develops may be enough different for each twin so that they do not develop along exactly parallel lines. One may be under the other; perhaps the upper one has one arm around the neck of the other and is thus in a more advantageous position. In fact, the "indirect effect of crowding" is one of the chief hazards twins run, according to Dr. H. H. Newman, who is one of the greatest authorities on the subject. "Lack of room in the uterus," he says, "very frequently forces the fetuses, one or both, to occupy positions that are unfavorable to normal birth," and sometimes the results are disastrous.[11] In addition, since one-egg twins have to share a single placenta, there is competition between the fetal blood vessels of the two individuals for a placental area usually occupied by only one. Hence it does happen sometimes that there are marked inequalities in the blood supply to each twin. This affects the development of each one differently: one of the two may be born weighing significantly more than the other, and usually one is perceptibly larger at birth. Mentally, too, they may be quite different, as Dr. Rosanoff and his associates have shown.[12] Among 1,014 pairs of twins, for instance, there were 142 pairs in which one or both twins suffered from schizophrenia. Among the one-egg twins there were 28 pairs in which both were affected and 13 pairs in which only one was affected. Such differences between identical twins are to be found all along the line of physical and mental development.

But all this does not mean that identical twins do not resemble each other very closely indeed—perhaps as closely as your left thumbprint resembles your right thumbprint in some cases, so that Aunt Harriet can never be sure which of the boys she saw putting the grasshopper in her salad. Identical twins are always of the same sex and they probably *look* as much alike to the nonspecialist as Tweedledum and Tweedledee.

Always Singe the Hair After a Haircut?

If you happen to enjoy the smell of burning hair, by all means urge the barber to singe after cutting. The only benefit, however, will be your delight in the scent. But there's no reason you should deny yourself this aroma if you go for it.

The idea may be on the wane these days, but not long ago it was generally "known" that hair bleeds when it is cut; that the "vital fluid" must be kept in, and the way to do it is to cauterize the ends.

In a word, No. Hair has no fluid in it, vital or lethal. It does not bleed. But it sure does smell when you burn it.

HAIR AND NAILS GROW AFTER DEATH?

A justly famous conundrum in the old days went like this: A large Negro and a small Negro were sitting on a log fishing. The small Negro was the large Negro's son; and yet the large Negro was not the small Negro's father.

The answer was so simple that people used to kick themselves after giving up.

Today's conundrum goes like this: Both hair and nails on a human body are measurably longer several days or weeks after death. Yet neither hair nor nails can grow if the body is dead.

In case you're still thinking about the pair fishing, the big Negro was the little one's mother. And the reason the hair and nails are measurably longer a week or so after death is that about one-sixteenth of an inch represents hair shaft and nail which was padded by skin while the body lived—skin which gave supporting tissues to both hair and nails but which after death collapsed and shrank. Now you see it; then you didn't.

Hair and nails cannot grow after death, because growth means multiplication of cells—and the body stopped all mathematical activities promptly after the arrival of death.

WE ARE PHYSICALLY WEAKER THAN OUR ANCESTORS?

"When our houses were of willow," proclaimed the old saw, "then were our men of oak. But now that our houses are of oak, our men are become of willow." In other words, everybody is living a soft life and losing his toughness as a result. The younger generation has been going to the dogs for so many centuries that it is shocking. When soccer was introduced into England, the old-timers were disgusted: here were tall youths kicking a ball around in the meadow by the river when they should be learning how to cut each other to pieces with swords. Ah, me. The lost generation. Effete, weaklings all.

Probably the whispering campaign about how much tougher our ancestors were came from retired generals and pensioned soldiers who, like Menelaus grown old, "waxed garrulous and sacked a hundred Troys twixt noon and supper," as Rupert Brooke put it. Any old-time truck driver will regale his listeners with how rugged the work was before power brakes and power steering; and if you know some Dartmouth graduate of the years 1900-1915, get him to tell you how nobody shaved between the Harvard game and Christmas. Or just let him ramble on at will. He'll get to it.

Actually, the researches of Franz Boas, Gordon T. Bowles, and a score of others have established beyond question that today's generation is stronger and healthier on the average than their grandparents. Any college that keeps records of parents and children enrolled there can document the fact that the Class of 1966 was taller and heavier than the Class of 1926. The same is true in Europe, in the industrialized lands: military records in The Netherlands indicate that the average size of recruits increased five inches between 1850 and 1907.

Science Service reported from Washingon in 1960 that "Young men and women in the United States today average about two inches taller than those 60 years ago, a study of the heights and weights of adults over the past 100 years shows.

"Miss Millicent L. Hathaway and Miss Elsie D. Foard of the Department of Agriculture's Research Service report that the younger generation in college in recent years has averaged about an inch taller than their parents. The sons weighed five to ten pounds more; the daughters, two to five pounds more."

When Gertrude Ederle swam the English Channel all the front pages told about it; but the other day when someone made the round trip—both ways without stopping—we can't even remember who it was . . .

THE SOLITARY MAN CANNOT SURVIVE IN THE JUNGLE?

We have been told so often that we do not have ripping-talon claws, rending-tusk fangs, or some other deadly attribute of the great cats in the jungle that most of us believe the folk myth that unless man had joined up in cooperation with a bunch of others of his species or made use of killing-tools he would never have survived the jungle. Our species is much tougher and hardier than it gets credit for. The human heart will outlast almost any mechanical pump ever made in terms of work output; and physically man is one of the largest and strongest of all earth's mammals. In the natural state there were not, probably, half a dozen of the many living things that he had any reason to fear, despite the fact that he inherited no protective armor of either fur or shell.

If you don't want to accept the story of Samson and the lion, you won't deny the written records of Carl Akeley, the explorer, and of Stewart Edward White, the writer, who were each attacked by a leopard and killed the attacker with their bare hands. True, they did not *seek* the encounter. But they won it.[13]

EARLY SHAVING ENCOURAGES BEARD GROWTH?

Many a chin, and many a manly chest, too, has been made to bleed untimely from razor nicks occurring when a valiant youth has sought to hasten the growth of his hirsute attestation to manhood. Probably in these days they're using electric shavers. But *they* won't help any more than the blades did. No amount of scraping the skin will increase the number or the activity of the hair follicles. The time of the appearance—and disappearance—of hair in the male is a matter of heredity.

Cognate with the early-shaving myth is the notion, once very current, that a balding man should shave his beard closely every day so that no nourishment should be diverted from the pate. Of course it doesn't make the slightest difference.

We don't want to spoil anybody's fun—or anybody's business either —but it seems that no evidence is available that any treatment or application is going to grow hair where the inheritance of the genes directs otherwise. Dr. Mildred Trotter took the time to explode three methods supposedly encouraging hair growth: the application of petroleum; shaving; and sunburn. All three had been supported by popular belief as being effective. Not one of them did a single thing to help, she reported.[14]

A PREMATURE BABY OF SEVEN MONTHS HAS A BETTER CHANCE THAN ONE OF EIGHT?

Among those who talk a great deal about these subjects, there is an old and widely held faith that for some reason the immature baby of seven months is more likely to live than one a month older—you might call this an old folk tale. Nobody knows where the idea originated, but the astrologer is sometimes suspected, because he gives the magic number 7 a favored place in his divinations. One John Maubray said in 1724, according to Spencer's *History of British Midwifery*, that because the eighth month is peculiar to the planet Saturn a child born under the sign of this planet is always weak; and if it does survive it has a tender constitution and may very well turn out to be half-witted. Now of course this is nonsense of a very high order. You'd have to get up pretty early in the morning to be more nonsensical than *that*.

With one exception, all babies have better prospects if they are full-term. The exception is to take care of those cases where the fetus is unduly large or postmature and thereby subject to birth trauma. In every other case the more completely developed the child the better his chances during birth and during the neonatal period. (Naturally this assumes that everything *else* is normal and healthy about the baby and the mother.)

The seven-month myth was laid to rest by Potter and Adair,[15] by C. McNeil,[16] and by Corner[17] once and for all as far as statistical proof is concerned.

What we forget because of the hazards attendant upon premature birth, of which so much is said, is that the prolonged pregnancy may be even more dangerous. According to Dr. Michael A. Zwerdling in a report to the American Association for the Advancement of Science at Berkeley, California, early in 1966, a study of 20,000 pregnancies that ran three weeks or more past the expected date showed that the death rates of babies before and shortly following birth were double the normal nine-month figures. He pointed out that in long-term pregnancies the infants are more frequently very large and can be injured during delivery because of their size; but he added that in actual practice babies weighing less than five and a half pounds in prolonged pregnancies are the riskiest. Long-term pregnancy babies have a higher death rate for at least the first two years of life, he said.

BOTH JAWS MOVE WHEN YOU ARE EATING OR TALKING?

Many famous men have asserted with absolute conviction that both jaws move. But stop and think for a minute. Let's see you move your upper jaw without moving the whole head. You can't do it. Up or down or sideways—if that upper jaw moves, so does all the rest of your skull. The upper jaw, obviously, is fixed; it is stationary. You can hold you head perfectly still and move your *lower* jaw to your heart's content, however.

Of course the upper *lip* moves, and maybe that is what deceives so many people. Try the question on a few friends—you'll be surprised how widespread the idea is that both upper and lower jaws do move. And some people won't change their minds about it either.

A Summer Cold Is More Tenacious Than a Winter Cold?

It is not hard to understand why some people are completely adamant on this subject: absolute granite, they are. To your joyful intonation to June, "Then, if ever, come perfect days. . . . Every clod feels a stir of might," meaning yourself, these people answer bitterly, "If she be not so for me, what care I how fair she be?" meaning June. But the difference in your viewpoints has really nothing at all to do with the colds you both get in the summer, from time to time. Appearances indicate that your cold clears up in two weeks and theirs takes a month, which is reason enough to say, "It lasts forever with me."

In full truth, no. While the viruses causing summer and winter colds may differ somewhat, there is no evidence that there is any difference in the duration of the colds they induce. They have the same incubation period and run the same course, December or June.

But in the summer there are many other airborne irritants to which some people are allergic. We know a gentleman with a nose of prodigal proportions at whose feet Cyrano could have sat weeping in jealous rage. This nasal appendage captures the very first whiff of opening buds before the rest of us feel that spring is even around the corner. It then enters a state of supreme indignation, reddens, fills with liquids of one sort or another, and keeps its poor master in a continual state of sniffing driers or spraying medicaments. This man *knows* that he always catches a cold in May and that it stays until July, and it would be physically hazardous to tell him that a summer cold is no worse than a winter cold. So it just depends on what one means by "A cold in the head."

Quick Bud, Quick Dud?

This one cannot be answered with the assurance with which most human nonsense can be refuted and dismissed: it is very general in its appeal and has behind it many an apothegm of sage and poet and seer. Behind the prophecy is the notion that too intense a light cannot be expected to last long. Miss Edna Millay said she burned her candle at both ends and didn't expect it to last the night. She was enthusiastic, however, as one recalls, at the candle power she was generating. The flaming Mr. Algernon Swinburne, for his part, reminds us that birds quick to fledge and fly at call are quick to fall; and Shakespeare portrays Juliet as fearful about the outcome of a love so fierce and intense as that between herself and Romeo—"Too rash . . . too sudden, too like the lightning, which doth cease to be ere one can say, it lightens."

Some such idea is behind the popular notion that precocious development, bodily or mental, is an indication that the child will die young. A prototype is Alexander of Macedon, king at the age of twenty, and supposedly weeping because there were no more worlds to conquer thirteen years later as he lay dying at Babylon. One could probably produce as many cases of prodigies who did not die young, however, if one set about it; and we are inclined to wonder if there is any final verdict on this question. No statistical data exists to prove it, so far as we know, one way or the other.

Men Have Mechanical Aptitudes Not Given to Women?

Rosie the Riveter is too recent an addition to our society for us to be able to say for certain whether the day will come in this country when men will regard manual dexterity with tools as one of the more engaging traits of femininity. Dexterity with a needle or a loom, and especially with a stove, have always been lauded as desirable characteristics on the part of the distaff side; and suspicion—perhaps jealousy—has attended the woman who outdid the men in the use of the tools of industry and factory, although employers now know that where precision and delicacy of handling are concerned women are not only equal to men but superior.

No, the hoary error about women's alleged mechanical ineptitude is one which has been encouraged—let's face it—by the women themselves. They want to exhibit those traits which are most pleasing to the male's idea of what a woman should be. And who wants to marry a female grease monkey? For that matter, who wants a woman around the house who is more dextrous in driving a nail or repairing a faucet than the master himself?

Ways to Keep Healthy (USA, 1925)

Who was the wit who said, "Never fool with a superstition—it might be loaded"? In Muncie, Indiana (taken as a laboratory for the study of the "typical" small American town by the Lynds in their famous Middletown), as recently as the mid-twenties (and perhaps right down to the present) some people had secret incantations for curing erysipelas, believed that wrapping old hatbands around the mother's breasts at childbirth would prevent all forms of breast trouble, and that tying a worn leather shoestring about the neck of a child would keep the croup away, or cure the child if he caught it. Also that a little bag of asafetida worn about the neck would prevent a child from catching contagious diseases. (It might, at that, if Dr. Johnson was right in saying that "the rankness of its smell occasions it to be seldom used but by farriers"—it would keep *everybody* at a distance and so protect the child from infection.[18] We have no idea why Dr. Johnson thought blacksmiths could stand the stench when other men could not.) The Lynds brought up these old superstitions in order to make the comparison between them and the faith people had in patent medicines. On a given day 37 display ads out of a total of 68 in the daily paper were devoted to various salves, soaps, cure-alls, and remedies—they are listed in complete detail on pages 437-438 of *Middletown*.

For Frostbite: Rub It with Snow?

Perhaps it is some association with the idea of a "blanket" of snow or of snow acting as a protection against the cold and the wind for the small creatures below that is responsible for the idiotic idea that rubbing the skin with snow is a good thing for frostbite. One of the men who knew the most about life in the killing cold climates, a man who lived off the land himself with no contact with the outside world for two years (and who was thereupon given up as lost forever), was Vilhjalmur Stefansson; and he himself said, in *My Life with the Eskimo* (p. 76), that "few things could be more absurd" than the snow treatment for frostbite. He pointed out that ignorant explorers, trustful of the old prescription of the folk, had frozen the whole surfaces of their faces by massaging them with snow when it was 40° below or more. "All you have to do," he said, "is to take your warm hand out of your mitten and press it on the frozen spot for a moment until the whiteness and stiffness are gone." Incidentally, it was Stefansson who proved that men could live and be healthy on a diet of nothing but meat for a considerable length of time. His party was given up for lost because the experts knew that he must have used up his civilized supplies long since and they *thought* they knew that our species could not survive on a meat diet. But the valiant son of Icelandic parents came back to give gentle but living reproof to that theory—and he was healthy and active until his death at the age of eighty-five, and had a never-failing sense of humor, which is another miracle.

Never Stop Moving if You're Lost in a Blizzard?

Stefansson also gave the lie to that companion piece of nonsense which asserts that it is fatal to sit down or sleep if one is lost in a blizzard, because there is no waking from such a sleep. One must continue stumbling along somehow, at all costs, according to this venerable lunacy and fight off sleep by sheer will power if necessary.

This particular illusion, says Stefansson, has caused dozens of arctic deaths; explorers, believing the old saw, have wandered on and on until they were utterly exhausted and their powers of resistance were reduced. Then they have collapsed and frozen to death, unable to twitch a finger in self-protection. But the experienced Eskimo knows better: the important thing to do is to conserve one's strength, not waste it in wild plunging. One should sit in the most sheltered spot available with one's back to the wind and get as much sleep as possible.[19]

For Burns: Apply Heat to the Affected Part?

This is the counterpart of the frostbite-snow myth. The homeopathic domestic remedy of curing similars with similars is probably a fairly recent invention as the history of man goes. Prehistoric man must have had many opportunities for burning himself. It is very unlikely that he ever thought of doing anything so foolish as to apply heat to the affected part. He probably did what any child would think of doing: get to the nearest cold water and keep in it whatever part of one's anatomy has been burned. Try it the next time you burn your finger and judge for yourself.

The cure for heat exhaustion is not exposure to the sun, but a cold bath or shower or hosing down.

SOME INFECTIOUS DISEASES ARE INHERITED?

When a person is sick, it always seems to be emotionally gratifying to be able to spot the source of the illness. If one can say, "I caught this cold right straight from Uncle Frank," that somehow relieves the sufferer of any responsibility for picking up the cold on his own; one is now suffering unjustly and obviously deserves a great deal of sympathy. Maybe this goes deep into the abysm of time when an illness was proof of one's being punished by an evil spirit. At any rate, it is a common belief that certain infectious diseases are inherited, and let us say immediately that this is fatuous: no infectious disease can be inherited.

On the heels of this statement should come the acknowledgment that an unborn child can contract some diseases—syphilis especially—in the womb and is therefore born with it; but the disease was not an inheritance in the sense that it was contained in the genes derived from his parents. He picked it up at one stage of his own life, although of course without any fault of his own.

A *weakness* can be inherited which makes one liable to develop a certain disease, so that the person is predisposed to fall a victim to it if the conditions are right, where a normal person would not.

It used to be an accepted "fact" that tuberculosis was more frequently inherited than any other disease; but it is known now that this is not the truth. That t.b. runs through some families is now believed to be because a predisposition to it was inherited, an infection occurred, and the child was subject to the same environment in which the parents lived when they were afflicted.

ABSOLUTE CHASTITY—BAD FOR THE HEALTH?

It is not hard to understand how some healthy sybarite with normal appetites might convince himself that complete sexual abstinence is a very bad thing for a person's health, and that excursions must be permitted at intervals. Perhaps this is where the notion originated—we do not know. It does exist, and it is entirely false.

Absolute continence may be injurious to the *mental* health, like any other powerful frustration; but that it is not necessarily so is perhaps indicated by the relative sanity of many persons in late middle and early old age; and we are given to understand that there are some spinsters who cannot be characterized as *non compos mentis*, although they can be said to be chemically pure.

That complete sexual abstinence has any deleterious physical effects, however, the record does not show. Sorry!

However, the struggle against the sexual impulse in the mature person, especially between the ages of 18 and 45, may seriously affect the development of the personality. Abundant evidence is at hand in the *Confessions* of St. Augustine, in Schopenhauer (who gave thanks when old age released him), and particularly in the story of the temptation of St. Anthony, which is the classic illustration of the psychological conflicts to which complete continence gives rise. Such continence may produce ills ranging from powerful mental confusion to a pathological aversion to the opposite sex and compulsive jealousy of those who do enjoy sex, as well as other serious complexes.

One of the theories to explain the alleged harmfulness—the physical harmfulness—of continence is that the accumulation of unexpended sexual substances flows into the blood stream and may cause grave danger as the blood circulates through the body. Of this theory, Kahn says:

"Probably the contrary is true. The inactive sex glands work less and therefore produce less hormones, like all unused organs. There is no example of such a condition and it would contradict every probability if an unused organ should produce more than an organ that has a normal function."[20]

Kahn then proceeds to endorse a piece of learned idiocy which is also shared by the illiterate folk, namely, that years of inaction of the organs of sex "without any doubt exert a disadvantageous effect on the sex glands," adding that men who do not use these glands "lose their secondary sexual characteristics . . . assume the feminine eunuchoid type which is often met among those living in celibacy. The women dry up to become old and, since the suppressed sex impulse is transformed into aggressiveness, 'evil virgins.' "

Unfortunately for Dr. Kahn's "without any doubt" statement, the secretion of the hormones subserving the function of reproduction and sex are in no way dependent upon sexual activity. They are a part of the normal functioning of the body. So is the elaboration of spermatazoa in the male and the monthly process of ovulation in the female. Neither of these processes is ever suspended by inaction of the sex organs.

On the evidence, then, there is no information to show that continence is harmful physically; and neither is there information to show that incontinence is harmful unless disease accompanies the incontinence: Catherine the Great lived to be 67; Casanova died at 73; scores of instances could be cited. But the witless myths of sex will continue to flourish because the subject is so interesting that it breeds myths and rumors as does any other subject that is surrounded with mystery and half-knowledge. And God forbid that sex should cease to be surrounded with mystery!

A Pinprick Is More Dangerous Than a Needle Prick?

It seems to be a very widespread notion that if one needed a drop of blood for a test or something it would be much safer to use a needle than a pin. One can remember from youth some howling non sequitur to the effect that since a needle was steel and a pin was copper or some baser metal or alloy, obviously the steel was safer. Why? One never asked. Steel: fine. Steel is somehow honorable. Excalibur, forged by fairies in Avalon, was finest steel. . . . Well, it makes for lovely romance, but extremely poor medicine. Like the legend of the rusty nail or the rusty pin being more dangerous than the clean one, it's pure nonsense. Of course if the pin has been lying around the house and the needle has been in a closed case, there's less chance of the needle's point being the resting place of bacteria; but it will be the bacteria, not the metal, that will cause an infection if there is one. The rust on a piece of steel or iron is harmless oxide of iron—ferrous or ferric, we never could get that part straight—and won't cause infection. But here again one has to remember that a rusty nail is probably also a dirty nail, and may be a more cheerful home for bacteria than a shiny new one. After all, the bacteria like *their* comfort, too.

If You're Hungry a Lot—Tapeworm?

More or less universal is the understanding that a tapeworm eats so much of its victim's food that normal servings are not enough for the host and he is liable to be perpetually hungry. Fact is, increased appetite without marked increase of weight is more likely to be an indication of some disturbance in metabolism rather than the presence of a tapeworm. In reality, a tapeworm eats very little, so little that the amount is scarcely noticeable. The parasite, indeed, gives hardly any sign at all that he is present.

It used to be thought that if you ground your teeth at night you had intestinal worms, but there's nothing in that either.

Constipation Leads to Self-Poisoning?

Many people have worried themselves silly with the idea that auto-intoxication follows a siege of constipation. Somehow the theory has been accepted that the body absorbs poisons from the clogged intestine. But the feces are not poison. Certainly there is a normal aesthetic revulsion, once children have been taught that the excreta are "nasty." They do not come by this idea without teaching, however, as any child psychologist and most mothers well know. But all humans, savage or civilized, develop a taboo against any association of mouth and anus, and it is a very powerful taboo. The body, however, does not absorb poison from the feces, and that's the fact at issue in this particular popular error.

It has even been suggested by some authorities that man is safest from autointoxication from intestinal poisons when he is constipated, since bacteria would tend not to increase under such conditions, but would do so rapidly under the more moist conditions in the intestinal contents introduced by laxatives.[21]

There is discomfort during constipation, but it comes not from any poisoning but from the feeling of overfulness in the large intestine. The familiar feeling of relief immediately after a much-needed evacuation should be sufficient proof of the fact that it is the elimination of the mechanical pressure rather than the removal of poison which has occurred. The effects of poisoning would linger.

Regularity in evacuation, as prominently advertised everywhere, is a consummation devoutly to be wished, as is the normal functioning of every other physiological process; but constipation will not poison your child—or yourself. It will at most make you uncomfortable.

The Bugaboo of Hydrophobia

Through the ages one of man's most feared and dreaded diseases has been hydrophobia. Prior to Pasteur, the agony and the convulsions of the afflicted, together with the inescapable death which awaited them, created an extreme horror in the human mind—and as so often happens when a terror of unknown character must be dealt with, all kinds of ghastly legends and beliefs came to surround it. Today it is doubtful if many doctors have seen a case themselves in human beings, or even know anyone who has seen it.

The disease attacks the throat, causing swelling and painful spasms. It becomes impossible to swallow; the thirst becomes dreadful. In fact, it was the sight of sufferers trying desperately to swallow the water they craved, and undergoing spasms in the effort, that led to the erroneous conclusion that some mysterious fear of water was involved in the disease. This idea was crystallized in the Greek name given the sickness: water fear, hydrophobia.

Now of course all you have to do is put the thing in Greek and you've got a sale. Who dares contradict? In addition, since the disease usually came from the bite of a rabid dog, people came to believe that the afflicted took on the behavior of a dog, barked, tried to bite people. The notion also arose that dogs go mad especially at such a time as Sirius, the Dog Star, is bright in the sky. This occurs toward the end of summer.

It was also believed that rabies can be transmitted by dogs only. In fact it can be transmitted by cats, wolves, skunks, chipmunks, squirrels, bats, and lots of other animals. Another piece of nonsense is the idea that rabies in dogs accompanies hot weather only. The weather has no influence on the disease whatever.

THE COMMON COLD—CAUSED BY COLD WEATHER?

"Button up your overcoat when the wind is free," went the lyrics of the old song. "Take good care of yourself—you belong to me." You won't find three people in a hundred, probably, who are not thoroughly convinced that one can "catch a cold" by being careless about wrapping oneself up properly when the wind, in that lyrical phrase, is free. But the chill alone cannot *cause* an infection—and when we use the word *cold* to mean a disease, what we mean is a respiratory infection if we are speaking of man. In domestic animals, for those who collect these cornerpieces, the word is *coryza*.

The chill can be a contributing factor to one's catching a cold; and so can a run-down condition, fatigue, and so forth. But the low temperatures do not cause the common cold, as was most brutally and inhumanly illustrated at several of the concentration camps where men were forced to stand in the autumn winds at Auschwitz, still wet from their showers, naked and dispossessed. (Victor Frankl's *From Death Camp to Existentialism,* reissued in a later edition as *Man's Search for Meaning,* provided agonzingly poignant testimony to this fact, as did many other books on the same subject; but Frankl's was a firsthand report by a trained psychiatrist, now practicing and teaching in Vienna.)[22] "We were anxious to know . . . what would be the consequences, for example, of our standing in the open air [at Auschwitz] in the chill of late autumn, stark naked, and still wet from the showers. In the next few days our curiosity evolved into surprise; surprise that we did not catch cold" (p. 15).

Before the Nazis there were many reports from polar explorers, describing in some instances how they had struggled along, even although exhausted, exposed, and undernourished, without catching a cold at any time; but when they returned to civilization they came down with colds immediately. Sometimes they caught colds in the arctic when they opened packages of supplies which had been packed for them in the cities.

Medical authorities today therefore believe that the common cold is caused by a virus. It is clear from experience that one cannot build up a resistance to the virus of the common cold with chilly showers and the rugged life in general. In fact, the famous influenza epidemic of 1917-1918 showed very grimly that the most "vigorous" among us were the special prey of the little monster.

Some things we do know: the cold virus flourishes at low temperatures more than it does at warm ones—which shows that the folk wisdom of connecting colds with the cold is not entirely without reason. It is a fact that colds occur least frequently in June and July, and most frequently in September, October, and November. Colds are also known to occur most frequently in the Temperate Zone. In Alaska and among the Eskimos colds were very rare until the virus was introduced.[23]

A Persistent Cough Is a Strong Suggestion of Tuberculosis?

When our hearts have gone out—over the footlights—to the gentle, white lady of the camellias because she is beginning to cough a good deal and we know that this is going to end with her death from t.b., we are in no condition to listen to an abstract from the laboratory. First the stage and the auditorium must bathe in a flood of tears, and we must all think, "So much beauty, so much gentillesse, so much je ne sais precisely quoi—ah!"

Later perhaps we can think about it.

It was a convention that the cough meant the disease. Everybody understood it. But in fact, and in medical terms, it was a dangerous belief. There are many kinds of tuberculosis besides the pulmonary; in fact, some authorities will insist that all pulmonary t.b. is secondary to some other infection. But even the pulmonary t.b. is not always accompanied by coughing or the spitting of blood. Just because the cough is there—or is not there—is no way to make a judgment; many a sufferer, because there was no cough, has failed to seek expert advice until it was too late. The truth is that a prolonged and violent cough is much more likely to indicate bronchial rather than pulmonary sources.

Actually, the cough is a protective reaction. It is needed, and it is desirable. In fact, its failure to operate, as Dr. Haggard points out, "may be attended with a greatly increased danger of pulmonary infection."[24] In other words, it's a signal; and a valuable one.

ELIMINATE HUMAN DEFECTS BY STERILIZATION?

Ever since the most primitive experiments in genetics—which go back at least as far as Bible times—when men learned that they could improve the livestock by selective breeding to give more milk, more eggs, or more white meat, there has been the dream of improving our own race through the control of hereditary factors. But, as Logan Clendening pointed out in his vastly amusing book, *The Human Body*, it is not going to work unless you eliminate the influence of love in the selection of a mate. "Men are not going to embrace eugenics," he said. "They are going to embrace the first likely, trim-figured girl with limpid eyes and flashing teeth who comes along, in spite of the fact that her germ plasm is probably reeking with hypertension, cancer, haemophilia, color-blindness, hay-fever, epilepsy, and amyotrophic lateral sclerosis."[25] Unless we become slaves to some nightmare government like that in 1984, we will not mate scientifically, no matter what the computers hint or how strongly their correlations agree.

The old dream is given a shot in the arm by Dr. Glenn T. Seaborg, chairman of the Atomic Energy Commission, when he says he expects to see scientists create life in laboratories before 1970. Perhaps, with control so impersonal and the need so obvious, the boys in the lab will improve on evolution's sad product. Dr. David Krech told assembled scientists in Berkeley that control of the mind is just around the corner. "If not today, then tomorrow," there will be "genuine breakthroughs into the understanding of the mind. . . . I need not spell out for you what such understanding of the mind may mean in terms of the control of the mind." They've linked the process of human memory with ribonucleic acid, *that's* what they've done, and the editor of the *New York Times* on December 29, 1965, said that we'd better prepare for "the biological and psychological reshaping of human beings" that will result from the fantastic progress being made in molecular biology.

The obverse of the coin is that if you can improve the race, then why can't you eliminate misfits by breeding them out? Why can't you deliberately eliminate future feeble-minded offspring and other constitutionally defective humans simply by sterilizing the known parents or potential parents of such offspring?

The popular and imbecile belief of the folk is—and has been—that you *can* do this. It is a very widespread notion, wherever a knowledge of sterilization exists. Breed 'em out! Breed out the criminal, the crook, the rapist, the dope addict, the homosexual . . . and so on down to the nonconformist, depending on who's running the shop.

The trouble here is that one is assuming that the only persons carrying genes which produce defectives are those who exhibit the defects. This is so far from the truth that we deliberately used the word *imbecile* just a few lines back. The truth is that practically every living human carries genes for some defective conditions. In most persons those genes are recessive—not expressed, not active. But let one of us mate with a person carrying similar defective genes, and the likelihood is that some of the pairs will link up together with the results we want so much to avoid. We cannot possibly know all the kinds of genes our mate is carrying, although we can know some of them. Hence it is impossible to prevent the birth of a certain proportion of defective offspring in each generation. In fact, H. S. Jennings estimated that "the prevention of the propagation of all feeble-minded in the United States would reduce the number in the next generation only by about 11 percent if carriers are widely distributed in the population, or up to 30 or 40 percent if the carriers are concentrated in small groups. In later generations, preventing the propagation of the feeble-minded would have little further effect save to keep the number down to that already reached."[26] In cases of defective recessive genes, sterilization would bring about no noticeable effect on the numbers of defectives in less than thirty or forty generations.[27]

But there is an "however." It is this: Where the defect is due to a dominant gene that manifests itself in 100 percent of cases, and early in life, the propagation of congenital defectives originating in such genes can be effectively reduced by sterilization. But such conditions are not always recognizable, not always even probable, and almost never absolutely certain. Socially, then, sterilization is no answer. Individual human rights intervene, except in the *1984*-type of state.

The case against negative eugenics, stated rather formally, goes like this:

The aspect of eugenics that suggests the negative control of the multiplication of undesirable traits is, in general, misconceived. The objections to negative eugenics are clear, unequivocal, and unanswerable. The recommendations of negative eugenics are (1) theoretically unsound and therefore (2) practically unjustifiable, not to mention the dangers of political misapplication; (3) fertility is generally reduced in those affected by recessively determined abnormalities; (4) even when such individuals breed, their offspring in most cases are normal; (5) even if it were possible, sterilization of the recessive carriers would waste an enormous potential of normal births; (6) conditions due to rare dominant genes usually result in infertile individuals, and in (7) other conditions due to unfavorable dominant genes the fertility is low, hence (8) most conditions due to defective genes are self-limiting; (9) carriers of defective genes also carry a large number of normal genes that in the paired or homozygous state often give rise to above-average traits; (10) many hereditary disorders are amenable to environmental alleviation; (11) the increase in human mobility and the collapse of innumerable barriers to intermixture between large numbers of the members of populations that were hitherto separated reduce the chances of deleterious recessive genes coming together; (12) sterilizing homozygous individuals who show a defective trait due to recessive genes still leaves by far the greater number of individuals carrying the gene in the single gene or heterozygous state to circulate it freely throughout the population. If, for example, the frequency of a recessive gene in the general population were 1 in 1,000, this would mean that the homozygote in whom the defective trait was expressed would occur in 1 out of 1 million individuals. Supposing the homozygous individual carrying the pair of recessive genes were sterilized, this would still leave 999 heterozygotes to those carrying a single recessive gene to distribute the gene. Clearly a rather inefficient and ineffectual way of dealing with the problem; (13) since the number of genes of any given sort in the human species is usually very large, any artificially induced changes in their number in any local portion of the species is likely to have very little if any effect upon the total frequency. As Penrose has put it, "The wider problem of genetical improvement of the human race must be viewed against the background of gene frequencies in the world population and the relative fitnesses of different phenotypes* in different environments"; finally, (14) because negative eugenics overlooks such facts, it would certainly do more damage to the human species than defective genes are capable of doing.

All right, now, if everybody has given up the idea of sterilizing someone else, we have an interesting human-interest side issue to introduce at this point. You remember that we used to say how dangerous it is to marry your cousin, and all that—and we used to point to so many royal families, inbred for generations. Americans used to love to point to George III, for instance. Well, what do you know? It turns out, according to Dr. Richard Hunter of the National Hospital for Nervous Diseases (in London) and Dr. Ida Macalpine (his mother!) formerly of St. Bartholomew's Hospital (London) that they have evidence which "clears the House of Hanover of an hereditary taint of madness imputed to it by the long-sustained but erroneous interpretation of George III's illness." They had a look at some papers in the Windsor archives, hitherto unpublished, and they are quite certain "that George III's malady was not mental." He had a "rare metabolic disorder recognizable as acute, intermittent porphyria." Porphyria is a disturbance of porphyrin metabolism, characterized by excretion of wine-red urine, sensitivity to light, anemia, enlargement of the spleen, often accompanied by nervous symptoms. While possibly clearing the House of Hanover of the taint of insanity, the fact remains that George III was intermittently so. That he provoked the American colonies into the Revolution may or may not have been related to his madness. There are some to be found so cynical as to believe that this

---

* Phenotype, the overt expression of the genetic constitution or genotype.

was the wisest thing George III ever did. At any rate, let us give him his due: he is the real Founder of the United States—mad or not.

Lemon Juice to Remove Freckles?

Nothing will remove freckles. At least, nothing will remove freckles *only*. There are preparations which will remove the skin, if that's what you want. Then the freckles disappear.

The phenomenon known as freckles is a series of small areas of pigmentation which are usually evoked by exposure to the chemically active ultraviolet (actinic) rays of the sun. Pigment granules move toward the surface of the skin and form separated clusters. But since most of these pigment cells do not actually reach the corium or dead surface layer which forms the outermost portion of the skin, it follows that no substance applied to the surface of the skin can actually have any effect on the pigment cells which lie in the deeper portions of the epidermis.

Girls have long believed that lemon juice will help. All it can possibly do is irritate the skin, and one would have thought that the first to try it would have passed the word along to her sisters. Maybe she did; but they weren't listening. Some firms are marketing corrosive chemical compounds under fancy names, beautifully packaged, and advertised to remove freckles. They can do permanent injury.

For Vigorous Health: A Cold Shower in the Morning?

It is a great pleasure to expose this nonsense for the madness it is. If you are already a normal and healthy individual, the cold shower may be refreshing, in a numb sort of way—at least you'll be so pleased to come out that by comparison you'll feel wonderful. But anybody with any circulatory troubles of any kind should eschew a cold shower like the plague: it constricts the blood vessels supplying the skin.

The point of taking a shower in the morning is to get clean. That's a fine idea, and your friends, as the advertisers have been quick to suggest, will applaud your effort. But a cold shower is no better than a hot one. It's true that it wakes you up. So does a two-inch salute exploding directly beneath the bed. If that's the way you like to wake up: all of a sudden—then write for our booklet, *The Quick Awakening*. (We haven't written it yet, but we will if the orders come in.)

WEARING TIGHT HATS CAUSES BALDNESS?

Many men are bald; many men used to wear rather snugly fitting hats; many of the hats were derbies and in order to be worn at the proper angle had to fit tightly; and *quod erat demonstrandum,* by the logic of folk wisdom: tight hats make for bald heads. The notion still persists in some circles. The proof used to be that Indians don't wear tight hats—usually they wear no hats at all—and Indians are never bald. Who ever heard of a bald Indian? So there's your story.

The answer is that Mongoloids are frequently bald. Indians are Mongoloids. Further, if anybody tried to wear a hat tight enough to be in effect a tourniquet, he'd be screaming with pain in a matter of minutes.

The scalp is supplied by arteries which are both surface vessels and deep ones. One could constrict the surface arteries—with great pain to the patient—but the deep arteries would then take over the functions of those no longer active. This is just as true of veins as it is of arteries; and therefore the nutriment to the scalp would continue to be provided. A tight hatband, even a tournaquet, could not stop *that.*

No, gentlemen: we have said it before and we will say it again: baldness is hereditary. You can't avoid it; and you can't produce it. (Of course we are speaking of normally healthy persons—not of persons suffering from diseases of the scalp and skin and what not.)

A CHILD PICKING ITS NOSE IS INDICATING POOR HEALTH?

Heaven alone knows where this one came from; but it is current, and in some communities it is even believed that when a child picks its nose over an extended period it is indicating the presence of worms.

One is almost tempted to repeat the old slapstick vaudeville comment: "There is no law against picking your nose; but it is forbidden to pick your *neighbor's* nose." This one used to draw guffaws from the 50-cent seats.

Publicly or secretly, everyone picks his nose: let's face it.

And why not? Dried mucus makes you whistle when you breathe, or it clogs up one nostril completely perhaps. And you are supposed to sit with you hands in your lap and breathe through your mouth? Come on! V. V. Rozanov, the Russian writer, wrote in his *Solitaria,* the "private life is above everything. . . . Just sitting at home, and even picking your nose, and looking at the sunset."[28] There, at least, is one honest man. It is touching that on his deathbed Aldous Huxley should have remembered this passage from Rozanov, and quoted it to Christopher Isherwood.[29]

Books have been written by psychiatrists and other specialists on how to stop children from picking their noses and on the reasons why they do it, and so on. They tell us that the youngsters are always exploring with their hands and fingers: exploring their own bodies and anything else that comes within reach. An uninhibited child will pick at his ears, a lock of his hair, his lips, genitals, or any other part of his body. Is he supposed to skip the nose? Did *you?*

Bite Your Nails—and Get Stubby Fingers?

Biting the fingernails turns out to be a very complicated matter psychologically—too complicated, indeed, to deal with in a few lines here where the authorities have given volumes to it. Aesthetically, many people are digusted by deeply bitten nails. To them, the practice seems barbaric. Nail biters can snip so deeply that infection results, and this can cause permanent injury to the form of the nail. But with stubby fingers it has nothing to do. Bitten nails make fingers *seem* to be more stubby. But they don't actually affect the shape or size of the fingers at all. Bite if you must. But for heaven's sake, do it when we're not looking.

Night Air Is Unwholesome?

There may be something to be said for the idea that cold air at night is less than desirable for a person who has been breathing warm air all day; in fact, there has been some attempt to equate the instinctive gesture of the hen sleeping with her head under her wing, or the fox with his nose in his bushy tail—both effectively warming up the air that is breathed in—with the wisdom of shutting the windows at night in the nursery. But we're not talking about *cold* air, but of *night* air. The two tend to become mixed and we should be clear.

Fear of the night air very likely goes back to our natural fear of the dark. Around the campfire there was no danger. It was only out there, where the leaping flames could not penetrate the black, that the hobgoblins of imagination lay in wait. We forget, in these days of electrically lighted houses and streets where the turn of a single switch can bring almost the equivalent of daylight to every corner, what an extraordinary and recent thing the incandescent bulb and the fluorescent tube are. But anyone who ever lived in a farmhouse illuminated by oil lamps knows that day ends with sundown. A century or more ago a person traversing the streets of London employed a bodyguard and a light-bearer. The night was a period of darkness, of terror, when evil was abroad, and it was "unwholesome."

In malarial countries, of course, the "bad air" (mal-aria) was held to be responsible for the disease.

But there has always been a notion that the night air was "unpurged" by the action of the sun and therefore full of noxious vapors and pestilential dampness. Brutus, his wife complained, stole out of his wholesome bed "to dare the vile contagion of the night, / To tempt the rheumy and unpurged air."

It is not difficult to understand how the idea became general that the night is dangerous. This is the hour, wrote Kipling, of pride and power and talon and tusk and claw. Quite. But there's nothing unhealthy about the night *qua* night. It's what happens in the night, not the air.

Frequent Washing of the Hair Causes Baldness?

In a society in which the cult of youth is as powerful as it is in America, the male fear of baldness is perhaps comprehensible. If every father wants to look as young as his son, baldness is not going to help. And when somehow the idea gets around, that washing one's hair often—for instance, in the daily shower—leads to loss of hair and baldness, it gets reinforced by the strong emotional need to seem young and therefore tends to persist even after it has been shown to be nonsense.

"It is almost incredible," says Dr. Howard Haggard, "how long some otherwise cleanly persons are willing to go without washing their scalps in the mistaken belief that cleanliness is harmful to the hair. It is not. Failure to remove the soap and failure to dry the hair may be injurious to the scalp. Cleanliness is not. Twice a week, even three times, is none too often for a shampoo for a man, for his scalp, because of his shorter hair, tends to become dirty more quickly than that of a woman."[80]

Frequent washing may actually serve to rid the scalp of incipient or light attacks of dandruff; but in no case will it produce baldness—although it will not prevent the development of baldness in those persons who are genetically destined to become bald. Baldness, except for *alopecia areata* (a disease in which all the hair suddenly falls out and later grows back again completely), is strictly hereditary, usually, but not exclusively, in the male line. As Clendening puts it, "The degeneration of the hair follicles on top of the head is laid down in the germ plasm to begin at a definite time in life," usually not in youth.[31]

You Can Get Appendicitis by Swallowing Seeds?

Even among otherwise well-educated people one finds the idea firmly entrenched that if you swallow grape seeds there's a good chance that some of them will lodge in the vermiform appendix and cause an irritation which will end only on the operating table. But surgeons report that the discovery of any foreign body in the appendix is so rare that most specialists never see a case of it; and even if such a thing as a seed were to lodge there by some incredible series of circumstances, there is no reason to believe that it would cause the disease: appendicitis is an infection produced by bacteria which are normally found only in the large intestine.

To demonstrate absolutely that a seed cannot possibly cause appendicitis is a proposition not unlike an absolute demonstration that the Big Dipper has not sprung a leak. The evidence is all one way; but as of this writing, nobody can speak of his own knowledge either about the Dipper or the seed. Maybe by the time this is printed men will be examining the Dipper, and then we'll have to revise our thinking.

To those who like to swallow seeds, we say: Swallow them. To those who don't like to, we say: Spit them out. Unless you're at the movies. In that case, put them in your pocket.

Regular Habits Make for Better Health?

It sounds so very sensible: get up at a regular time after having slept for a standard period, eat a regulation breakfast, train the bowels so that they will perform by the clock, eat a specified luncheon at 12:30 sharp, get the precise amount of exercise in an appointed way at some regular hour—and so forth through bedtime. How much better, one would say, than roistering some nights until the small hours and having a hangover the next day, eating too much at one meal and then going without food for the rest of the day, and living the irresponsible, unplanned existence. Nine people out of ten would tell you the former, regulated life is better: and so would the advertisers of laxatives.

Strangely enough, many anthropologists today believe that the old regimen in which for many millennia man gorged till he could hardly stand, and then slept until he was hungry again, was a pattern to which our prehistoric ancestors responded very favorably in terms of health; and that good health today is better served when there is variation from too strict a regularity. Not that they advise going to extremes; but variety appears to be a way of nature, and machinelike regularity is more liable to bring to the surface whatever weakness the particular system has to which one is being true.

In general, strict regularity as a health measure is nonsense.

SOFT LIVING MAKES NATIONS WEAK?

In a way this asinine idea is related to the legend that our forebears were made of tougher stuff than we; it is also based on the typically old-Prussian ideal of the blond brute with a sword slash on his cheek to prove his manhood. Lovers of peace become effete. Such was the message of General von Bernhardi in *Germany and the Next War* (1912). "This desire for peace," he said, "has rendered most civilized nations anemic, and marks a decay of spirit and political courage such as has often been shown by a race of Epigoni." (There is a nice point here: the general certainly intended "Epigoni" to be a pejorative; and in American usage an epigone is an inferior imitator of a distinguished artist; but any classicist among our readers has already spotted the Epigoni as the revenge-seeking descendants of the seven princes who marched against Thebes. These avengers, under the leadership of Adrastus, were successful and the city fell to them. Hence the Epigoni were heroes. Maybe they didn't teach the classics very thoroughly in the schools von Bernhardi attended.)[32]

In like vein, Heinrich von Treitschke taught: "It has always been the weary, spiritless and exhausted ages which have played with the dream of perpetual peace. War is a biological necessity of the first importance, a regulative element in the life of mankind which cannot be dispensed with." Possibly when he penned those words von

Treitschke was unaware of the fact that his countryman, Immanuel Kant, had written a book of that title, *Perpetual Peace*.

Some of that spirit has been part of every generation: we worship the athlete in training as a sort of ideal. The soft and easy life must be bad for nations.

And yet the soft and easy life, which is softer and easier for Americans than it ever was before, has shortened the hours of work, increased leisure time, seen increased wages, and more than doubled his life expectancy. Up to about 1860 man had a life expectancy of about thirty-three years.

Before anybody gets hot under the collar about this argument, we had better agree on what we mean by "soft and easy." We do not mean lolling around on silken cushions and eating vast quantities of starch and sugar. We mean living in good shelters with adequate clothing and enough or more than enough food, plus reasonable cleanliness and medical care. That's more than most nations on earth have been able to achieve in the millennia since our species stood upright; it is now possible, as we are told on every hand.

Extra food means extra strength and size. In Oslo, Norway, it was found that 14-year-olds who were fed a breakfast no more luxurious than a glass of milk, half an orange, a slice of whole wheat bread, a pat of butter, a small piece of cheese, a rye biscuit, and a spoonful of cod-liver oil increased their average height over the national average by four inches, and their eyesight, insofar as vision is affected by diet, was twice as good. In 1936 Orr reported that the sons of the poor in their early teens averaged five inches less than the sons of the rich of the same age.[33] The great arctic explorer Stefansson, speaking from long experience, declared that young men brought up in comfortable homes were better material for polar expeditions than run-of-the-mill sailors off the docks or laboring men, because, he said, they endure hardship better, are more cheerful in adversity, and can withstand cold and pain better.

"The son of wealthy parents," he said, "who is used to eating fifty different articles of food in a week will take readily to the fifty-first; but a farmer's son who from one year's end to another has lived on nothing but fat pork, potatoes, bread and tea, is likely to be so wedded to the idea that nothing but pork and potatoes is fit to eat that when he meets with a new dish, the fifth or sixth one of his experience, it strikes him as an unheard-of thing and unfit for food. It is common knowledge among guides in such out of the way places as Iceland that the wealthy travelers who visit the country will readily and with enjoyment adapt themselves to the food of the peasant, while the servants who accompany their wealthy masters have to be specially looked after by the guides and insist on being fed on provisions such as they are used to having in their own country." Incidentally, he said the same is true of dogs; the Eskimo dogs would almost rather starve than change an article of diet.[34]

North American, British, and Scandinavian studies all show that there has been a steady gain in both weight and height over the past century. The average gain between 1880 and 1950 was about ½ inch and 1 pound a decade at ages 5 to 7 years; increasing to about 1 inch and 4 pounds a decade during adolescence, and decreasing to about ½ inch a decade for the fully grown adult.[35]

Harvard students in 1920 were, on the average, 1¼ inches taller and 10 pounds heavier than the average student had been a generation earlier, and the trend continues.[36] There are innumerable corroborative studies of a similar sort. World War I U.S. soldiers had an average height of 5 feet 7¾ inches, World War II U.S. soldiers had an average height of 5 feet 8½ inches, the U.S. soldier after 1958 had an average height of 5 feet 8-9/10 inches.

Yet every so often we read in the press that the armed forces are rejecting more men than ever before. The rejects had jumped from 31 percent to 42 percent between the First and Second World Wars, according to the surgeon general's report. The causes for rejection were listed in order of their frequency: eye trouble, mental defects, bone defects, syphilis, hernia, t.b., and diseases of the cardiovascular system. One wonders how these ailments are supposed to correlate with soft and easy living? It seems more likely that they were caused by malnutrition, overwork, worry, and lack of medical care; and could represent an aftermath of the depression fare when these men were growing up.

A Clean Tooth Never Decays?

A well-known toothpaste used this phrase as a slogan so persistently a few years ago that the shibboleth passed into the folk language; it is like the paint manufacturer's "Save the surface and you save all," and seems to make just as much sense. But it doesn't.

The health of a tooth does not depend entirely on its surface condition, but also on the diet and general health of its owner. It is impossible to get any tooth that is still in place in the owner's gums surgically clean, entirely free from bacteria.

But who can imagine an advertiser saying, "Other things being equal, a clean tooth—that is to say, as clean as brush and dentifrice can get it—decays less rapidly than a dirty one"? Such a remark would not cause a mass movement toward the drug counters.

A Boil Draws Impurities Out of the System?

The firm belief that a boil had purifying powers used to be quite widely held; there was a country saying that "a boil is worth $20." Perhaps this was to comfort those who did the suffering; there is no record of any patient being unwilling to part with his twenty dollars' worth.

A local infection by some member of the group of staphylococci, usually in the form of an abcess of the root of a hair caused by bacteria which have penetrated the skin—that's a boil. It may be caused by friction from being constantly rubbed by a scratchy shirt or even by a collar stud, if you know anybody who uses collar studs. Usually the sufferers are males, and the boils are usually on the neck or buttocks.

It is almost always a restricted process around the root of the hair, and in no way represents a drawing off of impurities from the body. To the contrary, all boils represent the external evidence that potentially dangerous impurities have been introduced *into* the body. Boils on the nose constitute particularly hazardous conditions owing to the connection of the nasal veins with the cranial venous sinuses.

Sun Increases the Growth of Hair?

Many men with hirsute cheeks have stated positively that their beards grow faster in the summer; and many ladies have complained that the delicate down on their (excuse the expression) legs is more profuse during their period of estivation. Perhaps it's because one has more time to pay attention to these things during vacation. We cannot prove that there is no truth in it; but we point to the two classes of men who probably spend more time outdoors than any others—time spent under the sun whenever the sun is out: farmers and sailors. We cannot see that as a group either one of them is any hairier than the rest of the men.

Making a Child Walk Too Early Gives Him Bowed Legs?

Without taking a scientific poll, it's a tossup how widespread this belief is—but we've all heard it and probably most of us have believed it. Stop worrying: it's not true. Malnutrition will develop bowed legs in a youngster whether he walks ahead of time or late; if the child is properly fed, forcing him to walk early will never give him bowed legs.

Compound Fractures—Means Two Breaks?

The idea held by many people that a compound fracture is a double break is really not so much a matter of nonsense as it is word usage: the term is a technical one and it means the misfortune of having broken a bone has been compounded with an open wound—either the bone protruding through the flesh or the wound being made from the outside by the impact of whatever caused the fracture. Such injuries are serious because the wound so often becomes infected.

Double-Jointed People?

We have all heard of double-jointed people, and some among us are willing to testify that they have known such persons. Sorry, but no. There is no such thing as a double joint. You may have seen people who have joints that seemed almost fluid, they were so movable owing to the comparative elasticity of the attached ligaments. This condition is usually an inherited characteristic, and a person with such joints can sometimes perform incredible gymnastics with his bones. In fact, however, he has no double joints.

The Heart Is on the Left of the Chest?

Because the apex of the heart is situated a little to the left, it is easier to hear heartbeats by listening on the left side of the chest; but actually the heart originates in the middle of the neck region and descends in the mid-line into the chest: the heart is in the middle.

Hence that other folly that it is bad to sleep on the left side for fear of compressing the heart is manifest nonsense.

The heart-on-the-left myth is very ancient. And no matter how often it is refuted, the legend persists: our ears tell us! But they tell wrongly.

SUFFER FROM ACID INDIGESTION?

If you happen to be one of the estimated 190 million Americans who suffer from acid indigestion—the estimates in this case being the presuppositions of the TV advertisers—then the thing for you to do is to alkalize. Yessir. No doubt about *that*.

The rock in this snowball is that nobody can possibly know whether he suffers from excess acidity unless the contents of his stomach have been analyzed. Disturbances of the digestion may indicate many different things; and only a competent gastroenterologist can determine with precision what your particular disturbance means.

But, come! We can't be bothered with all that. Burping, are you? Got a little gas in the stomach? Probably overacid. Better alkalize. Like that good-looking female in the picture: remember how she didn't think she could go to the dance at all, just a few minutes ago? And now look at her—full of pep. What you want is some of those same pills. Never mind what they are. Get the big family size and watch 'em fizz! It's a free country.

WANT TO ACHIEVE REGULARITY?

What the pharmaceutical advertisers mean by *regularity* is anybody's guess, since they never define it. Presumably—this is just one guess—they really intend the word *regular* to mean "according to a rule." In that case, they must mean that people should train themselves to have a bowel movement at about 7:30, or whatever time is selected, every morning and make that the rule. Okay. Then the next thing, of course, is to find some pill, liquid, capsule, or something that will cause the rule to be followed, if such a thing exists, which it does not; but wait. Let's not spoil the advertisement before it has even been *written*.

The fatuity lies in the acceptance of the suggestion that regularity can be purchased in a bottle. Every responsible medical authority tells us that the frequent use of laxatives is a harmful and dangerous practice. One of the surest ways to produce constipation—chronic constipation—is to use laxatives habitually. It is known—not guessed—that this produces dehydration of the colon and tends to produce a permanent contraction of its walls.

Americans have a pure terror of constipation. They're sure they are poisoning themselves. Advertisers tell us we feel dragged out and so forth from being constipated. What we feel dragged out and so forth about is their interminable irresponsibility in presenting laxatives for our use with utter indiscrimination when (a) their products will not produce regularity but the opposite if used frequently, (b) that acquiring the habit of using laxatives is downright harmful, and (c) that the constipation against which they warn us with such fearful symbols is not dangerous in most cases and will cure itself in nature's good time. And if it doesn't, then it's time to see Old Doc Bones, M.D., and no fooling.

What Causes "Heartburn"?

If one wished to employ that professional jocosity which is based on a supposedly innocent literal-mindedness assumed by certain lecturers, one could say that the answer to "What causes 'heartburn'?" is "The imaginative mind of man." At any rate, the term is a splendid example of a popular misunderstanding combined with a popular misinterpretation given a local habitation and a name. For no such thing as heartburn exists. Under no conditions, even when parts of the heart are inflamed, is that organ ever the seat of burning sensations. What is actually felt is a reaction in the stomach, or less frequently in the intestines, owing its existence to excessive amounts of hydrochloric and other acids which irritate the lining of the stomach and can result in excessive regurgitation of these apparently "burning" acids. The hyperacidity producing the burning feeling is most commonly caused by worry, nervousness, excitement, overwork, and excessive indulgence in coffee, tea, alcohol, and tobacco.[37]

Webster's first definition is the medical one: "A burning sensation in the stomach, often with the inclination to vomit; cardialgia." The second, and only other, meaning is figurative: "Discontent or enmity; envy; jealousy." Under "cardialgia," which indeed is derived from the Greek *kardia*, heart, and *algos*, pain, Webster gives this: "A burning or gnawing pain, or feeling of distress, felt near the heart and usually a symptom of indigestion." It is probable that such emotions as anxiety and stress do give rise "to the formation of atheromatous plaques" leading to coronary attacks. In fact, "we see and hear altogether too much of persons in stress jobs . . . who, under stress conditions, are stricken on the spot, not to believe that this factor is very important in triggering many a case of coronary thrombosis."[38] But that's not heartburn, nor does the sensation known as heartburn threaten the heart. So take it easy.

THAT THE STOMACH IS THE ORGAN OF DIGESTION?

Most people, including most educated people, believe that the stomach is the organ of digestion. It is not, not much more so than the mouth. Digestion, which is the process of converting food into materials fit to be absorbed and assimilated, occurs mainly in the small intestine, which is about 22 feet long in human beings. The main function of the stomach is to provide temporary storage for the ingested food and to bring to bear upon it the hydrochloric acid and enzymes which turn it into chyme, a semifluid mass which is spurted into the duodenum and small intestine, during a period some two to six hours after the ingestion of food. The chyme remains in the small intestine from two to eight hours. Here it is acted upon by the bile, pancreatic, and intestinal juices to be broken down into the materials which are then absorbed through the walls of the intestines, by the various vessels which carry them to those parts of the body for which they are destined.

Since the major part of digestion occurs in the small intestine and not in the stomach, it is possible to remove a diseased stomach completely (gastrectomy), without in any way interfering with the nutrition of the individual.

THAT THE EYES CAN BE RUINED BY EXCESSIVE USE?

This is what one expert has to say about that:

Another matter which has achieved the status of folklore is the widespread belief that eyes can be "ruined" from excessive use, or use under unfavorable conditions. The Greek physician Paul of Aegina, in the seventh century after Christ, cautioned his patients not to hurt their eyes by too much reading, while the Persian physician Rhazes issued a warning in the tenth century against books with small letters, and advised exercising the eyes by looking at large letters and pictures. Today many patients tell me that they have only themselves to blame for a cataract or other eye disease, since they have done much close work for years in poor light and neglected to wear their glasses. Unnecessary worry could be avoided if it were generally understood that healthy eyes are not ruined, or even damaged in any way, by excessive reading, small print, fine work at close range, poor illumination, fluorescent lighting, lack of glasses, incorrect glasses, glasses in need of adjustment, cheap sun glasses, or devotion to television. Lack of proper glasses can result in discomfort, headache, inefficiency, and automobile accidents, and for children glasses may be very important in the correction and prevention of cross-eyes and walleyes, but in the vast majority of cases glasses merely improve vision and relieve the symptoms of what is called eyestrain, and do not save the eyes from disease or blindness. Strictly speaking there is no such thing as eyestrain, for the use of the eyes in the most difficult circumstances does not strain them at all. Eyestrain is simply a convenient, though inexact, term for the discomfort that accompanies the effort to see clearly under adverse conditions.[39]

It is possible through undue muscular effort to strain the extrinsic muscles of the eyeball, that is, the muscles that move the eyeball. But it is not possible to strain any of the structures within the eyeball by this or any other kind of use.

MONSTERS AND THROWBACKS AMONG HUMANS?

Once in a while a baby is born with a tail—if you can call a small projection of nothing but skin a tail—or with a rich growth of hair all over the body, more or less; and occasionally one hears of a child born with a scaly skin, or some other peculiarity at variance with human usage but familiar in the evolutionary scale. Then the sages around the campfire pull on their pipes and mutter explanations in terms of atavism, and everybody listens with rapt wonder.

Atavism is a relatively new word deriving from the Latin *atavus*, ancestor (or perhaps from *atta*, daddy, and *avus*, grandmother, as Webster III suggests). The Oxford English Dictionary dates it at 1833 and quotes Bagehot: "Some mysterious atavism. Some strange recurrence to a primitive past." But it is Webster that falls into the folly of attributing the occurrence of an atavism to "recombination of ancestral genes," and this is the folk error behind the whole idea, right in tune with the campfire sages.

With the resurgence of science and of scientific inquiry in the nineteenth century somebody got the idea that we "are" a combination of the potentialities of any one of our limitless ancestors straight back to the edge of the sea and further. If the genes get mixed up in some way so that we show up with gill slits in the throat—as sometimes happens—then it is because some of our ancestors once used to breathe water and derive their oxygen from the sea; and we're showing up as a throwback.

Which is nonsense, and we hope the editors of Webster III pay close attention so that Webster IV will get it straight.

The peculiarities improperly called atavisms are not throwbacks at all; they are more or less aberrations of normal developmental processes. Any part of the body can undergo an arrest of development—for reasons not entirely understood—at any period within the growth from cell to mature organism or can suffer a failure to arrest further development.

Thus the so-called gill slits represent the arrest in development of the fistulae which normally occur in this region during the embryonic period;[40] the so-called tail—very rare—consists of an appendage of skin, without any bone at all and no different from the rest of the skin, and is due to a disturbance in the rate of development of the coccygeal skin region as compared with the neighboring buttock region in the fetus, the former growing faster than normal (or the gluteal region could have grown with abnormal slowness, so that the effect of a little tail is given). But throwback—no. Neither in man nor any other animal has such a condition ever occurred, as far as admissible evidence has accumulated. Admissible evidence does not include the gammer's hearthside folklore, lovely as that is in another context.

In short, there are no such things as atavisms.

At Puberty We Become Fertile?

This is one of the prize errors, being both popular and learned. The meaning of *puberty*, given by as exalted an authority as Webster II, is "the state or quality of being first capable of begetting or bearing offspring; the period at which sexual maturity is reached." This would be correct, especially the second part of it, if we accepted puberty to mean what Webster has *said*; but Webster means the first menstruation in the female and the first ejaculation in the male. The most authoritative work on the subject, *Marshall's Physiology of Reproduction,* and other standard works such as L. I. Dublin's *Factbook on Man* both fall into the same error.[41]

In mankind, as in most mammals, the first menstruation, or the menarche, is not at all a sign that the organism has become fecund. If we regard this as the beginning of puberty—and we do—then we must stop thinking of puberty as meaning "period of fertility," which it is decidedly not.

In the first place, conception is impossible without the presence of two basic conditions, both of which are usually not present at the time of the menarche; and in the second place, the ability to conceive is not in itself to be equated with the ability to bear a child, since other changes must occur before a child can be carried to term.

The conditions which must develop before pregnancy is possible are as follows: First, ovulation must occur; this cannot occur in the absence of the secretion from the pituitary gland of the follicle-stimulating hormone (FSH). The secretion of this hormone does not usually reach a sufficiently high level until several years after the onset of menarche. When ovulation does occur, it is quite impossible for the ovum to attach itself to the inner wall of the uterus, which it must do if further development is to proceed, until the pituitary has secreted several other hormones. One of these is the luteinizing hormone (LH), which organizes the area on the ovary through which the ovum has emerged into a temporary gland, the corpus luteum. A third hormone, luteotrophin, from the pituitary is necessary before the corpus luteum becomes actively secretory. Luteotrophin causes the corpus luteum to secrete the pregnancy-preparing hormone, that is progesterone. It is only when this series of changes has occurred that pregnancy becomes possible, and the fertilized ovum can attach itself to the uterine wall. The highest incidence any female ever has of anovulatory menstruation—that is, without the shedding of an ovum —occurs during the first two or three years of the menstrual cycles. In this period also the cycles are most likely to be of irregular duration, while the organism, as it were, is settling into its new character. This is why Malinowski's Trobriand Islander girls, in their early youth, despite unlimited opportunity, did not become pregnant; and why it is that in cases of child marriage pregnancy usually does not occur until the third year following marriage, which generally occurs shortly after menarche. In short, there is an appreciable period following most onsets of menstruation when the female is infertile, and when the organism is developing the greater complexity of differentiation which marks the mature being from the immature. This interval is known as the adolescent sterility period.

In other words, puberty is not a single event; it is a period of maturation. And to identify puberty, menarche, and nubility, or the ability to reproduce, as three of a kind is incorrect. Through a progressive series of developments involving hormones of the anterior pituitary and estrogens released from the ovaries at the appropriate stage of development, the female advances to the first stage of puberty, the beginning of menstruation. Development then continues until the organism is ready for ovulation and the formation of the corpus luteum and its secretion of progesterone, and it is then, and not until then, that pregnancy is possible.

Growth and development is presided over by the master gland of the body, the pituitary gland. With increase in complexity (development) the pituitary increases the amount of follicle-stimulating hormone it pours into the blood, thus causing growth of the ovarian follicle and filling of its central cavity with follicular fluid containing the hormones called estrogens. The estrogens are responsible for those changes in the genital tract which result in menstruation and also in the development of the secondary sexual characteristics. But estrogens alone cannot produce ovulation nor the ability to carry a child. For this the pituitary and other hormones already mentioned are necessary.[42]

The steps in reproductive development may be schematized as follows:

At an average age of 13½ years Adolescent sterility period Duration: 13-16 years of age	Puberty	{ *Follicle-stimulating hormone** increases in amount by about 40 percent, producing *Follicular growth* *Menarche*, characterized by *Anovulatory cycles*
Nubility Duration: 17-22 years of age		{ *Follicle-stimulating hormone** *Luteinizing hormone** *Ovulation* *Estrogen* *Corpus luteum*
Maturity: Duration: 23-28 years of age		{ *Follicle-stimulating hormone** *Ovulation* *Estrogen* *Luteotrophin** *Corpus luteum* *Progesterone*

* Pituitary hormones.

In Pregnancy, the Blood of the Mother Is the Blood of the Child?

One speaks rhetorically of the blood of one's ancestors coursing through the veins of later generations. It makes a good trope; it is a fine figure of speech for inducing pride of family, loyalty to the Mac-Gregors. I walk, sir, with the blood of kings in my veins.

Well, don't walk out in the hot sun, friend.

Yet it is tempting to take the rhetoric literally. Tempting, but foolish. This idea of ancestral blood, for instance. The closest relationship we ever have with another being over any protracted length of time is with the mother during the period of gestation: and even in *that* relationship the maternal and fetal circulations are separate. While a few blood cells may pass across the placenta from the maternal to the fetal circulation, it is not blood that normally does so, but the various substances carried on the surfaces of her red blood cells, molecules of protein, of carbohydrates, of minerals and vitamins, of oxygen and other chemicals. These pass through the fingerlike processes, the villi, which reach out like so many roots into the maternal blood pool to take up the nourishment it contains. The substances on the surfaces of her red blood cells pass through the thin walls of the villi, and thus enter the child's circulation. At no time do the two blood streams mingle; they are entirely independent. Blood cells are normally far too large to pass through the walls of the villi or through any part of the placenta.[43]

This, admittedly, is relatively new information. Oliver Wendell Holmes, who was associate justice, 1882-1899, and then chief justice of the Massachusetts Supreme Court, 1899-1902, ruled from the Massachusetts bench that an unborn child is not an individual but "part of its mother's bowels," and this ruling has been used as a precedent in later cases.

There are many mysteries still confronting medicine—cancer, for example—but as recently as Hans Holbein the Younger (d. 1543) the educated man knew literally nothing of anatomy. Holbein, as anyone knows who has seen his paintings of Henry VIII and his queens, was an exact observer of the living face; but his woodcuts in the *Dance of Death* series show incredible errors in the structure of skeletons: to-day's schoolboy could do better. Our knowledge is very young; and popular error clings to our language through the proverbs and epigrams and because it is easier to repeat an old saw than to disprove it.

The mother's-blood–child's-blood fallacy therefore tends to remain with us; but those of us who are not dropouts from high school should really know better.

4

Misconceptions About the Human Mind

Mistaken ideas about our minds and how they work are no less widespread than those about our food and the bodies we inhabit, and in many instances it is less easy to present definitive proof in the area of psychology than in the other two. At any rate, we know a great deal more about the working of the human mind than we did a few decades ago. But one of the first ideas we should examine is the notion that certain mental states are "unnatural" or "abnormal." Deep in our hearts we suspect that when we use those terms we are not being entirely honest. To commit murder, for instance, we say is abnormal—it is an extreme deviation from ordinary conduct. And we are very eager to send the wife-killer to the electric chair or the gas chamber. Good enough for him! Yet how many of us are there who have never felt the *urge* to kill?

The very fact that a state or an action exists is proof that it is within the order of nature. Therefore "abnormal psychology" is fully as absurd a term as "abnormal physics." The ways of the "savage" are fully as *natural* as the ways of the Lord Mayor of London—and both have moments of being faintly ludicrous from the standpoint of the other man: the Lord Mayor insists on dressing for dinner, no matter how hot and uncomfortable the night may be; he chokes himself with linen and starch, instead of ripping off the silly shirt and letting the soft breezes cool his fevered skin. The "savage" laughs at this; yet if his own mother-in-law comes between him and the moon so that her shadow falls upon the food, he will not eat at all that night, because of his personal taboo. What the Lord Mayor does may be equally as ridiculous as the conduct of the savage; but neither is unnatural. "The unnatural," said Goethe, "that, too, is natural." Agreeing, George Bernard Shaw held that pretending that certain ways of thinking or acting are unnatural is a conspiracy to convict Creation of indecency. However, the type of mentality which Mencken used to characterize as the Philistine convicted Creation of indecency without a qualm; and so did Anthony Comstock—and lots of other people suffering from a burden of guilt which they could not admit to consciousness.

So it's agreed, is it, that we are talking only about natural phenomena?

THE MAN'S INSANE!

One quick look into the eyes of the fugitive, and the hawk-eyed detective realized that the poor creature was out of his mind. Any experienced operator can tell at a glance. Or at least that is the nonsense which is prevalent and thoroughly believed by thousands of readers. In this department nothing is less reassuring than to be confronted with a score of newspaper photographs and be required to rate the owners of the faces as villains or geniuses. Try it on your friends. The scowling rascal who has obviously just removed the dagger from between his teeth turns out to be the learned Bishop of Omaha; and the baby-faced choir singer turns out to be—guess who?

Actually, the "wild" look sometimes observed in the eyes of the insane is nothing but a superstition. Some insane persons do have a wild and furtive look; but so do some supposedly normal people. As a rule, mentally sick people look just like other persons.

THE FACE BETRAYS THE MAN?

"There's no art," says Duncan the King, "to find the mind's construction in the face. He was a gentleman on whom I built an absolute trust." And so he executed the Earl of Cawdor and gave his properties to Macbeth.

Yet our literature and our folklore are always reading character in the person's "wide, intelligent eyes," or in his "thin-lipped cruel mouth that turned down at the corners," or his "jutting chin that proclaimed the belligerency for which he was famous."

Any attempt to take the part for the whole, any simple rule-of-thumb interpretation of so complicated a matter as character, is folly. We don't even know why it is that we like certain faces at first sight or fear others. One case study was made of a child who bawled his head off upon the close approach of Santa Claus; and the fear was traced back to a shaggy dog who had upset the crib years before. The youngster had forgotten all about the incident and so had everybody else; but he had not forgotten the fear of furry things close to him. Thus the entire subject of personal love and distrust, of attraction and repulsion, can be extremely complicated and delicate.

Probably there is a correlation between character and appearance—but the connections are so minute and varied that no simple explanation can account for them. But we still seek the simple answer: a fat man is jolly; a long face is sad; blue eyes are honest; red hair means a hot temper; black men are lazy; Chinamen are inscrutable. We have to take short cuts to truth inevitably, but we should be aware of our probability of error. John Bull is not really England; Uncle Sam is not really the United States; Mlle. Fifi is not really France.

HERE WALKED HERCULES

Judging by the footprint, the old saw held, Hercules must have walked this way. And very possibly he did; but the footprint is only an indication and not a proof. To judge human character by the face alone or by the handwriting or the footprint is hazardous business and fraught with the possibility of error; yet we habitually judge the whole by a part of the whole, perhaps on the theory that we can never get to know the whole anyhow. Maybe we have to do it that way. All the more reason why we should be conscious of the incompleteness of our knowledge and avoid being absolute about an opinion which is necessarily based on less than total information. There have been theologians, as someone remarked, who have described the nature of God with a detailed assurance from which an experienced zoologist would shrink in explaining the genesis of a black beetle. But we do tend to accept judgments made on the basis of the footprint alone. *Caecorum in patria luscus imperat omnis* (In the land of the blind men a one-eyed person can be king of everything), as Fullonius was so fond of saying.

With this warning, we can now report that the colors which a woman selects for her personal attire provide a clue to her personality. Self-confident girls favor neutral grays and beiges, fewer warm colors, hues of medium value—not too dark, not too light. Those who are insecure pick brave, bright colors, plus extremes of very light and very dark cloth. So says research expert Beverly S. Cave after testing some Penn State coeds. The aura of nonsense attaches to these findings only if one accepts them as more than indicative possibilities—the part which *may* indicate the whole.

THERE ARE RECOGNIZABLE TYPES OF MEN?

The criminal, the saint, the greedy, the ambitious, the fearful, the courageous—these and other types of men can be spotted by the trained eye, according to the wisdom of the folk. And not of the folk alone but also of the academy. The late Professor Earnest Hooton of Harvard held that "criminals are physically differentiated according to the types of offense which they commit and they are biologically as inferior to humble but law-abiding citizens as they are sociologically."[1]

Hooton popularized the subject of anthropology—even *Life* devoted occasional pages to his writings—and he was fun to read; but he could get as much mileage out of a skidding banana peel as the traffic would bear. In the citation just given he was dead wrong.[2] Among those who specialize in these matters it is a favorite parlor game to line up photos of most-wanted criminals and mix them up with photos of most-respected clergymen and jurists, and then allow some innocent at the party to select the vicious from the beneficent. The results are often fantastic, and seldom accurate. Maybe this means that at bottom all crooks are potentially clergymen and jurists, and vice versa. We must investigate that rich vein. Meanwhile beware hagiography, star readings, and uncontrolled use of LSD.

LUNATICS—THE HAPPY ONES?

"How happy is the moron," sang Dorothy Parker, "he doesn't give a damn!" In much of popular fiction the demented are represented as enjoying their condition, sometimes to the point of actual bliss. "I am Napoleon, and it's wonderful. Of course, I have a great many responsibilities, but it's worth it." Was it not Dryden who wrote:

> There is a pleasure sure
> In being mad which none but madmen know.
> The Spanish Friar, Act II, sc. 1

In support of this popular fallacy, one must admit that in the manic-depressive psychoses there are certainly manic states of wild elation, and perhaps it is these, in part, which are responsible for the generalization that lunatics are happy in their illusions.

However, those who have worked with the mentally sick know all too well that there is no state so bitterly tragic as mental illness. The misery of the mentally disturbed is beyond the conception of those who are unfamiliar with it. Patients who have endured a severe mental disturbance and have recovered thoroughly enough to be able to give a coherent account of their feelings while ill agree on one thing—that the suffering is intense beyond all comparison with anything else they ever knew.[3]

Can the Thinker Have a Tail?

If it was shocking, sinful, heretical, and just plain awful for Galileo to demonstrate that the earth is not the center of the universe, think how terrible it was for Darwin to demonstrate that man, far from being little lower than the angels, was in fact an animal himself, subject to the laws governing all animals. The favorite defense among those who had to admit Darwin's evidence was that, if man was an animal, at least he was the only rational animal: he was the only animal that could reason. The idea, despite the findings of Freud, lingers. It is one of the most tenacious among popular fallacies: only the tailless wonder can reason. Thus Daglish: "No beast has the power of reasoning out a course of action and of moulding its behavior on a preconceived plan."[4]

We know better today, whether we like to dwell upon the subject or not. The minds of men and the minds of animals are alike; they differ only in degree. The evidence showing that the great apes solve many problems logically and reasonably is "abundant and convincing" to Yerkes. In his book The Great Apes, and in evidence supplied by investigators such as Köhler, Kohts, and numerous others[5] the last doubts are removed.

One of the most convincing demonstrations—and most dramatic—was conducted by Dr. W. N. Kellogg, who for a period of nine months adopted a chimpanzee and brought him up along with his own year-old son. The chimp was, in fact, a few months younger than the boy. There was no question but that the young ape was temporarily more intelligent than the baby: he could remember better, understood more words, perceived more readily how to use tools, and was brighter in many ways. Toward the end of the period the human baby was beginning to outstrip the ape, as expected; but this doesn't mean that the chimpanzee did not continue to "reason" within the limits of his mental powers.

Indeed, any reader of Gertrude Lintz's accounts of her chimps, Joe and Maggie, can have little doubt of their intelligence. "Chimps," she says, "can put two and two together, which is all that thinking amounts to."[6]

Confronted with such evidence, there are those who will still retain their conviction that only mankind can reason because man alone can laugh. But that bastion, too, has fallen. In both his books on apes Yerkes presents conclusive proof that these mammals do laugh.[7] According to Yerkes, man's distinction is that he alone sheds tears, which is a dismal substitute indeed. Let him weep alone.

Despite anything said in this book and despite any proof adduced, we can have a warm assurance that most of mankind will continue to believe that our species alone can reason. Aristotle said so himself; and the Church for twenty centuries taught that man alone has a soul, the ability to reason, and hence the freedom to make choices between good and evil from which moral responsibility derives. And, more than that, the human ego is fed so comfortingly by the conviction that only man is wise. No—we're not going to drop the idea; not this afternoon, anyhow. But for those who like to pile up illustrations in case of argument, consider the facts as set out by Loeser and innumerable other investigators, who have shown that every animal is capable of some degree of intelligence.[8]

Spiders do not spin their webs from a single instinctual pattern: they adapt their work with consummate skill to the requirements of the particular location in which they are working.

Some spiders will use the web of another if possible, rather than go to the trouble of spinning their own. Even an old, dusty, abandoned web with the roof falling in, as it were, is sometimes preferable to all that spinning needed for a new pad.

If a spider is feeding on a captured fly and another fly zooms into the web, the spider will fasten down the first fly securely, grab the second and spin a net around it, and then return to the interrupted meal.

And some spiders, says Loeser, "which had lost one or more legs were seen to give up weaving webs and go hunting for food until their limbs had grown again."[9]

Similarly, adaptations which bees make to an environment for which instinct could not have prepared them give the appearance of reasoning: ordinarily a honeybee goes about preparing the comb as a first order of business; but if offered a ready-made comb, it will skip that step, ignore its "building instinct," and immediately set about the business of hatching. Duplication of effort seems to offend its sense of orderly procedure. In the same way, if bees are given unlimited supplies of sugar, they abandon their "instinctual" storing away of honey for the off-season.

In the Loeser book already cited (p. 81 and elsewhere) that scientist's observation is that there are no "instincts" in the old sense of the word in the entire animal kingdom: nothing that sets a whole pattern of behavior to work at a given signal. All animals, he thinks, are aware only of simple sensations and they respond to these as they occur. Most psychologists today maintain that this is even more true of man than it is of any other creature.

Man's Mind Is in His Brain?

That argument need not detain us; we can observe the incredibly clever manner in which a hermit crab places a sea anemone on the shell of the mollusk in which he is making his home, and then we can call that action anything we like. If you cannot accept the proposition that animals are capable of thinking, you'll call this instinct. To others it will appear as intelligent action. As John Ray, the seventeenth-century English naturalist, wrote in his *Collection of English Proverbs* (1670), "Let him make use of his instinct who cannot make use of reason." Jennings concluded in 1906, after an exhaustive study of unicellular organisms, if they didn't think, they certainly behaved as if they did.[10]

Hoary with age is the notion that the mind of man is a specific organ located in the head or the brain; nothing could be further from the truth—but one would never guess it from our language. Look up "lunatic" in a thesaurus and you find "softhead," "shallowpate," "saphead," "numskull," "dumbhead," "blockhead," "lunkhead," "fathead," "clodpate," "harebrain," "bats in the belfry," and scores more, all indicating the profound conviction that the human mind is up there in the attic for sure. In Shakespeare's day the brain was thought to have three "ventricles"; one for the imagination, one for the reason, and one for the memory. This is a rich field for folklore; but we must skip all that to establish some facts in the case.

We think with our whole bodies and not with the brain alone. This fact was really known long before psychosomatic medicine became a science, but not by the folk, most of whom still think the mind is in the brain.

What we call "mind" is the accumulation of the experiences which have come to us from every part of our bodies. Those experiences make their impressions upon the whole body, too; but the brain is the central organ which stores and serves to integrate one experience with all the others.

Another way of putting it is to say that "mind" is behavior; and it is the body as a whole that does the behaving, not just the brain encapsulated by the skull. The brain is the receiving and transmitting station, and a great and complicated mechanism it is—but it is dependent upon all of the rest of the body for what it receives, and it is beautifully and wonderfully integrated with every other part of the organism. An isolated brain would be powerless to do anything, however. And so would a body without the central nervous system and the brain.

Kraines and Thetford illustrate what happens by using the brilliant analogy of the ballet: "Just as the rhythmic, smooth, and unbroken movement of the trained dancer seems to be a graceful undulating movement, but is in reality composed of innumerable small contractions of individual muscle fibres moving in such rapid succession as to 'appear' smooth, so the mind, seeming to make decisions and to solve problems with relative simplicity, is in reality merely reacting to stimuli in terms of patterns established by countless hitherto experienced pains, frustrations, and successes."[11]

Indeed, moving a finger—that simple gesture—is as much a mental activity as it is a muscular one. Mind might well be defined, in fact, as an expression of the body. The brain acts as organizer or inhibitor so that traffic moves one way at a time; if it did not, there would very shortly be chaos and everything would come to a standstill—which is exactly what happens during an interval of indecision: when the brain is frozen, the body is frozen. In a word, the *mind* is frozen.

"Nervous Breakdown" Comes from Overworking the Brain?

Somehow one has never heard of a "nervous breakdown" resulting from too much gardening or too much wood chopping—the overwork that caused the breakdown is always mental. And the term *nervous breakdown* covers everything from a tantrum to insanity; it is employed so often to cover up some disgrace that a person of sensitive social graces, once he hears that "Henry has had a nervous breakdown," pursues his questioning no further, lest skeletons be heard rattling in family closets.

The truth is that a nervous breakdown, whatever form it may take, always has a long history of mental conflict or frustration behind it. The breakdown represents the crisis which has brought the whole conflict to a head. At this point the sufferer must find the solution to his problem—or withdraw from society in one way or another. Some manage it, others do not.

The people who are deemed to be in greatest danger of facing a nervous breakdown through overwork of the brain are the high-tension executives in business who are running the machinery too fast and without a rest; or the intellectuals, scholars, scientists too devoted to their labors to take an afternoon off at the ball park. It is commonly held that these people either wear out the brain tissues or cause them to be inflamed in some way.

There is not the slightest ground for such beliefs.

Any part of the body can suffer from fatigue, including brain cells; but brain cells cannot be fatigued by mental work; no amount of this is capable of exhausting the brain. No one ever uses more than a small fraction of the potential brain energy he possesses. But anxieties and bodily fatigue or illness can make sustained mental application difficult. Which is quite a different thing from saying that the condition is the *result* of the concentrated mental work. Stop worrying: you may overwork the body—it tires fairly easily. But you're not going to overwork that marvelous mechanism up where the gray begins.

The idea that the mind becomes tired from working is a popular fallacy derived from a false comparison with muscular work. The whole psychosomatic organism may become weary; but the brain itself is no more fatigued than is the conducting wire which carries electricity to your light bulb. Man, it has been variously estimated, is born with between 10 billion and 14 billion brain cells.[12] It has also been estimated that from the age of 35, and often much earlier, we begin to lose between 10,000 and 50,000 of those brain cells a day. But don't worry, a simple arithmetic computation will show you that by the age of 70 you will still have at least 9 billion brain cells left.

Do You Walk in Your Sleep?

There is a most curious notion firmly established in the folkish mind that if you do happen to walk in your sleep there's nothing to worry about because you are perfectly safe—that is, you are in the hands of God, so to speak—as long as nothing suddenly wakes you up. As in the old flicker cliffhanger thrillers of Harold Lloyd's, you may walk out onto steel construction skeletons of skyscrapers, right along on one of the beams overhanging Madison Avenue a hundred stories below, reach the end of the beam and decide to turn around and come back—and end up safe and sound in your own bed. As long as you are walking in your sleep you're presumably safe. But if you should be awakened on that high steel beam you'd be subject to all the normal fears that flesh is heir to, and probably lose your balance in terror. The popular myth, incidentally, is usually not at all interested in sleepwalkers until they are on a ridgepole, a cornice, a high girder, or the edge of a cliff—at least the walker is envisioned in some very great peril to which, awake and in command of his faculties, he would by no means commit himself.

In discussing this particular popular fallacy we can only begin by pointing out that there are no recorded cases of persons sleepwalking themselves into situations of great peril. Into situations fraught with potential social embarrassment, yes—like walking into the crowded living room in one's pajamas. But onto high girders, no. Apparently the only real danger in suddenly awakening a sleepwalker—especially a child—is that the awakening confronts the sleeper with a confusion between what he thought was going on and what he now sees *is* going on which can mount to a point where the walker cannot be sure which is real and which dream. Prolonged confusion in this department could invite powerful emotions which might be inhibitive or otherwise dangerous. None of this would be true in the case of the awakened person who instantly saw his predicament and recognized the real and the imaginary.

Seeking the origins of this very widespread belief that sleepwalkers are immune to harm unless suddenly awakened, we find ourselves pretty deep in primitive religion. We are dealing now with the wandering spirit—soul, ghost, essence—which goes where the body cannot go and remains after the body has died; the spirit that watches over a man when his faculties are dormant; the little white mouse-soul that comes out of a man's mouth when he is asleep and actually does the things of which the sleeper dreams (this is a German version; in another form of the story the white mouse becomes a little bird). In most of these old stories the central fear is that the soul may not rejoin the body by the time the body awakes—and this would be very bad; it might even cause the death of the sleeper. And right there, perhaps, we have put our finger on the deep source of the popular belief about sleepwalking.

Among many nonliterate peoples it is believed that it is dangerous to wake a sleeper, because his soul is away and may not return in time. If a sleeper *must* be awakened, it should be done gradually so that the soul will have time to return.

No human mystery is more common to people everywhere than the adventures of a dream which seem to be as real as any experience can be. The reader can undoubtedly recall dream experiences of his own which were so real that the ordinary ritual of rising, washing, dressing, and having breakfast are all merely semireal until the spell wears off. It would be interesting to determine whether there is any relationship here with the equally widespread fables of invisibility, where the protagonist, by virtue of some magic object, can go where he will without being seen. Usually the magic object is a cloak, a cap, a ring, a stone—although it can be something considerably more esoteric, such as a dragon's crown or the heart of an unborn child. Thompson's index lists twenty-eight such objects which render one invisible. The invisibility magic, in its turn, seems to be associated with other such excellent props as inexhaustible purses or pitchers, caps conferring wisdom, swords which cannot fail, rings and other objects which (compare Aladdin) summon spirits, and so on. Where is my wandering soul tonight?[13]

In a Dream of Falling, It Is Fatal to Hit Bottom?

Since it is not possible to state surely what a person is dreaming about from watching him sleep, we would not be able to connect his dream with his death if he happened to die without waking. Hence the answer to the proposition that you will die if you hit bottom while dreaming of falling is one we cannot answer. However, we know that plenty of people have dreamed that they were falling, and wakened to fall again another night.

The psychoanalysts tell us that the dreams of falling are symbolic of personal anxieties, and this is not hard to believe—nor does it increase our knowledge very much. Freud attached an erotic significance to such dreams, as nobody will be surprised to hear. He says, "Nearly all children have fallen occasionally and then been picked up and fondled; if they fell out of bed at night, they were picked up by the nurse and taken into her bed.[14]

The most we can say about this is that there is no evidence that hitting bottom will cause death, since the only information we have is from those who did dream of falling, did hit the bottom, and lived to recount the horror of it all. If anybody wants to double his anxiety by thinking that he'll die if he hits bottom in this dream of falling, the thought is there for the taking.

Human Nature Never Changes?

"You can't change human nature." "It's only human nature." "Human nature is the same everywhere, always was, always will be." These are ideas which one hears expressed again and again. "What can you expect? It's only human nature." "Human nature will not change," said Abraham Lincoln.[15] *Natural expellas furca, tamen usque recurret,* wrote Horace. "If you drive Nature out with a pitchfork, she will soon find a way back."

The truth is that because human nature is the most changeable thing in the world we are human. A baby is not born with human nature: he acquires it through learning. A child that was deprived of the humanizing process to which all children, with a few exceptions, are normally exposed, would not develop as a human being. Every child is born with the potentialities, the capacities for being human, but he does not become what we recognize as essentially human unless he has undergone the socializing process which makes him so. All of us are born with the capacity to speak, but none of us would ever have learned to speak unless we had been repeatedly exposed to speech. A human being *learns* to be a human being, and it is because of his two million and more years of such learning that he has acquired a genetic constitution which makes him the most educable creature in the world, and by the same token the most naturally capable of change.[16]

The endowments of biological potentialities with which each child is born are, within broad limits, similar, but the manner of their development will depend upon the patterns prevailing in the particular culture to which they are made to conform.[17] Man, as an acting functioning human being is custom-made, tailored according to the prevailing pattern of the culture in which he learns to be a human being. Human nature is what a human being *does* by way of being human, and what he *does* may vary infinitely, as we "survey mankind from China to Peru."

The basic substrata of potentialities which make it possible for the child, under the appropriate socializing conditionings, to develop as a human being do not remain stationary. They, too, change. Man has not ceased to evolve, and there is today every reason to believe that his potentialities for human behavior are as subject to evolutionary pressures as they ever were.[18]

It will always be possible to pick up scattered kernels of evidence to support the nonsense that human nature is always the same everywhere, if you call it evidence that Thucydides (died 400 B.C.) says that many things have happened and always will as long as the nature of man remains the same—meaning that it will remain the same. Personally, we don't call that evidence at all; just because a famous Greek historian held that opinion does not make it a fact: the same historian thought the world was flat. With our immensely strong wish to believe what we want to, we tend to collect the evidence that supports our opinions and so very easily we tread blindly past those which contradict them; hence the apothegm of the folk that the devil can quote Scripture to his own ends.

More Human Nature That Changed . . .

The Jewish people during the Middle Ages were bitterly persecuted by Christians who blamed them for the death of Christ and honestly believed that to kill a Jew was to earn credits toward heaven. As a result, many jobs were not open to Jews, and they tended to band together in city ghettos. Thus over several hundred years the Jews gained the reputation of being naturally adapted to city life and to fiduciary concerns, particularly as moneylenders. Christians did not lend money, because they could not, by law, charge interest. Jews did lend money and charged fair rates of interest—for which again they were hated. But our point is that the Jews had the reputation of being city-bred people with a sharp eye for the handling of coin of the realm. Yet when they were given a chance to become agricultural, as in Israel, it was immediately clear that they could make the desert blossom at least as fast as any other people. In short, Jews are no more bent toward mercantile pursuits by "nature" than they are toward husbandry.

Perhaps the most dramatic change in "human nature" is the change we have seen in Western civilization—and now throughout the world —in the status of women. Western woman, above the rank of peasant, was inferior in strength physically and intellectually. She was supposed to have a smaller brain than man, and so on and so forth. The past half century has seen this very same species—if you want to call her that—prove that it can do everything a man can do except become a father. To balance that sad inferiority, one might recall that men have not been bearing babies much lately either.

THE ONE THING THAT NEVER CHANGES IS HUMAN NATURE

Taken out of any specific context and allowed to stand as an absolute statement in its own right, the headline above is simple nonsense, and is so proved with great ease as follows:

1. Human nature apart from humanity does not exist. Agreed?
2. Human beings—humanity, that is—are known to change both individually and as groups: that is, as families, tribes, or nations.
   a. Illustrative examples are filled in here.
3. Q.E.D., human nature does change.

It so happens that we have with us a few handy instances to slip into 2-a, "illustrative examples," and we would like to assume that the reader would be pleased to have them.

Elizabethan England was one of the most musical nations in Europe; the people of Renaissance Britain loved to sing and dance and play instruments. In part this could have been overcompensation for the sad state into which music in England had been driven by the Civil Wars and the Reformation; and in part it was certainly due to the contributions of Huguenot refugees and Flemish weavers escaping from persecution. Psalm singing was a real rage, as W. Barclay Squire of the British Museum points out, citing the fact that "from 1560 to 1600 alone there appeared in England some ninety editions of metrical psalms with music."[22]

Popular music outstripped the church music; there were itinerant "pipers and fiddlers" in every tavern; and all the great noble houses had their own resident musicians, both to perform and to teach. After the defeat of the Armada in 1588, national music in England burgeoned and the booksellers offered all kinds of music books. Shakespeare, of course, refers to singers, musicians, and the art of music in scores of passages.

Yet today when one is asked to name a musical people, how many will name the English? The socioeconomic interests of the English were strong enough to lead the national effort in another direction—and history awards this people a garland of success in world trade instead of in music. The nature of the English nation—this was our point—did change within relatively few years. With their decline as a world power, the English seem to have turned to music once more.

Perhaps the Japanese people display an even more dramatic example. Only a little time ago—little more than a hundred years—they held themselves in isolation from contact with the West and even refused trade with American ships. In fact, more than fifty attempts were made by this country to establish trade relations with Japan prior to 1854.[23] American whalers wrecked in Japanese waters were brutally treated and ports were closed. Commodore Biddle, for instance, anchored in Edo Bay in 1846 but was refused any consideration. Perry's first visit elicited strong antiforeign responses and he was not able to get any agreement until his flotilla returned in February, 1854, when two ports were opened and America was named in the treaty as a most-favored nation. Even then Japan was not "open" to trade. The treaties were signed only by the shogun (called the *tai-kun* or *tycoon* by Westerners) and the people were powerfully antiforeigner in attitude. Murders of Westerners were not uncommon.

Today, as we all know, Japanese industry itself reaches out for world markets—one can get cheaper radios, tape recorders, binoculars, cameras, and all kinds of gadgets from the Japanese than can be made in the land of the free and the home of the brave. Technologically the Japanese are a different people entirely from the old days of the home factories specializing in ceramics and a few other specialties. Within a few generations they were able to change their old ways so completely that they have altogether lost some of their original traits along with the ability to produce certain exquisite objects of art, the best examples of which now reside in museums. They have Westernized their culture, adopting the vices of the West, alas, along with the material prosperity.

In short, human nature is what one makes of it. It would be possible to cite scores of other illustrations, from the statement attributed to the sage Saïd of Toledo in the eleventh century, that the races north of the Pyrenees "lack all sharpness of wit and penetration of intellect," back to the remarks of Galen in the second century, that the reason for the levity, excitability, and emotionalism of Negroes was due to a weakness of their brains, resulting in a weakness of intellect.[24]

As for those who say that human nature never changes, perhaps they mean that there are certain generalizations which can be made of all living organisms more or less always, more or less everywhere— like the tendency to avoid painful experiences and to seek pleasurable ones (which is about as broad a generalization as you can get!). But that is rather a different thing from saying that human nature is constant. And of course one can always find exceptions: the masochist, for example, deliberately *seeks* pain; the martyr seeks death; the suicide woos the bullet. And what about the moth and the flame?

Or perhaps what these people are trying to say is that we live in an orderly universe where the laws of nature are dependable and that in this dependable universe there is no effect without its cause. But they would be closer to the truth to say that the very essence of all life is change itself.

THE HUMAN IQ IS A CONSTANT?

If it were really possible to construct a scale for every person which accurately reflected his biological age and his mental age in such a way as to show indisputably the extent to which his innate intelligence potential had been reached at any given point, that scale would indicate what we loosely call a person's IQ, his "intelligence quotient."

We take a rough reading in that direction today by saying that a 10-year-old should have the following intellectual attainments, and this particular 10-year-old measures below or above that level and therefore has an IQ of 140 (well above his age expectation) or of 90 (somewhat below what is expected). But there are so many variations that the scale itself and the IQ figure are nothing but probabilities. Yet parents of a 140 IQ child preen themselves, and so would you and I.

That the intelligence quotient is an unchanging figure, the same at four that it will be at ten, is generally agreed in lay circles. But the fact is that there are dozens of factors which can and do change the IQ. For example, Professor T. R. Garth, in 1935, attempted to discover whether the score of American Indians rated about 80 IQ could be modified if their children were placed in white homes in a white environment. In a very short time Garth found that the children in white homes obtained an average score of 102, while the brothers and sisters of these children who remained in the Indian environment obtained an average score of only 87.5.[19]

Even more striking is Rohrer's report on the Osage Indians of Oklahoma. As a consequence of the discovery of oil upon their reservation the Osage were able to improve their living conditions substantially. On one test, the Goodenough "Draw-a-Man" test, the Osage children obtained an average score of 104 while the white children's score was 103. On a test which made use of language the Osage children made an average score of 100 while the white children scored an average of 98.[20]

Actually, the idea that the IQ cannot change is cognate with the notion that human nature is always the same; and that old notion is allied to the belief that "you can't improve nature," a belief dear to certain granite-headed village prophets who want things done as grandfather did them and not otherwise. The first troglodyte who managed to build a fire in a cave was improving on nature.

What the IQ in fact measures is for the most part socioeconomic, emotional, and schooling experience, and very little else.

Back to the IQ: It has been shown that a child whose tests show him to have a low intelligence quotient is quite capable of raising that score if he is exposed to stimulating, pleasurable schooling early enough in life. Further, the investigations carried out on monozygotic twins separated in childhood and reared apart, as conducted by Professor Newman at the University of Chicago and by others,[21] show that education and environment can indeed produce appreciable changes in IQ.

In short, human nature can be changed; IQ can be changed; and even animal nature can be changed, as witness the beloved axolotl: here is a little creature six to eight inches long, resembling a tadpole. He has external gills. If he is left in water, he stays an axolotl. But if the water is allowed to evaporate slowly, the animal loses his gills and fins, develops eyelids, and leaves the water to become a salamander. Thereafter his nature is not axolotlish but salamandrine. Any questions?

WHERE IS MY WANDERING MIND TONIGHT?

We have already pointed out that mind and body are one and not two, but the myth of duality dies hard. Probably this is natural enough; a dreaming man may be out on the mountain hunting the roan deer while his body lies quiet on his bed—and when he tells his experience of the dream, those who were near him all night may assure him with oaths that they saw him on his bed: he knows where he was. He was out on the mountain. The only explanation must be that the soul goes wandering. Yes, to be sure: he was abroad mentally, but at home physically.

For thousands of years mankind has been assured of its double nature, mental and physical, mind and body, spirit and flesh. Indeed, the Gnostics of the first century believed that everything was spirit, that what we see as physical is merely an aspect of spirit—it just *looks* or *seems* to be material. The mystery cults were imbued with this idea, and some religious views still teach the same thing.

This is a reflection of a human characteristic which it is hard to call by any other name than stupidity: while nothing is more important to us than the functioning, use, and health of our own organisms, our own body-and-mind totalities, we actually know less about them than we do about most things. We are close to complete ignorance—but that does not bother us, because we have our totemic, traditional, rich supply of nonsense to substitute for knowledge. Superstition can be much more credible than fact. If you say that the body is evil and the spirit is good, who is going to dispute you? All the godly know it's true. Lechery, greed, envy, pride, cruelty, selfishness—are these not sins of the body? So that the pure and conscious mind must drag the body before the spiritual magistrate, shaman, priest, or worse still, before the tribunal of the human judgment, to be punished. One recalls that Jurgen, visiting his father in hell, found the old gentleman complaining bitterly because the attendant devils were too lazy to torture him as much as he thought they should; and when Jurgen advised him to leave well enough alone, the old man cried out, "But my conscience, Jurgen!"

And so it occurs that, despite the plethora of articles in the mass media on the subject of mental and physical health, we continue on our way without learning very much. It is possible that the reason for this is that there are hundreds of ways in which we can avoid facts, but no way in which we can avoid the need for self-esteem: we must think well of ourselves. Hence if a fact comes up against a myth, a stupidity, an error, or a piece of nonsense, and if the fact tends to make one look less admirable than one likes while the myth allows one to retain the rose-colored spectacles, one will choose—guess what!

Aside from that consideration, errors about the human body are accepted on the basis of very little evidence, on none, on hearsay.

Further, there is a magic in language which, for everyone but those persons who have been trained to be critical—that is, trained to seek for alternatives before coming to a conclusion—seems to establish as fact almost anything that is *stated* as fact. If you drink sea water you'll go crazy—did you know that? No, it never occurred to me; but you must be right because the Ancient Mariner and heaven knows how many other sea tales of shipwreck and open boats all indicate the same thing. So it must be true. Yes, sir—drinking sea water drives men mad. . . . We are not saying, mind you, that drinking *enough* sea water *under certain conditions* will not increase the irritation caused by a lack of fresh water and perhaps increase the torture of thirst to the point where the brain goes foggy—possibly even to the point of insanity. But your correspondents have themselves drunk sea water. . . . We will quickly deny the corollary allegation which we can plainly see coming to the reader's lips.

Statements made by persons of authority are naturals for public credence. Even if the person making the statement happens to be an authority in mathematics and not in anything else, he can make headlines by condemning this or that act of the government, as we have seen so frequently in our own time. Several times the American people have elected a man to head the nation merely because he had been a famous military leader.

And of course fifty million Frenchmen can't be wrong: if enough people say it, it must be true. This characteristic of our species is behind the satire in Kipling's jungle story of Mowgli's being captured by the great apes. "We are great, we are free, we are wonderful. We all say so, and so it must be true," they chanted to him. Fortunately Mowgli was able to see an alternative—to wit, that they were wish-thinking, herd-minded, and basically pretty thick behind the ears. Perhaps Kipling had somebody else in mind besides the Bandar-log.

Sound Body a Must for a Sound Mind?

The old classical ideal, *mens sana in corpore sano*, simply meant that a supreme good, for which everybody should make the old college try, was a healthy mind in a healthy body. It still is an unspeakably wistful ideal, and it is impossible to imagine anyone not wanting to achieve it, just as it is a wee touch doubtful that anybody ever does. But ideals are to aim at. That's an editorial comment.

The motto has somehow become distorted, perhaps largely by the physical culturists, who are in a position to judge only the second half: the sound body part. That emphasis has tended to spread abroad the conceit that a sound mind can exist *only* in a sound body—which is nonsense taken right out of the mother lode, pure and unadulterated. Darwin had a dyspepsia which made it often impossible for him to work for more than four hours a day. Thomas Henry Huxley suffered from severe gastric troubles, and so did Herbert Spencer. John Keats did some of his best work when his lungs were being eaten away by t.b., and so did D. H. Lawrence. Steinmetz, the wizard of electricity, the first man to make artificial lightning, had an irremediable deformity of the spinal column. And Freud for half his life had cancer of the jaw and larynx. Milton wrote when he was sightless; Beethoven composed magnificent works when he was deaf. You could load a hay wagon with examples if you could find a hay wagon.

Of course a disease which attacks the central nervous system can make a difference; but no parent should get the idea that having the tonsils removed is going to improve the mental capacity of a child. It may possibly take the child's mind off his discomfort so that the mental apparatus can *work* better. But a very much twisted and un-healthy body can be governed by a fine, unspoiled brain. Not that it always *is*.

SOUND MIND, SOUND BODY—SECOND STANZA

Having just gone to some trouble to prove that a perfectly function-ing cerebral cortex can exist in a twisted body, it is perhaps only fair to the Greeks to say that the ideal still holds: a healthy mind has a much better chance in a healthy body; or, more strictly, it is much more likely that a healthy mind will be found in a healthy body than in a twisted and diseased one. We are now thinking, of course, of the findings of psychosomatic medicine in which the word *mind* means something a great deal wider than brain.

No reader of these pages, surely, has not experienced the debilitat-ing effects of the extreme, muggy hot weather on the thinking appara-tus. You know that you can "think" better in a cool place. You wouldn't want to take a final exam in a sticky, dripping-hot room with no air conditioning. Industry found this out long ago. Much as they love their workers, the big corporations would not have made life so much more comfortable for them—at enormous expense—if it did not pay off in terms of production. Let us not be naïve.

Further, the keen mind can be in part shaped by the hurt body: it is a question whether the savage satire of *Gulliver* would have occurred to the mind of Jonathan Swift if he had not suffered from what is now thought to be labyrinthine vertigo which first made him partially deaf and later probably drove him insane. That this proud and bitter genius died insane is history. The sharp mind, first affected by the unhappy body, finally lost its hold.

If the Greeks had said "a healthy cerebral cortex in a healthy body," the issues would have been more clearly drawn. Funny one of them didn't think of it.

CERTAIN DISCIPLINES "STRENGTHEN" THE MIND?

In the old dichotomy mind and body, thought of as being totally apart and different, like the spiritual and the physical, Psyche and Eros, it was no trouble at all to have a thought picture of the mind structured somehow with muscles which grow stronger the more they are exercised. Now of course if one practices a great deal with the discus, a particular set of muscles becomes more powerful; and those same muscles can be called upon for throwing a javelin or a rock or a rotten apple. The transfer of power to the javelin from the discus is close to total.

Therefore, by analogy, a study of geometry should increase the "muscles" of the brain so that they can handle problems of logic in general: you become successful at solving geometric problems, and as a result you are able to handle the problems of state in later life. Train a child to become a good chess player, and he'll turn out to be methodical, well organized, and keep his closet clean and his room picked up.

That's the theory. Plato suggested subjects that were good exercise for the mind and kept it in trim, like an athlete in training. Even as recently as Woodrow Wilson it was conceded that studying Latin and math was great stuff for mind training: "The mind takes fiber, facility, strength, adaptability, certainty of touch from handling them," he asserted in a 1902 article. In short, there is a transfer of the ability to handle Latin over to the ability to handle problems in general, like the transfer of the discus thrower's muscles to spear throwing.

The theory was forced to surrender to facts when Thorndike and Woodworth began their researches in the psychology of learning; and now we know that a mind disciplined to solve problems in algebra may become expert in solving problems in algebra; but very little of that skill will be transferred to solving problems in other fields. The training in math may instill a love of exactitude and orderly procedure —these attitudes are the concomitants of learning; but a lawyer's skill in presenting a good defense owes practically nothing to his earlier training in math or Latin: it developed out of presenting legal defenses —which will not help him one whit in his golf score.

"Experiments on transference ranged, during the first twenty years of the century, through all psychological fields—memory, skill, judgment, thinking and reasoning. In all the amount of transfer found was amazingly small—quite insufficient to justify educationally the attempt to train a habit in any field other than that in which it is most required."[25]

All this, of course, caused a revolution in American education: one studies the classics to become versed in the classics; Latin to become able to read Latin; math to do mathematical calculations—but *not* the classics because it's good for the mind or Latin because it develops fiber or math because it disciplines the brain to be exact. And of course the college entrance requirements have reflected this new understanding. In 1900-1920 one had to have Latin to enter any Ivy League college, to select only one of the changes.

You can train the mind, the brain, the cerebral cortex: but you can't build muscle into it: you can't "strengthen" it. Neither can you tire it out. So feel perfectly free to use it any time you want to.

Making Whoopee Rests the Mind?

Some people make whoopee by running and dancing or playing a mad set of tennis or doing some physical act that uses up a lot of bodily energy; others, by going out on the town and painting it red— and perhaps getting soused in the process. Anything extravagant. And they justify the extravagance on the basis of the popular nonsense that putting the body to great exertion automatically gives the mind a rest. It is true that much of the whoopee-making gives the thinking apparatus a *vacation;* but since it wasn't the cerebral cortex that was tired in the first place, violent physical activity is no "rest" for the brain.

Now, this is not to say that mental fatigue, so called, cannot occur. It can, just as an electric motor can burn up its oil and finally stick; but the copper wire leading electricity into the motor did not wear out, tire, or run short of oil. The wire will carry electricity in proper amounts for ages. And the cerebral cortex is like that copper wire: it does not tire or clog. What does get fatigued is the whole organism: and since body and mind are one, we say the mind is tired.

Idleness, sleep, lolling on the beach, or playing a hot game of tiddlywinks would give the "mind" as much rest as anything. What's required is a change, a holiday from the mental activity that has engaged the whole organism. Perhaps you'd rather scream and shout and jump up and down; in that case, by all means do so—but don't strain yourself.

Do Intelligence Tests Test Intelligence?

The word *intelligence* is derived from the Latin *legere,* to perceive, and *inter,* between or among. According to Webster, it means, first, the power of understanding; second, the "power of meeting any situation, esp. a novel situation, successfully." In other words, it is the perception of alternatives. If the organism is confronted by a problem situation—such as being trapped behind a wire fence or cage with the only opening at the top—and it tries to force its way out by going straight ahead into the wire, time after time, without seeing any alternative way of attempting escape, that organism is less intelligent than the one which, after a few trials, looks around for another way, such as up. The lobster in a fisherman's trap remains, and is finally eaten, because he does not try enough alternatives. He is not locked in there: a way out exists. But not for an organism of his intelligence. Fortunately for lobster lovers.

The ability to discern alternatives is one which can be learned. If one's experiences within the environment are strictly limited, intelligence naturally does not grow as it would under richer surroundings. That was given as one excellent reason why the Nazi soldier was inferior to the American soldier when both were thrown into unforeseen circumstances: one had learned to obey unquestioningly; the other had been trained to act independently and imaginatively until the time of his induction; and those early years counted in terms of intelligence: the Yank saw alternatives.

But the so-called "intelligence tests" do not measure intelligence. They measure an expression of socioeconomic, cultural, and schooling experiences, and very little else. If they come anywhere near measuring the genetic contribution to intelligence, it is at a considerable distance removed.

IQ tests have their uses in telling us where a child stands at his age level in relation to other children of the same age level, in terms of the performance arbitrarily established by the tests themselves. Used as an administrator's tool for placing children in more or less homogeneous classes in a school, they may have their place—although the whole question of homogeneous classes in a democracy is still moot. The tests at least will be reasonably accurate in separating the efficient readers from the inferior readers, if that's the way you want to group children in a school.

From another point of view, however, these famous tests have done more harm than good, operating as a tyranny determining the teacher's attitude toward an individual child. If little Willie is shown to have an IQ of only 90, then is it not foreordained that his performance will be inferior? So why bother with him?

Actually, the low IQ child may have intelligence far superior to that of a child ranking high on the tests. Perhaps he simply lacked the environmental conditions necessary to develop his full capacities, since intelligence is learned. A low score is no more a test of the quality of intelligence than a high score is an indication of genius; and the injustices committed against low scorers in our schools often have grave consequences, especially for the underprivileged. We know that when the environment improves the scores on the tests improve.[26]

5

Absurdities About Race

In the paragraphs that follow we are maintaining that the term *race* as applied to a group of human beings to explain hereditary traits is meaningless and nonsensical, and we are supplying the reasons for saying so. A word derives meaning from the context in which it is used and from the idea it attempts to map out in a verbal symbol—the thing or action it refers to. *Race* has eight meanings as a noun before it is used for "descendants" or "people": the act of rushing forward; the onward course of life; a running in competition; a strong current of water; a channel for water; a machine guide; a fenced lane; and the space between two points (now obsolete). After that it has been commonly used to indicate a tribe or nation presumed to be of the same stock—lineage, breed; and then "a division of mankind possessing constant traits, transmissible by descent." It is only in the last meaning that the word becomes nonsense, a term without real referents. *Race*, however, is far from standing alone as a word without reference to anything in the real world: the language is rich in such terms. For example, the British guinea, 21 shillings, does not actually exist as a coin or as paper money: it's just an idea meaning 21 shillings—one shilling more than a pound. But if a lawyer's fee is 50 guineas, you pay him 50 pounds plus 50 shillings, so it is not difficult to understand why the myth is perpetuated.[1] *Race* as a rationalization designed to

151

hang the idea of inferiority or superiority on any group we choose to call a "race" may be useful to the ego of someone who thinks he derives his higher status from a biological inheritance; but he does not so derive it, as we hope to show.

About three and a half billion samples of a species to which we laughingly refer as *Homo sapiens* walk about today on Sun's Planet Number Three and not one of them is quite like any other in terms of inheritance, experience, or fingerprints. On the other hand, from the Cheshire Cat point of view, they all look so much alike that you can't tell one from the other: two eyes, always in approximately the same place; one nose just so; and always, always a mouth under the nose—no variation at all.

Except as a shadowy background, however, these three and a half billion people mean nothing to you and me. We cannot "think" three and a half billion. Some of us have trouble "thinking" ten.

Therefore we begin to classify these people. Things begin to make a little more sense if one says, "There are about 200 million Americans," although the 200 million is still meaningless. But separating people into nationalities does help to begin to find a way out of the chaos suggested by three and a half billion human beings.

Scientists studying mankind began by dividing the species into four great divisions and called these Caucasoid, Negroid, Australoid, and Mongoloid. These were the four major groups of mankind. Each major group consisted of certain subdivisions called *races* and were distinguished from each other on the basis of such characteristics as skin color, the color of the hair or shape of the head, and other such traits. In the course of its development the term *race* was forced by strongly partisan pressures into a nonsense-word to account for supposed inferiorities in terms of natural endowment—and thus support elitist claims of "racial" inferiority or superiority.

The nonsense is this: that a prime determiner of all human traits, capabilities, and potentials, physical and mental, is something called race—a fixed and immutable part of the germ plasm transmitted from generation to generation. This thing called race is inescapable, of course, and is either decidedly limiting, as in the case of the Negro, or decidedly beneficient, as in the case of the Master Race, the white or Nordic hero race. Such is the nonsense aspect of the word *race*.

It would be comforting if we could assure ourselves that this use of the word was limited to the period of the abolitionist controversy in the United States. But this is only where it flowered, in support of the plantation system, once the cotton gin had made the use of slave labor suddenly very lucrative. The moral judgment that slavery is wrong and that all men are brothers and born with equal rights was answered by the argument that you cannot fight Old Mother Nature, who made one race inferior by definition, as it were. Not only in the American South in the mid-nineteenth century has this nonsense-use of *race* been employed, but in all countries where some kind of elite (of birth, or wealth, or of control) has fought the democratic idea: the millowners versus the sweatshop labor or child labor—it need not be between black and white.

The first codification of these ideas appeared in France during the period of the Second Empire. The author, an aristocrat, Orientalist, diplomat, and manufacturer of inferior plays, incompetent novels, and execrable poetry, was Count Joseph Arthur de Gobineau, who looked upon the egalitarian philosophy of the Revolution as the confused insanity of a degraded rabble, and determined to set the record straight. In Paris in 1853-1855 he published his four-volume work, *Essai sur l'inégalite des races humaines.* The first two volumes were published in an American translation by H. Hotz in Philadelphia in 1856.[2] Since he gave the Germans the accolade of being the "master race," the work was very popular across the Rhine and Gobineau Societies were founded all over Germany. Gobineau is still cited in some circles. His teachings culminated in that stupendous miracle of nonsense, *Grundlagen des neunzehnten Jahrhunderts* (Foundations of the Nineteenth Century), written in 1899 by a renegade Englishman, and son-in-law of Richard Wagner, Houston Stewart Chamberlain. The translation was introduced to the English-speaking world by Lord Redesdale, grandfather of Unity Mitford, who later became an intimate of that gentle shepherd of the master race, Adolf Hitler.[3] The book became the Bible of the German racists and Kaiser Wilhelm II called it "my favorite book." Both the Gobineau and the Chamberlain were spiritual predecessors of *Mein Kampf.*

One would hope that in this day and age, and to the audience to which this volume is addressed, it is hardly necessary to state that the idea of race as a prime determiner and so forth has no basis whatever in scientific fact nor in any other kind of demonstrable fact, but is purely myth. Since it is still believed by millions, we must place upon the brow of this myth a fresh green laurel wreath for being the greatest existing single exemplar of folk nonsense. It really has very few competitors, and certainly none in the depths of its imbecility.

And yet the myth is really a very young one; an infant Hercules, possibly. Mankind had never entertained the idea of biological inferiority as the basis for discrimination until the late eighteenth century. Discrimination there had been, as we know, by land and by sea—persecutions for religion, silencing of critics, execution of nonconformists such as Socrates, and discrimination on the basis of sex—for centuries; but it was left for the years following the Industrial Revolution to develop organized attacks on a human group because of biological differences.

This is a grim kind of nonsense, but it deserves some examination.

How did the biological basis for persecution come to be accepted by millions?

Here we are in some danger of oversimplification; yet the outlines are fairly obvious. All the governing, directing, planning, and policing of the British Empire and of America was in the hands of whites. It was the white man who opened up the new lands, who tamed nature, who built the ships—and who wrote the books and kept the records. It was also the white man who set up the conditions for the slave market; and it was he who obtained, transported, and sold slaves to a white buyer.

Since he was able to compel obedience from the slaves in much the same way in which he obtained obedience from his horse, the white man considered it plain on the face of it that he was superior to both slave and horse.

In the case of the horse, the white man had Scripture on his side: God had given man dominion over the beasts of the field. In the case of the slave, although the creature had the shape of a man it was clear that the black man was of inferior clay. It was the biological difference that set them apart, and this, too, had to be the will of God. The white man was intended to rule, to command, to enjoy the finer things of life; and the black man was intended to serve him. The thing was self-evident. There was something about being black which per se limited a creature in human shape to activities of a very low cultural order, and nothing could change that. It was a racial "fact." Inherent natural differences had made the relationship between white and black inevitable.

Now, this theory suited the white man right down to the ground, of course; and therefore nobody paid much attention when, as early as 1848, John Stuart Mill wrote:

> Of all the vulgar modes of escaping from the consideration of the effects of social and moral influences on the human mind, the most vulgar is that of attributing the diversities of conduct and character to inherent natural differences.[4]

Or, if they heard him they agreed with Julius Caesar: "He is a dreamer; let us leave him." Bagehot, writing in 1872 in his *Physics and Politics,* echoed Mill: "When a philosopher cannot account for anything in any other manner, he boldly ascribes it to an occult quality in some race."

The war, which has never ended, over the place of the Negro in the life of the United States, and the ever-growing imperialist power of England, made acceptable as a fact of everyday observation the proposition that "inferior races" are characterized by peculiar, and usually unattractive, physical attributes invariably associated with limited mental capacities. Writers such as Matthew Arnold,[5] Thomas Carlyle, Charles Kingsley, Lord Acton, and Rudyard Kipling subscribed to the natural racial superiority of the (mythical) Anglo-Saxon race, and of course the especial and particular superiority of the English branch of that "race." Among scientists similar views were held by distinguished men like Thomas Henry Huxley, Francis Galton, and Karl Pearson. Kingsley rejected John Stuart Mill's view that the impoverishment of Ireland and its inability to govern itself was due to anything but a "peculiar indolence and *insouciance* in the Celtic race." In his famous *Ode to the North-East Wind,* Kingsley encapsulated it all:

> Conquering from the eastward
> Lords by land and sea.
> Come; and strong within us
> Stir the Viking's blood;
> Bracing brain and sinew;
> Blow, thou wind of God.

"Science has now made visible to everybody," wrote Arnold, "the great and pregnant elements of difference which lie in race, and in how signal a manner they make the genius and history of an Indo-European people vary from those of a Semitic people."[6] Carlyle's *Heroes and Hero Worship* (1840), his *Past and Present* (1843), and his notorious essay *The Nigger Question* (1849), made his racist views abundantly clear. It was the moral obligation of England, he averred, as the nation destined to rule the world, to secure the blessing of Anglo-Saxon civilization to the backward races.

> In what land, the sun does visit
> Brisk are we, whate'er betide:
> To give space, for wandering is it
> That the world was made so wide.[7]

The sense of world-mission and of "a race apart" found its most vigorous exponent in that born storyteller, Rudyard Kipling. His pulse-stirring rhymes embody the racist thinking of jingo imperialism, and in none of his verses more stirringly than in his famous "The White Man's Burden" (1899).

> Take up the White Man's Burden,
> Send forth the best ye breed,
> Go bind your sons to exile
> To serve your captive's need;
> To wait in heavy harness,
> On fluttered fold and wild—
> Your new-caught, sullen peoples,
> Half-devil and half-child.

Thus the symbol of Anglo-Saxonism, "To serve your captive's need." The terrible thing is that Kipling and millions of his fellow Englishmen believed this canting nonsense, and took it to be no less than the gospel truth. Acton, who had no particular love for nationality, nevertheless attacked the historian Buckle's view that "original distinctions of race are altogether hypothetical" as "a great absurdity."[8]

Thomas Henry Huxley, one of the most distinguished scientists of his day, a man of generous heart and great public spirit, could write immediately after the conclusion of the Civil War, that it was simply incredible that when all disabilities from which the Negro had suffered have been removed, "and our prognathous relative has a fair field and no favor, as well as no oppressor, he will be able to compete successfully with his bigger-brained and smaller-jawed rival, in a contest which is to be carried on by thoughts and not by bites."[9] Galton's protégé, Karl Pearson, first professor of biometrics in the University of London, and one of the most distinguished minds of his time, asserted that it was "to the real interest of a vigorous race to be kept up to a high pitch of external efficiency by contest, chiefly by way of war with inferior races, and with equal races by the struggle for trade routes and for the sources of raw material and of food supply." "This," added Professor Pearson, "is the natural history view of mankind, and I do not think you can in its main features subvert it."[10]

And so we graduate from natural history to politics, national welfare, and finally to ethics, and nowhere is this more clearly set out programmatically than in Karl Pearson's declaration, in 1900, that "It is a false view of human solidarity, a weak humanitarianism, not a true humanism, which regrets that a capable and stalwart race of men should replace a dark-skinned tribe which can neither utilise its land for the full benefit of mankind, nor contribute its quota to the common stock of knowledge."[11]

Codifying such thinking, Bernard Bosanquet, the English philosopher, in his book on the state wrote that "The nation-state is the widest organization which has the common experience necessary to found a common life." "According to the current ideas of our civilization, a great part of the lives which are being lived and have been lived by mankind are not lives worth living, in the sense of embodying qualities for which life seems valuable to us. This being so, it seems to follow that *the object of our ethical idea of humanity* is not really mankind as a single community. Putting aside the impossibilities arising from succession in time, we see that no such identical experience can be pre-supposed in all mankind as is necessary to effective membership of a common society and exercise of the general will."[12]

As Hobson has so sagely remarked in a passage that might well be recommended to our domestic imperialists, "That the power to do anything constitutes a right and even a duty to do it, is perhaps the commonest, the most 'natural' of temperamental fallacies."[13]

Myths in the service of imperialism—and never was there a more useful myth in its service than "race"—are idealizations, rationalizations of social conditions, so that with respect to the matter of inequality the main function of the myth is to explain the origin of differences in ways that satisfy the needs of the group. Myths that account for social differences correspond to, and often have, the force of legal fictions, while the legalistic attempt to justify the status quo provides the myth with an aura of historical authority.

VARIETIES OF THE HUMAN SPECIES—REAL OR IMAGINARY?

If you thought we were going to jump off the bandstand waving a pure-white flag and shouting, "We are all alike and therefore all men are brothers!" you picked up the wrong signal. Not one of us is precisely like another and very few persons are motivated by altruism. The richness of our species in its variety is one of the continuing wonders of life; but the even greater wonder is the unity within the variety, thus:

We take an Australian aboriginal and place him side by side with an advertising executive from Madison Avenue, and we see at once that each is a product not only of a different physical type but of a different culture; and it is not the physical type that is responsible for the behavior of each, but the cultural experiences which each has had. Not the color of the skin, not the shape of the head, not the physical type—but the culture which has shaped his experience determines his behavior. And since neither the aboriginal nor the executive is responsible for the milieu into which he was born and in which he was raised, it is obviously the height of folly to make a pejorative judgment against either one on the basis of his cultural experience, just as it is ridiculous to blame a trout for not being a muskellunge. Mankind everywhere has always proved to be extremely plastic, adaptive, and sensitive: the species will always truly reflect its particular culture; and since cultures differ, allowing for individual genetic differences, so do the mental and cultural levels of the citizens of each.

The inhabitants of the British Isles just two thousand years ago—at the time of the Roman conquests—were people of the Iron Age phase of culture. They painted their bodies with woad, believed that babies born with one or two teeth were vampires or at least fearsome creatures, held that divination of the future could be attained through magic rhymes—and celebrated a bloodthirsty ritual in which human sacrifices were made by burning people in wicker cages. There seems to be some evidence, for instance, that *eeny, meeny, miny, mo*—which almost certainly goes back to the Druids—was originally a divination rhyme or else a system for selecting the victim for human sacrifice. In short, the ancestors of today's English gentleman were living in a state not far removed from that of many nonliterate peoples when the Romans appeared on the scene and began taking the captured aborigines back to Italy for the slave market, and the word got around that they were not a very good buy. Too untutored.

In this particular case, as time has shown, it was Roman opinion itself that was being primitive: at least it was accepting the idea that there is something in a people which makes them unable to learn and progress—some racial deficiency.

While there is an enormous variety within the species of man, in terms of shape, weight, height, and various inherited capabilities or deficiencies, men are largely the products of their cultures, and if those are changed the people are changed. And here it should be emphasized that cultures have been observed in which changes take place only with glacial slowness, and others in which cultural changes occur with comparative rapidity—but the time element is no criterion by which to judge the adaptability, intelligence, or potential of a people.

Indeed, Margaret Mead gives us in detail an account of the transformation of the people of the Great Admiralty Island popularly known as Manus, northeast of New Guinea, from an isolated "cluster of stone-age head-hunters into a community asking for a place in the modern world" in a single generation (from 1928 to 1953). When she first saw them, they considered a sea voyage of twenty miles "so dangerous that people wept when a canoe set off across the reef and wept again when a returning canoe was safely beached with all its crew alive," but when she saw them the third time, in 1965, "the school children were writing essays—in English—about space satellites." For her this experience "helped correct the widely held belief that slow change, however uneven, was preferable to rapid change." And of course the rapid change was made through the acculturating ferment induced by contact with millions of American fighting men in World War II.[14]

Thus in all cases the irritation, stimulus, or cross-fertilizing effect of new experiences is the indispensable and necessary condition for the production of cultural change. So Western man, who has somehow packed more experience into the past couple of thousand years than has fallen to the lot of the Australian aboriginal, and other isolated peoples, in their whole cultural history—especially in terms of contacts with various other societies in different parts of the world— shows a proportionately quicker ability to make cultural advance.

As Boas puts it: "The history of mankind proves that advances of culture depend upon the opportunities presented to a social group to learn from the experience of their neighbors. . . . The tribes of simplest culture are on the whole those that have been isolated for very long periods and hence could not profit from the cultural achievements of their neighbors."[15]

In a word, there is no inherent tendency in *any* group of mankind which distinguishes it from any other in ability to develop from a barbarous to a highly cultured state.

Variety—yes. "Racial" intelligence—no.

Occasional Wars—Necessary for the Fitness of the Race?

Even in the second half of the twentieth century there are national leaders and social philosophers who are sufficiently the victims of educational lag to believe that the sinews of their "race" need to be knitted into tight condition, as a prizefighter conditions himself for self-defense, by occasional exercise of the art of fighting.

Either these people have no real idea of what modern warfare is or they are carrying over from the older Darwin days the mistaken notion that evolution means nothing but the struggle for existence and the survival of the fittest. This habit of thought has done considerable harm, as well as being factually inaccurate; it concludes that evolution is a continuing process in which survival depends upon being perpetually aggressive. All animals are, of course, capable of aggressive behavior, but only under certain conditions. There also exist powerful drives toward cooperative behavior. All these forces operate as parts of a whole pattern, not as isolated actions. In terms of fact, the evidence strongly indicates that of all the drives cooperation is the most dominant and biologically the most important. Certainly man's future lies in the further development of this drive; and without it (mutual assistance, sociability, collective action, synergy) the improvement of the organism and the strengthening of the species becomes incomprehensible. Indeed, as a negative paraphrase, the last clause is the message of Jesus.

Modern war calls for the careful selection of the best of the species, and the placing of that superior and younger segment in a position where death is a logical outcome, not from meeting with and being conquered by other "best" men who will survive to father future generations but from an impersonal bomb dropped from the sky or a shell lobbed from ten miles away. Would any husbandman put the best of his breeders into dangerous situations and coddle the weaker in safety? As a selective agency, therefore, war is very efficient at conserving the weak and losing the strong and thus at weakening the species. Yet we find such bizarre comment—accepted thoughtlessly by many—as Sir Arthur Keith's, "Nature keeps her orchard healthy by pruning; war is her pruning-hook."[16]

THE AMERICAN INDIAN IS DYING OUT?

It is no wonder that the noble white man would like to be relieved of the contractual and other obligations he owes to the noble red man, and if the latter would just go away, disappear, like an amiable fellow, life in this department would be much more pleasant. This being the case, and the sources of news being what they are, the general absence of the American Indian from the headlines feeds the notion that the redskins are quietly dying out except for a few special groups retained on purpose for ceremonials and as tourist attractions.

The only trouble with the idea is that it is false. Ever since that fateful summer day at the Little Big Horn—June 26, 1876, it was—when General Custer and 264 stout lads were annihilated by the Sioux the Indian population has grown annually. By 1890 it was stated by the Census Bureau that there were 248,000 American Indians still left in the country; thirty years later the figure was 287,000; in 1940 the total was 334,000 in round figures; and the 1960 figure was 524,000. The American Indian population is currently increasing at the rate of 1 percent per annum, and among some tribes, such as the Navaho, Hopi, and Papago of the Southwest, the rate is 2 percent per annum. The truth is that the American Indian is the fastest growing minority in the United States, and by the end of this century will undoubtedly surpass the million mark.

The American Indians are not very well organized and their Washington lobby is weak as compared, let us say, with the electric power industry, which would like to build dams in reservation territory; but as the great Indian authority, Dr. Clark Wissler, wrote in 1940, "The birth rate of Indians has always been high and shows little inclination to fall; but the death rate is constantly dropping. . . . There will be more and more Indians in the future."[17] Wissler's prediction has been realized in every particular.

The White "Race"—Inherently More Intelligent Than the Rest

It is no trouble at all for the white man to accept, with a certain equanimity, a certain blushing acquiescence, the obvious "fact" that Caucasians are ever so much smarter than African tribesmen or the famous poor Indians, or the Orientals.

It is possible to raise the question: If the white man is so much more intelligent than the Oriental, then why did the Congress of the United States on May 26, 1924, totally exclude the Japanese from this country by a new Immigration Act which abandoned the famous Gentlemen's Agreement of 1907? Afraid of competition? (And of course the answer is a resounding negative and some such statement as that the Japanese were considered "undesirables.")

The only point we are making is that the Caucasian believes in his own superiority and that his political action (exemplified here by merely one well-known instance of exclusion) proves it.

Not that the white man is the *only* type of mankind with the superior feeling. Most peoples seem to suffer from a touch of xenophobia, and history is full of stories of attempts to wipe out the opposition, root and branch, and salt the ground so that nothing may ever grow there again—as was said to have been done at Carthage. After the Battle of Hastings the troops of William the Conqueror performed what has been called "the harrowing of the north," during which not a man, woman, child, or beast was left alive in Yorkshire.

That the superiority has never been demonstrated and is almost certainly factually incorrect and therefore a nonsensical attitude to maintain, we have already seen. Otto Klineberg, our leading authority on "racial" and ethnic psychology, has shown that the range of inherited capacities in different ethnic groups is very close to being identical. Median Alpha scores of white and Negro recruits for the U.S. Army, compiled even as long ago as World War I, showed Negro recruits from five northern states scoring as high as or higher than whites from eight south central states. Lest this be challenged, we give the figures:

MEDIAN ALPHA SCORES OF WHITE AND NEGRO RECRUITS, UNITED STATES ARMY, FIVE NORTHERN STATES, EIGHT SOUTH CENTRAL STATES[18]

	Median alpha score, white recruits	Median alpha score, Negro recruits
Five Northern States		
New York	58.3	38.6
Pennsylvania	62.0	34.7
Ohio	62.2	45.5
Indiana	55.9	41.5
Illinois	61.6	42.2
Eight South Central States		
Kentucky	41.5	23.9
Tennessee	44.0	29.7
Alabama	41.3	19.9
Mississippi	37.6	10.2
Arkansas	35.6	16.1
Louisiana	36.1	13.4
Oklahoma	42.9	31.4
Texas	43.4	12.1

The highest median among the whites from the southern states listed were from Tennessee, 44.0; from the Negroes from the North, 45.5 (Ohio). Ohio Negroes did better than the whites from eleven other states. In addition to those listed above they did better than whites from Arkansas, 35.6, North Carolina, 38.2, Georgia, 39.3.[19] The tests were administered and rated by white army officers. It is true that whites from all states did better than Negroes from the same states—but no one will deny that whites in each case enjoy superior social, economic, and cultural-educational advantages to those available to the Negro, especially in 1917-1918. Where the northern Negro enjoys greater cultural advantages than the southern white, the black man is superior. Many other investigators have proved this point, a point to which attention was drawn by Ruth Benedict and Gene Weltfish of Columbia University. Their popular little pamphlet, *The Races of Mankind*, published by the Committeee on Public Affairs during World War II and purchased by the War Department "for the use of officer-instructors as background material to help counteract the Nazi theory of a super-race," was suppressed through the efforts of Congressman Andrew J. May of Kentucky because the authors, as he said, "described northern Negroes as the equals in intelligence of southern White men." Which is not what the authors had said at all, although their figures allowed the inference—and, indeed, showed the superiority of the northern Negro!

Objection was also raised to the pamphlet on the ground that "Adam and Eve are depicted with navels." While Congressman May was involving himself in these omphalogical niceties, which he asserted were "inimical to the interests of the people and the Government," the ever so devoted congressman was engaged in taking bribes from a munitions manufacturer, an "error" for which he was subsequently tried, found guilty, and imprisoned—with, of course, benefit of a Congressional pension.[20]

The stupidity of censoring views which are not cheerfully received by those in power is another idiocy which is so often exposed that one would suppose the word would get around; but it is still a very popular game and any number can play. The ecclesiastical murder of Giordano Bruno in 1600 for his heliocentric view of the solar system stopped just short of repeating itself thirty-three years later in the case of Galileo. *Eppur si muove.*[21] Yes, the earth does move. But even such cultural pillars as the Encyclopaedia Britannica continue to censor academic freedom in the twentieth and most enlightened century.[22]

THE SPLIT CARTILAGE PROVES YOU'RE A WHITE MAN?

Whenever the issue of "race" becomes socially or politically significant, as it did during Hitler's persecution of the Jews, there are sure to arise certain folk rules of thumb which prove, in one easy application, whether one is pure Aryan or perhaps one-eighth Jewish or one-sixteenth Negro or one-thirty-second Indian. These tests are used for discrimination in one's favor as well as against a person; but usually they are intended to weed out the undesirable.

One test to prove that a person is a true white or a true Negro was to press a finger on the tip of the nose: a split in the cartilage proved at once that 100 percent Caucasian blood pounded through those all but royal veins. But if there were no felt division at the tip of the nose, but only a straight, unbroken cartilaginous tip, then the owner must immediately be pronounced a Negro.

Such an error becomes serious when men like the famous Dr. Victor Heiser give it authority. Dr. Heiser was a pioneer in public health work and wrote the best seller, *An American Doctor's Odyssey.*[23] On page 146 he is pointing out that certain Philippine Negroes "were true Negroes." And his proof: ". . . shown by the one-piece cartilage in their spreading noses; all other races have a split cartilage. Even the octaroons show this negroid test of Negro blood."

Where Dr. Heiser got this piece of misinformation it is difficult to imagine. The fact is that no split cartilage appears in any man, ape, or monkey; and that there are no significant characteristics of the nasal cartilage except size to distinguish the Negro from the white nose. But we have not heard the last of the split cartilage, that's for sure. It's too much fun.

PAGING THE ARYANS . . . WHAT! NO ARYANS?

The myth of an Aryan "race" originated in the writings and teachings of Professor Max Müller, the great German philologist and student of mythology and religion. He published his lectures entitled *The Science of Language* in 1861. Based entirely upon his linguistic studies, he made the assumption in the beginning that the Indo-European (Aryan) mother tongue of which he had found indications must imply the existence of an Aryan "race" that used the language. Upon deeper reflection, however, it became clear to him that Indo-European could have been used by peoples of many diverse "racial" origins; and with rare intellectual courage and honesty he repudiated the "racial" theory and continually urged thereafter that when he said "Aryan" he referred to language alone.

"I have declared again and again," he wrote, "that if I say Aryans I mean neither blood nor bones, nor hair nor skull; I mean simply those who speak an Aryan language. . . . To me an ethnologist who speaks of Aryan race, Aryan blood, Aryan eyes and hair, is as great a sinner as a linguist who speaks of a dolichocephalic dictionary or a brachycephalic grammar. It is worse than a Babylonian confusion of tongues —it is downright theft. We have made our own terminology for the classification of languages; let ethnologists make their own for the classification of skulls, and hair, and blood."[24] Müller had very little interest in anthropology or ethnology. His great work was his edition of *Sacred Books of the East* (51 vols.) on which he was still working when death came to him in 1900.

As for the Aryan language, the Indo-European mother tongue, it is itself a hypothesis: as if one should say, "Let's assume for a moment that such a tongue once existed and that various branches and dialects and variations of the speech developed in different cultures, as French and Spanish and Portuguese developed from the Latin. Would this not explain—" and then the specific example of a word which seemed to be cognate with another in a distant language might be brought up. The hypothesis seemed to be helpful and was used by many scholars as a useful tool. But, as Bender has shown, "Not a line of Indo-European (Aryan) literature has been preserved, and not a single skeleton, inscription, weapon or other object has been identified as Indo-European. The problem is fundamentally a linguistic one and its solution must be looked for primarily in the province of comparative mythology."[25]

Hence we must soberly arrive at the conclusion that the Aryan "race" is nothing but a piece of verbal nonsense and without meaning. Professor Snyder reasonably reminds us, "When a language has spread over a large territory, there is no reason to believe that all people who spoke that language belong to the same race"—by which he means the same ethnic group.[26] Even if they had been of the same race at the start, mixing with other ethnic groups over the centuries would have absorbed them. Which is why the Nazi claim that the Germans represent the true Aryan stock, and that all Nordics are members of the Aryan race, is factually empty and utterly nonsensical, however useful it may have proved at the time for purposes of rallying the pride of the nation in a mad venture to rule all lesser "races" and to eliminate the Jews entirely. Indeed, it is a fascinating—if revolting—study in psychology to observe the black-haired, rat-faced little monster Goebbels drumming up enthusiasm for the blond, blue-eyed supermen and claiming to be one of them. Perhaps it was something like this which Mr. Cabell was satirizing when he presented the red-haired Gerald who proclaimed himself Lord of the Third Truth because he could not be satisfied that there are only two truths—that we copulate and die.

Such myths as this would be harmless enough playthings except for the fact that people incline to take them seriously, and eventually come to believe them with a religious fervor which renders them capable of the most monstrous conduct.

THE SAVAGE—A BLOODTHIRSTY CREATURE?

There are two equally laughable ideas about man in a so-called state of nature: the first was very popular in the eighteenth century when the idea was to get back to nature, to lead a natural life such as we enjoyed in the first lovely garden, now so sadly lost. This period presented the ideal man, the Noble Savage: an Indian, perhaps, silhouetted against the sunset, arms calmly folded over his chest—a man who speaks with one tongue and is not a liar like the rum-drinking merchant-adventurers; a man of dignity and honor. . . . Unfortunately, a realistic appraisal turned up the fact that he had fleas, no concept of cleanliness, and would be no addition to your party. The other, equally ridiculous, idea was that he was a murderous fiend who would drink hot blood at the drop of your head.

Actually, he was neither. The savage, yesterday and today, was and is merely another human being, the product of his environment like the reader, no more so and no less. If his culture was isolated and his people did not come into contact with other tribes and other usages, then his behavior reflected a more or less unchanging and static society; but if his people were at the crossroads of commerce—like the early Jews in Palestine, for instance—then the culture was more varied and so was human behavior.

Savage originally meant "of the forest" and hence "untamed," and from that to "cruel." The Latin source, of course, is *silva,* the same root that produces *Sylvanus,* the god of the woods and fields; and *silviculture,* a somewhat pompous word for forestry; and—to put a tall silk hat on it—*silvicolous,* "forest-inhabiting," as in the sentence, "The Indians of the plains differed from the silvicolous tribes."[27] To Captain John Smith the natives were *savages,*[28] but he appears to have got along so well with them that he preferred the New England coast to any other part of the world. "I would rather live here then any where," he asserted at the age of thirty-seven.

The years have given a ferocious emphasis to *savage,* nonetheless: we may see a mental image of a dog tearing at his prey, or something equally unrestrained. When the White Rabbit feared that the Duchess would be savage, he meant that she would be in a foul temper, not that she would be acting like an aborigine. In this way many harmless and innocent words have taken on darker hues than they possessed originally: *villain* indicated simply a farm laborer at first; *boor* meant nothing but a farmer; *churl* originally meant a serf; *knave,* like the German *Knabe,* merely indicated a boy; and *varlet,* to go no further with this, was simply the Old French diminutive of *vassal,* which meant "boy."

But back to the human savage. There certainly have been—and perhaps still are—savages in the territory of New Guinea who are not averse to an occasional tidbit of human flesh. Today, perhaps, they are more likely to be satisfied with the sing-sing, a two-day period of cavorting, dancing in costume, and feasting on conventional comestibles, as the tribes do now annually, usually in the middle of May. The men melt away into the forest and spend hours painting their bodies with intricate designs and making bird of paradise headdresses; then they come out to dance and shout and shake their bows and ten-foot spears while the throb of lizard-skin drums beats out a powerful rhythm. Many thousands gather for this event, some of the tribesmen walking for a week over the mountains to be present.

There have been, and perhaps still are, head-hunting tribes who would value your noggin for a trophy; and others who kill all strangers on sight. These people are "savage" within the ferocious meaning the word has come to connote. But we know of other island people who welcome strangers—and these people are also "savages." The fact is, the white man could learn a good deal about decency and ethical behavior from such "savages," among others, as the Eskimos and the Australian aborigines.

As someone once said: "There are only three races—men, women, and children. And none of them speak the same language."

Intellectually we can accept the fact that the concept of "race" is nonsense, but unfortunately there is a visceral concomitant which is not so easily disposed of—for the reason that it is backed by emotion. The white man who despises the Negro is not stopping to consider that his ideology reflects nonsense. He cannot hear the voice of reason under such circumstances. Thus we find the Negro in the civil rights battle in 1966 beginning to cry aloud for Black Power;[29] and we find at least one white man masterminding a plot to kill the entire Negro population of the United States by poisoning gelatine to be sold to them at a discount.

This is nonsense which must be taken seriously. Everyone has to help bring insanity of this kind to an end.

THE NEGRO'S KINKY HAIR PROVES HE IS CLOSER TO THE APE?

The Western use of the word *ape* as a noun (*simia* in Latin), while it soberly refers to any monkey, and particularly to the larger and tailless varieties, the great apes (orang, chimpanzee, gorilla) and the gibbon, is customarily touched both with awe and with disdain: with awe because the ape is so startlingly similar to man; and with pejorative connotations because, in the opinion of mankind, the ape never quite makes it. Our familiar couplet, apparently written by that master poet, Anon. "The ape, though clothed in silks he be/Is ape to all eternity," is the descendant and heir of dozens of antecedents—such as Lucian's *Simia simia est, etiam si aurea gestet in signia* (The ape is still an ape even though wearing golden insignia). Erasmus, Florio, and Ben Jonson, to name no more, all said more or less this same thing. Other writers amused themselves by remarking that the higher an ape climbs the more it shows its bare rump (Montaigne, George Herbert, Francis Bacon, and others). One suspects them of the use of *double-entendre* and of the intention to deliver a homily on the folly of overreaching. Another group said, in effect, "How ugly the beasts are, and how like us!" (Thus Heraclitus, Plato, Cicero, Swift, and others). But probably the most familiar literary reference is leading apes in hell, the fate reserved for old maids. George Gascoigne's *Posies* (1575); Pettie's *Petite Pallace* (1576); John Lyly's *Euphues* (1579) —right down to Ben Franklin's *Poor Richard* (1735)—used the phrase; probably the most famous is Katharine in *The Taming of the Shrew* (Act II, scene 1): "She is your treasure, she must have a husband;/I must dance barefoot on her wedding-day,/And for your love to her, lead apes in hell." Beatrice uses the phrase also in *Much Ado* (Act II scene 1). Chaucer used the word *ape* to mean a dupe, a fool ("Right as him liste, the preest he made his ape"; "Canon's Yeoman's Tale," line 760), but that is obsolete now.

Thus we have a word which over the centuries has indicated a large, tailless monkey who looks frighteningly like us but who, the more he tries to act like a man, becomes the more ridiculous; who tends to mimic our ways; but who is separated from us by not being *quite* human. Ape.

Fresh from the slave pen and with only a few half-understood words of English and no knowledge of the American culture, the Negro may have seemed slow to learn when he tried to adapt to being the servant of a white family in a strange land. He may have seemed less than Caucasian, shall we say. It would be pleasant to think that applying the sobriquet was done jocosely and kindly; but it certainly took on overtones of hate when the black man showed signs of wanting to progress beyond apehood.

Among the outward signs that the Negro belonged to a lower order, according to certain racists, was the inevitable tightly curled hair, which was asserted to be characteristic of apes and therefore proved that the Negro was very closely related.

The fact of the matter is that the straight hair of whites is much more characteristic of apes than the kinky hair of Negroes. The gibbon, chimpanzee, orangutan, and the gorilla all have straight hair. None of these has hair anything like that of the Negro.

PRIMITIVE PEOPLES DEVELOP FASTER THAN WHITES— BUT THEN STOP?

Almost everyone has heard some version of this myth: its purpose is to establish that the "unlettered" peoples, like the "lower" animals, develop rapidly after birth and are able to take care of themselves long before white children become independent of their parents; but then— at the age of twelve or thirteen—they stop developing mentally and never attain to the mature brain power which is the heritage of the Aryan alone. In other words, the white man has ascended the evolutionary ladder to an elevation which the others are simply incapable of reaching.

The "fact" is applied most frequently to the Negro in American society, and the cognoscenti in these matters will explain to you without the faintest hint of a smile that the reason is that the Negro brain stops expanding because the sutures in the Negro skull knit early in life. With so plausible a reason, the lunatic statement is accepted as gospel and passed along as wisdom.

It is, of course, the purest nonsense. The Negro brain and skull develop in the same way and at the same speed as the Caucasian brain and skull. One would think that a moment's reflection would show that this must be so; but lacking that, we have the study of Drs. Todd and Lyon of Western Reserve: they made a study of cranial suture closures on 365 whites and 149 Negroes and reported that they found the order and pattern identical.[30]

LESSER BREEDS SEE THE WHITE MAN AS GODLIKE?

One of the most cherished pieces of nonsense in the cultures of the white man is the myth of the White God, in which a motley crew of adventurers under an English or Dutch or Spanish captain anchors off some native coast in the tropics and the canoes come out like mad, full of people who want to worship the palefaces as gods or magicians because of their ships, guns, armor, or other artifacts, as well as their wonderful, wonderful white skins. All the beautiful young females go crazy about the bearded gods and the island chief places the foot of the captain upon his, the chief's, head in sign of fealty.

It makes for an excellent musical, full of color and action and tender scenes; but it ain't necessarily so.

The original text in the Nahuatl of Sahagun's native informants which tells of the conquest of Mexico by Cortes from the Indian point of view shows Montezuma and his people thoroughly frightened by the visitants. That Cortes might possibly be Quetzal, the Fair God, returning to govern his people was not ruled out as a possibility; but Montezuma tried magic of all kinds against the Spaniards, and the Otomies of Tecoac came out against him in battle array (and were wiped out completely). It was the treachery of the Tlaxacaltecas, jealous of their neighbors at Cholula, which permitted the massacre there in the arena; and it was clear that Montezuma would have done anything to get rid of the Spaniards. If he couldn't do that, the next best thing was to make them happy and avoid trouble. And we know where *that* path led.[31]

In hardier climes, where the white man is at a disadvantage by reason of having lived a softer and more protected life than the natives —as among the Eskimos—the inhabitants of the land often consider the white visitor a pitiful caricature of virility. Many accounts of the frozen North recount such an attitude. Far from placing the captain's foot on his head, the chief is more likely to regard the whole crew as a bunch of weaklings, worthy to eat only among the women.

SCIENTIFIC SUPPORT FOR RACE PREJUDICE?

In complex societies, as Jacques Barzun points out, there seems to be a need to give a local habitation and a name to the vague hostilities we feel for those outside our own group, and we embody these hostilities by referring to the discriminated people as an out-group; we blame them for what goes wrong; we fear and curse the alien; and we build theories to justify collective hostility. It is particularly easy to do this when a member of the out-group is as visible, as quickly detected, as the Negro in a white neighborhood. And to avoid being intelligently critical about our aversion, we say that the Negro "race" has something about it which automatically condemns every individual in it.

Some such need and some such process must have been behind the popular fallacy, when chromosomes were first isolated, that Negroes have only 47 chromosomes as against 48 for the whites. This notion gave "scientific proof" of the inferiority of the Negro. Poor fellow, he could not help it; but what could you expect of a chap with only 47 chromosomes? He was really more to be pitied than censured.

Even after the statement was shown, again and again, to be false, it persisted where it was "needed"—Negroes have only 47 chromosomes. The truth is that whites and Negroes have exactly the same number of chromosomes, namely, 46, not 47 or 48—just 46.

CERTAIN DISEASES ARE "RACIALLY" SELECTIVE?

It is true that certain peoples develop an immunity from or a tolerance for a disease after long experience with it, which immunity would not be shared by a person from another part of the world where the species had not had any chance to develop such an immunity owing to unavailability of the disease. And it is true that where a people inbreeds a great deal—and for religious or other reasons declines to mix with other peoples—any defects in the genes stand a greater chance of pairing and as a consequence produce a predisposition to a particular disease. Those are things we can understand; anybody capable of comprehending the mechanism of vaccination can see this. (In passing, you might ask yourself why vaccination should be derived from *vacca,* cow. Score ten points for a reasonably correct answer.)

But that certain peoples, *ipso facto,* by the sheer fact of being Eskimos or Jews or whatever are susceptible to pulmonary afflictions or to the circulatory illness known as Buerger's disease—as has been charged to each, respectively—is true nonsense. Dr. Leo Buerger, himself a Jew, the discoverer of the circulatory disease that bears his name, taught that only male Jews—well, all but 4 out of 500 of his patients at Mount Sinai Hospital—develop the illness. He was shown to be wrong by Dr. Horton of the Mayo Clinic, who studied 948 cases of which only 262 were Jews. But that's not the point: the point is that there appears to be a tendency to identify a particular group with a particular characteristic or characteristics. Medical men, as well as the laity, are especially prone to look for such special traits. Actually, people are all alike with respect to susceptibility to disease except where environmental conditions, such as those just named, have affected them.

But it is not merely the folk who make this mistake. Professional men have erred in the same way. For example, it was at one time believed or at least asserted that amaurotic family idiocy (cerebro-macular degeneration) occurred exclusively in Jewish families of Russian provenience. Amaurotic family idiocy is a recessive genetic defect characterized by progressive blindness and paralysis with severe mental retardation. When the condition affects children under the age of 2 years it is known as Tay-Sachs disease. When children between 2 and 11 years are affected it is known as Spielmeyer-Vogt disease. In any event, it had been asserted by many medical writers that the disease was limited largely to Jews. For example, as late as 1966 Dr. Frank Ford writes, "It is with few exceptions restricted to subjects of Jewish race."[32] The adjective describing the condition, *amauroun*, to dim, also describes the state of knowledge of this disease which persists into the second half of the twentieth century.

The fact is that, while the disorder has an above-average frequency among Jews of eastern Polish origin, its frequency among Jews of other geographic origins is about the same as its frequency among non-Jews.[33]

The Hand of the Negro is Long, Narrow, and Apelike?

There comes that old "ape" comparison again; but we have to mention it because the popular notion that the hands of the Negro are more simian than those of whites is very persistent.

It is true that in the Negro the forearm is longer than in the white, and to the same extent the hand is longer also; but when it comes down to being narrow and apelike, the facts show that the width of the Negro hand can be expressed in terms of percentage of its length as 40.5 and that of the white as 41.6—which, as Todd and Lindala observe, is hardly worth calling out the National Guard for. Proportionately, both hands, Negro and Caucasian, are as much "the same" as human comparisons generally are.[34]

Brains and Cubic Centimeters?

Cognate with this attempted pejorative based on hand shape is the old canard about the restricted cranial capacity of the Negro along with the attempt to give that as a reason for innate mental inferiority. It is true that the white adult cranium has about 1,390 cubic centimeters as against 1,350—or 40 cc less—for the Negro; but it is also true that the Negro skull is dolichocephalic—a long skull—whereas the white's is usually brachycephalic—broad skull; and even among whites the broad skulls have slightly more capacity than the long ones. But in any event the difference is too slight to be the cause of inferior or superior brain power. In fact, Professor Franklin P. Mall of Johns Hopkins University and his associates demonstrated, when investigating an assortment of brains of various ethnic origins, said by Dr. Robert Bennett Bean to vary according to sex and race, that the brains of whites could not be distinguished from those of Negroes. Professor Mall therefore concluded: "In this study of anatomical characters said to vary according to race and sex, the evidence advanced has been tested and found wanting. It is found, however, that portions of the brain vary greatly in different brains and that a very large number of records must be obtained before the norm will be found."[35] He points out that the almost infinite number of marked individual variations makes it impossible to assign race, sex, or genius as the cause by itself, a fact complicated further by the personal equations of the investigators themselves. Levin and others have concurred in many studies since.[36]

Underlying these facts, however, is a still more important one—namely, that difference in brain size has no more to do with intelligence than has bodily size. If the white man wishes to pursue this subject a little, he will shortly discover that the average brain size among the Negro Kaffirs and Amaxosa of Africa, the Japanese, Chinese, American Indians, Eskimos, and Polynesians—to name a few—is larger than that of the average white. So if we're going to make brain size a criterion for social acceptance, the white man is going to have to accept a low place on the totem pole. In passing, it should perhaps be mentioned that Neanderthal man had an average brain size of 1550 cubic centimeters—about 160 cc greater than that of today's white man.[37]

To Mix the Blood of Races Is Dangerous?

Bon sang ne peut mentir, says the old French saw: Good blood cannot lie. Which is a delightful piece of wish-thinking deserving its own special niche in the halls of Romance. All those lovely myths about the king's son in disguise, whose royal blood manifests itself *au moment critique*—Prince Arthur at the Stone, or the kidnaped dauphin brought up among highwaymen who cannot bring himself to commit an unchivalrous deed—are echoed in all the literature of earth, as in Don Quixote's *La sangre se hereda*, Blood is an inheritance. The English say, "Blood will tell," but they also see the possibilities for humor in the notion: "You come of good blood," goes the adage, "and so does a black pudding."

Perhaps we are losing the old-time notion that blood differs according to social station or race or something else, now that blood banks have become so common; and yet among the ignorant it is still true that blood seeks out its own kind and especially that one must not mingle the blood of one race with that of another. Poor Butterfly! All the most virulent racists have pounded at this idea, along with the notion—equally untrue—that some races are mutually infertile; and nowhere more loudly than in the case of mixing white blood and black. You could have found southern gentlemen who would not have accepted a transfusion of Negro blood if it would have saved their lives. Perhaps you still could.

The bald fact is that the blood of a Negro is precisely the same as the blood of a white or a red or a yellow: the same, in every respect.

There are differences in the distribution of the blood groups: the Negro has a somewhat different frequency of certain blood groups as compared with whites. But the Negro has all the blood groups that whites have, and every element of Negro blood is the same as its parallel in the Caucasian or the Arab or the Chinese.

Undoubtedly the basic idea behind all the debate is that the blood is the carrier of hereditary characters—and this idea is a genuine popular fallacy: it is widespread among the folk, and thus popular; it is untrue, and thus a fallacy. The blood is in no way connected with the transmission of hereditary traits. The transmitters are the genes which lie in the chromosomes of the germ cells of both parents. The only parts of the organism which transmit and influence heredity are the genes in the chromosomes of a single spermatozoon and a single ovum. Nothing else.

Man—the Only Species That Eats His Kind?

This piece of nonsense must have originated in the days when the bestiaries were written to teach moral lessons; and the notion—which is completely mistaken—that only man will eat other members of his own kind must have been intended to support the moral invective leveled against man, the sinner, the greatest of sinners, the original sinner, whose children to the world's end must pay for the sins of the ancestors. The writers, to illustrate the complete degradation of man, then foist this canard upon our species. Yet every farmboy knows that chickens will eat chicken entrails greedily—and fight for the privilege. And every naturalist knows that nature's scavengers like the hyena, the gull, the skunk, the buzzard, even the common crow, will eat any meat found on the trail, in the garbage, at the town dump, or on the road where an automobile has squashed the life out of it. It doesn't matter to the crow whether it is crow meat he's eating or something else; the fact is, it is likely to be something else, because crows are very smart and don't get run over by cars. Stefansson fed his sled dogs on dog meat occasionally, and found they liked it just fine. He also found that bears will eat bears.[38] And we all know that fish eat fish. Which makes it a little difficult to understand what was eating Earnest Hooton when he said, "Cannibalism, as a cultivated taste, pursued with method, skill and persistence . . . seems to be restricted to the human carnivore."[39] Method, skill, and persistence certainly mark the food-hunting activities of every known fish-eating fish; and, on the other hand, very few human groups undertake methodical, skillful, and persistent head-hunting and cannibalism. Among most nonliterate peoples cannibalism is ritualistic rather than a search for nourishment: by eating some ritually preferred part of a warrior enemy one acquires his courage, as is well known. So one would eat this morsel, even if the taste seemed a little gamey, for the magical values involved.

The natives of the New Hebrides at one time had this matter worked out satisfactorily to all concerned, according to an account by Harrisson, who explains how these tribesmen uphold the national honor, keep a war going, and pay for it as they go by consuming those who die on the field of battle. He reports that they "fight and eat each other like gentlemen, leave the women and children alone, seldom kill more than three or four men per war, do not seek to conquer; wars can go on for months without a death; there is such a surplus of males over females that the welfare of population is not affected; while the outlet and play value of war is an invaluable dynamic."[40]

In any event, man is not the only animal that eats his own species; and man as a rule is not himself anthropophagus except for ritual purposes. After all, the diet is a rather expensive one.

CHILD BRIDES ABOUND IN INDIA?

The idea that most Hindu females become mothers when they themselves are between 8 and 14 years of age received a vigorous fillip in 1927 when Katherine Mayo came out with *Mother India*. This was seven years after Kentucky, by ratifying the 19th Amendment, the 36th state to do so, in effect made woman suffrage the law of the land, and the subject of the Free Woman was very much at its conversational apogee. The contrast of the poor little girls of India who were just beginning to appreciate their dolls, but had to put the toys away in order to attend to their precocious maternal duties, and the American usage in this department obviously gave our women a tremendous sense of superiority. In this country one had the impression that a stone tossed into any assembly of Hindus was sure to strike at least one child bride and perhaps carom off a few more.

For Katherine Mayo had said, "The Indian girl, in common practice, looks for motherhood nine months after reaching puberty, or anywhere between the ages of fourteen and eight. The latter age is extreme, though in some sections not exceptional; the former is well above the average."[41]

American women clucked their tongues and wore shocked expressions. The thought was too horrible. They looked at their own 14-year-olds—remember, this was at the end of the twenties, not the sixties!—and found themselves close to tears.

They might better have looked at a few statistics. In those days (using the 1930 figures) 125,000 American girls were married at or before the age of 15; and the Indian Census for 1931 showed the average marriage for girls as 13.35 years. We may think that is too young; but it is not eight; and it is not dramatically different from the United States. What the figures show is that child marriages even then were not the rule in India. A. H. Clark, replying to Mrs. Mayo in the *Atlantic* shortly after *Mother India* had taken over as a cocktail favorite, went to the Indian Census for 1921 and showed that even a decade earlier the majority of Indian women were not giving birth to their first child until the third year of marriage—that is, in the average girl's 17th year.[42] Studies made in Bombay and Madras showed that more than 85 per cent of the mothers were more than 17 years old. Which is another way of saying that only one-sixth of the mothers in those cities was younger than 17—back in the twenties.

This compares interestingly with an article in the *New York Times Magazine* of May 29, 1966, by Lasker Medical Journalism Award Winners Ruth and Edward Brecher which pointed out that the U.S. average in this year of emancipation shows one out of every six teen-age girls becoming pregnant out of wedlock. This is happening in a society where "doting parents and well-paying jobs are showering money on American teen-agers" to the extent of $15 billion annually.

Child brides, indeed.

"Native" Peoples Lack Moral Stamina?

The chief literary spokesman for the idea of the white man's burden was Rudyard Kipling. It was clear enough to him, and has been equally clear to generations of young British career diplomats, that the English sense of equal justice before the law imposed upon Englishmen the duty of whipping into shape the lesser breeds without the law. They would never make it on their own. Therefore continued British rule in India and Africa was a moral obligation which the Englishman owed to his little backward yellow, black, or brown subject.

The natives simply lacked the moral stamina to establish and then be loyal to a system of jurisprudence under which every man's house is his castle and yet the general welfare is protected. The "native" understands this, as Gunga Din did. It was only "natural" that the "backward races" should be in some sort of dependence upon and "protected" by the "civilized" Powers—with a capital P.

Benjamin Kidd, a liberal thinker and ex-civil servant, could write at the beginning of the century, "If we look to the native social systems of the tropical East, the primitive savagery of Central Africa, to the

West Indian Islands in the past process of being assisted into the position of modern states by Great Britain, or the black republic of Haiti in the present, or to modern Liberia in the future, the lesson seems everywhere the same; it is that there will be no development of the resources of the tropics under native government."[43]

Jews Tend to Have Hooked Noses?

Neither by a hooked nose nor by any other single trait or biological characteristic can a human being be proved a Jew or proved non-Jewish, although the rule of thumb about the hooked nose dies hard, aided by the cartoonists. Dr. Maurice Fishberg investigated nose form among Jews in New York, Eastern and Western Europe, Africa, and Asia. Typical of his findings were those for New York, where, among 2,836 adult male Jews he found 57.26 per cent with straight, or Greek, noses; 22.07 percent with retroussé, or snub, noses; 14.25 percent with aquiline, or hooked, noses; and 6.42 percent with flat and broad noses. Among 1,284 adult Jewish females, the percentages were, roughly, and in the same order, 59, 14, 13, and 14 percent.[44]

The fact seems to be that Bavarians, American Indians, many Asiatic, Alpine, and Mediterranean peoples show a much higher percentage of hooked noses than do Jews.

Jews Are a "Race"?

If by "race" one means some force that makes everybody within the circle more or less homogeneous, there simply is not a set of characteristics to be found which, taken together, identify a Jew. We dealt with the hooked nose, one hopes, convincingly. What else? Eyes? In Mogilev, Russia, figures taken shortly after World War I showed that only 4.9 percent of the Jews had light-colored eyes; but in Galicia 23 percent of them had light-colored eyes, and in Vienna the score rose to 30 percent. The Jewish Ashkenazi (from Central and Eastern Europe) in Jerusalem were 30 percent blue-eyed; but the Sephardim were under 10 percent blue-eyed.

Hair? Turkish Jews showed 5 percent blonds; Ukrainian Jews, 15 percent blond; English Jews 26 percent, German Jews, 32 percent, and the city of Riga, 36 percent.

The fact is that the figures for eyes and hair and other traits follow the population trends in the countries examined—the Jews tend to resemble the rest of the citizens in these respects. And why not, with intermarriage taking place as freely as it does? Jews differ from Jews as much as various geographic groups differ—in head shapes and sizes and eyes and noses and hair and all other particulars. It would be exactly as accurate to speak of the Catholic "race" or the Protestant or Moslem "race" as of the Jewish "race." Our own definition, when asked whether a Jew is defined by "race," nationality, tradition, or religion, is to say that a Jew is a person who is a member of the Jewish culture, exhibiting behavioral traits associated with that long tradition —but we're not triumphantly proud of the definition. At least we know it's not a matter of "race."[45]

HALF-CASTES, MONGRELS, HYBRIDS—INFERIOR STUFF?

The Earl of Kent's rightly famous curse, addressed to Goneril's steward, Oswald, makes eloquent use of the umbrageous connotations of *mongrel* and reflects royalty's scorn for anything not of royal blood: it will be remembered that it ends, " . . . knave, beggar, coward, pander, and the son and heir of a mongrel bitch: one whom I will beat into clamorous whining, if thou deniest the least syllable of thy addition."[46] In this case, *addition* is a term of heraldry and means something added to a coat of arms as a mark of honor; but in this case, of course, dishonor. George Lyman Kittredge used to explain that Kent was not merely calling Oswald a son of a bitch; he was giving the idea the added embroidery that Oswald was not only the son, thus inheriting the character, but he was also the heir, the eldest son in terms of primogeniture, who therefore inherited all the properties, not only of the bitch his mother but of the *mongrel* bitch of indeterminate ancestry so that anything at all might attach to her, including filth and disease, especially in the consciousness that bitch also was used to mean prostitute, so that son of a bitch also meant whoreson. Thus the curse is fairly complicated and thoroughly devastating.

Not only royalty demanded that the bloodlines be clear so that property would descend to the true son; the people also demanded that there should be no human mongrels in the royal line, and the most extreme care was taken upon the birth of a prince to see that witnesses were present who could attest to the fact that the youngster was no changeling. The people wanted to be ruled by the "true" king, who was, of course, the Lord's Anointed.

It is easy to see how this idea could be carried further by animal husbandmen trying to develop special breeds for strength, speed, endurance, digging, fighting, and so on. Even today, if a thoroughbred bitch gets loose from the kennels while she is in heat and happens to be served by some unknown dog, the owner will destroy the pups at birth rather than have mongrels around to disrupt the strain he is trying to build. The word *thoroughbred* elicits our instant applause: it is a good word. We approve of it. We would like to be thoroughbreds ourselves. But the word *mongrel* is sort of an insult, even if it is used as a kindly insult. Yet, as Albert Payson Terhune pointed out in one of his Sunnybank stories, we are all mongrels. The ancestors of a thoroughbred horse or dog must be invincibly clear and attested for four generations on both sides. How many of us can go back even three generations on both sides with absolute assurance?

It may make sense in animal husbandry; it may make sense even in a kingly line; but it is the strictest nonsense in the emotional connotation. Human hybrids have by this time been seen in almost all possible intermixtures, and in every case where the evidence is dispassionately analyzed the offspring represent highly desirable types. Mixtures in Hawaii of Chinese-Japanese-white strains and native aborigines have produced some of the finest kinds of human hybrids. Certain Negro mixtures have developed physical power and artistic grace.[47] Polynesian-white descendants of the mutineers of the *Bounty* on Pitcairn Island are a people of enormous health and vitality. So with the Javanese-Dutch offspring, and innumerable others.[48]

The idea of the potency of intermixtures producing *desirable* mongrels was in fact one of the most powerful notions underlying the optimism about America and the New World advanced by the school of Spencer, based on Darwinian discoveries and theory. Spencer visited the United States in 1882. He told reporters that this country had not yet developed to the point where it could make the best use of its democratic institutions, but that the facts of biology made the American future look very brilliant: the melting pot, by mixing up the varieties of the human species as had never before been done anywhere in the world, would inevitably produce "a finer type of man than has hitherto existed." America would face all kinds of difficulties because of this melting-pot action, but in the long run the country would produce "a civilization grander than any the world has known."[49] This idea was part of the intellectual climate of the period, which held that human perfection was not only possible but inevitable. Evolution—nature—was constantly improving species through selection of the fittest; Western civilization was obviously a part of this Plan; therefore, Noble Savage to the contrary, civilization was not artificial but a part of nature like the development of the embryo. The mixing of the kinds of men gave nature a fillip.

Negroes Have a Racial Odor?

That man's noblest friend, the dog, can positively identify his master regardless of any disguises is a fact customarily attributed to the canine sense of smell. The dog's master smells like a man, and like one special man; and the dog smells like a dog, especially when he is wet; but to the man he does not smell like any dog in particular. This is because the dog can catch a scent about twelve times as sensitively as a man, particularly a smoking man. We have now established the fact that both dog and man do have an odor: they smell, in the kindliest sense of that word.

It is a common piece of nonsense to say that an American Indian or a Negro or a Chinese has a smell that is characteristic of his "race." The odor referred to may be characteristic; but its cause is not biological. The odor of sweat depends upon what the man eats, wears, handles, on bacteria,—in short, on his environment. There was a Japanese student who spent four years at an American university. At the successful termination of his studies, three of his wealthy friends came to the United States to escort the student home in triumph, and they occupied the same cabin on the ship. But after the first day and night, the friends insisted that the student change cabins. In effect, they threw him out, complaining that he smelled like an American.

As early as 1903 the great Japanese anatomist Buntaro Adachi wrote an article on *Der Geruch der Europäer* (On the Odor of Europeans).[50] Here he explained that when he first arrived in Germany as a student he found the smell of Europeans and especially of Germans almost intolerable. Later he grew used to it.

A hundred years ago if you had stepped into a New England farmhouse kitchen in the winter, when the family lived for the most part in the kitchen—nobody in his right mind would have thought of going into the living room after dinner for the simple reason that one would freeze to death in there—the olfactory nerves would have identified your location instantly: the stove burned hard wood; the woolens were hung over the stove to dry; the guns on the wall gave off the instantly recognizable scent of the special oil used on them; a diurnal bath and change of underwear and other clothing were out of the question— once a week was the rule. Also, there had been coffee and fried pork and perhaps doughnuts or apple pie and maple syrup for breakfast along with potatoes and other tidbits, each with its powerful supplementary odor. Put them all together, along with the dog or dogs and the pipe tobacco, and be it ever so humble, you were unquestionably in a farmhouse kitchen. Those who have caught this total scent strongly are not likely to forget it—or to attribute it racially.

Nevertheless, be prepared to hear this hoary fable about racial stink over and over again. It comes in so handily to explain why I do not like your smell that I will not part with it, no matter what the scientific truth is. Carey McWilliams cited the excruciating folk wisdom that "when a white man sweats, salt comes on his skin to take the smell away; but when a nigger sweats, he's got no salt."[51]

Similarly the sociologist Alfred McClung Lee, investigating the 1943 Detroit race riots, cites a case of a man who became sick when the lights came on in a movie house and he saw that he had been sitting next to a Negro. "He smelled so bad!"[52] But the olfactory nerves had not been at work while the theater had been dark!

Dollard, during his study of "Southerntown," was told that even the cleanest Negroes have an intolerable odor. Some respondents described the smell as "rusty," others as "acrid." Dollard himself could detect no difference between whites and Negroes, given similar conditions of cleanliness, and so on.[53]

Klineberg refers to "an experimental attempt to throw a little further light on this question" in an unpublished study by Lawrence, who collected in test tubes a little of the perspiration of white and colored students who had just been exercising violently in the gymnasium. These test tubes were then given to a number of white subjects with instructions to rank them in order of pleasantness. The results showed no consistent preference for the white samples; the test tube considered the most pleasant and the one considered most unpleasant were both taken from whites."[54]

The fact is that sweat itself is odorless. Shelley, Hurley, and Nichols have shown that pure apocrine sweat as it initially appears on the skin is both sterile and odorless, and that any odor that may develop is due to the decomposition effects produced by the action of bacteria.[55] Morlan found in an experiment on the perception of body odor in which two Negroes and two whites were the subjects, in which the judgment of 59 persons in a total of 715 experiments was tested, that in all there were 57 incorrect answers, in 368 cases the persons tested said they could not tell, while in 190 attributions the answer was wrong. That is, in 52 percent of judgments there was a failure to recognize a distinctive odor, while in 22 percent of judgments the attribution was incorrect. In other words, in two thirds of the cases the judgment was a failure, and in only one third was it correct.[56]

The odor one associates with sweat is probably produced by a combination of substances.[57] Many kinds of bacteria are to be found on the surface of the skin, and particularly in the armpits, and they have many substances, secreted in the sweat, to work on: sodium chloride, phosphates, uric acid, vabric, caproic and caprylic acids, glucose, creatinine, aromatic acids, ethereal sulphates of phenol, skatoxyl, neutral fat, fatty acids, cholesterol, albumin, and iron. In addition to environmental differences and those in food consumed, individual variation in body odor may reflect either chemical differences in sweat or differences in resident bacteria or both. When an odor is present, it is the result of decomposition produced by bacterial action.[58]

Diet has an influence on the scent of sweat; frequency of bathing is a factor; and there are undoubtedly many other details as yet unknown to us. Some Negroes have been shown to have more sweat glands than whites; and this leads to the tentative conclusion that if there is any difference in the odor of the sweat it is probably one of intensity and not of kind.

And that is just about all there is to be said with assurance at the present state of our knowledge. It is enough to make nonsense out of the traditional broad generalizations which are based on prejudice rather than on fact.

A Low Brow Shows the Stupid and Base-Born; a High Brow, the Opposite?

It is very widely held that a low forehead indicates stupidity, probably because it suggests that apelike face of the "beast," our cousin of the jungle. The corollary is that the high forehead indicates nobility and intelligence. Both notions, and the parent idea from which they spring (namely, that one can read character in the face), are totally false, as it happens. Anthropologists long ago exploded this folly and showed that head shape and the size and form of the brain have no connection at all with mentality. The idea is, nevertheless, one of great primitive strength and has embedded itself in the language: highbrow and lowbrow. The first thing the makeup man does when he is changing Dr. Jekyll into Mr. Hyde is to lower the hairline. In fact, he adds hair wherever he can make it stick, including the backs of the fingers. Hirsute creatures are beasts, it seems, unless the hair is wholly on the crown.

Intelligence, however, depends upon the complexity of the microscopic structure of the brain and the organization of this structure by the cultural environment, not on the size or shape of the brain. Karl Pearson investigated head form in 1,010 Cambridge University students, 2,200 schoolboys of age 12 and 2,100 other schoolboys; he obtained their intellectual levels from teacher ratings and scholastic records (not necessarily infallible). What he found was that there was absolutely *no* correlation between intelligence thus determined and head form—and all subsequent studies have pointed to the same answer.[59]

Now for the lagniappe which often accompanies, through a benevolent serendipity, the cheerful pursuit of the character or history of words: both *highbrow* and *lowbrow* were "invented and first used" by Will Irwin in a series of articles in the New York *Morning Sun* about 1902. The claim, made by his widow, Inez Haynes Irwin, is quoted in Wentworth and Flexner's *Dictionary of American Slang*.[60] Not that this makes any difference: it is a useless piece of information if you like, such as the fact that it takes five to eight minutes to suck the yolk out of an egg after each end has been pierced with a pin (testimony of Detective Allen Gore, the arresting officer in the case against Queen Volga Adams of the Gypsies in an $118,000 swindle). To Bertrand Russell, however, there is a "delicious savour" in "useless" knowledge; and we hope and pray that we will never be too busy to enjoy that flavor. We consider this a very highbrow attitude.

ELDERLY NEGROES, BEING NATURE'S CHILDREN, HAVE CLAIRVOYANT POWERS?

Many people believe that a dog can foretell tragedy, that he sees it coming and howls. Perhaps this is not so surprising when one considers the routine matters that a dog can accomplish which are impossible to any man outside of Tarzan—smell the way along a trail, for instance; or pick out the owner of a hat when the two have never been seen together. Obviously a dog has something close to extrasensory powers compared to human abilities in the same fields.

But why the word gets around that an aged Negro man or woman can feel events coming more sensitively than an aged white we are at a loss to explain; it was noted long ago by the distinguished anthropologist, Malinowski, speaking of the attitudes of explorers to the natives, that whites have a "tendency to credit the members of the latter with mysterious demoniacal powers." Perhaps the drums, the voodoo, the hair-tingling activities of the night in the jungle are responsible.

The folly comes in believing that there is a fundamental difference in the nature of the white and the nonwhite.

There isn't.

It is a cultural difference, and nothing else. A white man can learn to hear as well, catch a scent as acutely, see as sharply, as any "savage" or child of nature. All he has to do is to be brought up in a culture in which such skills are part of the cultural conditioning.

"PRIMITIVE" PEOPLE ARE SIMPLE AND CHILDLIKE?

It is obvious enough to the citizens of Western civilization that "savages" or people of "primitive" cultures are mentally inferior to themselves; that they have simple tastes, simple minds, and simple languages. Give them a few colored beads and they'll sell you the island. And all the English they know is a crazy pidgin. They have no fine arts, no literature, no "real" religion. All these things must have a cause, and the cause must be that the primitive people do not have a mentality equal to that of the Westerner with his wealth, comforts, and television.

No nonsense could be more complete; and no part of it is sillier than the idea that "primitive" languages are simple. Simplification and generalization are the marks of sophistication in language, not of inexperience: classification, word families, a few symbols to handle the infinite number of events and facts and things—these come as language develops, not in the infancy of a language. Our 26 letters to take the place of thousands of separate symbols reveals a simplification which required centuries of evolution and experience. The languages of nonliterate peoples are complicated in the extreme.

We might take a sample from the Abenaki, since we happen to have some material at hand.[61] Take the irregular verb "to have." In Abenaki there exists the animate objective verb, *wajonomuk*, where the *muk* indicates the animate; and we have the inanimate objective verb, *wajonozik*, where the *zik* indicates the inanimate. And then we have the affirmative conjugation both in definite and finite, and the negative conjugations (e.g., "I have no fish," *O'da n'wajonow namas*) and both indefinite and finite, the endings differing in each case; to say nothing of the "dubitative" conjugation, ("Perhaps I have a trap," *Wskebi wajonal telaps*) and the "dubitative negative" conjugations ("Perhaps I have no horse," *Walma majonok ases*); and all these in the various moods, persons, and tenses. In addition, verbs have adjective meanings included; and noun meanings built right into the verb. For example, "To have a cow" is the simple infinitive *okaozemimuk*—and where is the *majono* root we just learned? And "to be white" is the nonpretentious *wobigimuk*. Or would you rather study the more "simple" English verb "to be" and let the savage Abenakis play with their toys?

As for the pidgin, it has been pointed out that the "savage" on the beach at least knows enough English to converse roughly with you in this "business" English while you know nothing of his island speech. So who's bright?

Incidentally, "pidgin" is supposedly the Chinese pronunciation of "business" originating in the ports of the South China Sea in the seventeenth century when the traders managed to communicate with the natives in a sort of English used with a Chinese syntax. Today between 30 million and 50 million people use pidgin as a second language.

Some native speech systems make a lot of sense. In Liberia, for instance, the native system of comparison goes like this: small-small (very small indeed); small; sufficient; plenty; helluva (very big).[62]

We deeply distrust all rules of thumb—probably because we are the heirs of a post-Tennysonian age which believes in accurate measurement, so that when we say "a foot" we mean "twelve inches." We gain and we lose by this process. In the old days a measurement was just-about: hanging a man higher than Haman (50 cubits)[63] was an emotional linguistic hyperbole, or if not hyperbole then at least a striking metaphor in rhetoric, whether or not one's mouth was to be full of stones: as Old Judge Brooke with his double chins said to the hospital doctors when he turned over to them the last of his hoarded claret:

> But if you give it to some damned layman
> Who doesn't know brandy from licorice-water
> And sports a white ribbon, by fire and slaughter,
> I'll hang the lot of you higher than Haman![64]

Nobody measured the height of the gallows. As for *cubit*, it derives from *cubitum*, elbow, and means the distance from the end of the third finger to the elbow, supposedly 18 to 22 inches. It's like the word "forty" in the Old Testament, meaning some reasonable stretch of time—not quite *helluva* but more than *sufficient*.

Thus our rule of thumb would come out like this: When you wonder whether this or that group of islanders or aborigines is different in one way or another from you, given the culture in which you have developed, you should ask, "In their culture what would I be like?" It can't hurt.

You Can't Say "Get Lost" to a "Savage"

Can one imagine one of Fenimore Cooper's dusky warriors being lost in the woods like a child? Or Tarzan losing his way in the jungle? Or Mowgli unable to find the trail leading back to Mother Wolf's gray side? Perish such infidelity! No, no, it is well known that the primitive has a sixth sense in these matters. Drop him down anywhere and he will toss some dirt into the air, sniff the breeze, examine the ground, and perform whatever additional rituals appear to be required, and then he will face directly toward the home tepee and start trotting. We all know that.

The only trouble with this lovely bit of romantic idiocy is that there's no whit of truth in it. In his local habitat the native knows the ways of the birds and animals and plants and the general shape and character of the terrain; he knows where the hills are and where the lakes and river are, and if he sees a beaver it may occur to him that perhaps there's a stream around somewhere.

As Stefansson explained, the native Eskimo or Indian can find his way about, in his own wilderness, much better than a visitor from the city or a sailor from a ship can, "but he is likely to fall behind the white man in experience in just about the proportion you would expect from knowing the greater advantages of training in logical thinking which the white man has had. The European who keeps his head and looks about him can, in a year, pick up all the essentials of the lore of the open country."[65]

In short, the aborigine is neither simple-minded nor gifted in any way out of the human generality.

"Savages" and "Primitives" Need a Bath?

Tourists returning victoriously from their various conquests of the rest of the world—which, as they had foreseen, was barbarous compared with Sioux City—may report with a shudder their impressions of the filthy little urchins on the docks at Marseilles who will leap into polluted water after a dime, or of the ragged and disreputable wharf hands who besides being dirty were obviously drunk also. In short, the natives and savages the tourist saw were living in slum conditions, not within the cultures of their tribes. Many observers have reported that under normal conditions "savages" tend to be as clean as men anywhere. They may not understand the laws of hygiene—as Dr. Victor Heiser discovered in various sections of the world when he was working for the public health service and trying to eliminate yellow fever and other epidemics such as cholera; but neither do the civilized whites until they have been taught. How long ago was it that Dr. Ignaz Semmelweis charged his colleagues with helping to spread puerperal fever because they came direct from the autopsy to the maternity wards? And they practically destroyed him for saying so.

Malinowski stated early that he found the Melanesians very sensitive to cleanliness and even to B.O. He said they smelled better than most European peasants and would never thing of breaking wind, for instance, in the presence of others.[66] Stefansson, reporting from the other end of the world, thought the Eskimos took too many baths and vainly tried to persuade them to wash less often. In the Mackenzie River area the natives looked upon bathing as "a thing of magic value, likely to promote good fortune and turn away evil influence."[67] Thus many eyewitnesses and trained observers have refuted the idea that the natives are dirty; just as they have refuted that other chestnut that the natives are atheists or irreligious.

Here again we bump into one of the tricks of the language in which umbrageous connotations attach to words which were once in perfectly good odor. Language usage, for the elegant, was formed at court or in noble circles—that is, among the supposed cognoscenti. Beyond the pale were the country bumpkins—and while their various dialects were also changing in the manner that any living language changes, nobody paid any attention: the status speech was that of the court. In the university centers the division was often between town and gown, the status resting with the scholars. Then, as now, the hayseed was regarded as either a clown or a rascal. *Savage* people dwelt in the woods and were wild outlanders; heath-dwellers, or *heathens,* were assumed to have false gods or none at all; and from *pagus,* a rustic, we get *pagan* (compare *paynim*)—again an ignoramus in religion. One could continue the list—for example, *hedge,* a symbol of the countryside, is associated with *Hexe,* witch; *hag;* and so on. The sophisticated, the urbane, the proficient—these are of the court; the bungler, the inept, the maladroit—along with the rascal and the naïve—these are of the barnyard and the woods and meadows. And yet the court will borrow from the country: Hamlet said he "knew a hawk from a handsaw."

It's the old nonsense of taking the part for the whole. Actually the so-called primitive cultures show extreme concern for religious observances and the avoidance of taboos. Elaborate religious requirements surround every act. Stefansson gave the opinion that the taboos connected with the eating of the mountain sheep alone are, among some Eskimo tribes, "as extensive as the entire dietary section of the Mosaic law."[68]

THOMAS JEFFERSON'S VIEWS ON NEGROES

Racists and others unfamiliar with the facts frequently cite Jefferson's views on Negroes, as expressed in his *Notes on the State of Virginia*, published in 1785. It was under "Query XVI The administration of justice and the description of the laws" that Jefferson set out his thoughts on the poor mental endowment of Negroes, and his belief that they should be emancipated, and then "be removed beyond the reach of mixture."[69] But with further experience of Negroes, it is seldom mentioned that Jefferson repudiated his earlier prejudices, for that is what he freely acknowledged them to be. Thus, writing in 1791 to Benjamin Banneker, the Negro slave-born inventor and mathematician, in praise of the latter's *Almanac,* Jefferson declared how much he welcomed "such proofs as you exhibit that nature has given to our black brethren talents equal to those of the other colors of men, and that the appearance of a want of them is owing merely to the degraded condition of their existence."[70]

Some seventeen years later, in a letter to Henri Gregoire dated February 25, 1809, Jefferson wrote: "Be assured that no person living wishes more sincerely than I do to see a complete refutation of the doubts I have myself entertained and expressed on the grade of understanding allotted to them [Negroes] by nature, and to find that in this respect they are on a par with ourselves. My doubts were the result of personal observation on the limited sphere of my own State, where the opportunities for the development of their genius were not favorable, and those of exercising it still less so. I expressed them therefore with great hesitation; but whatever be their degree of talent is no measure of their rights."[71]

Many honest and well-meaning men of sharpest intelligence have held the view of "race" as something which determines physical and mental development. Everyone is sure that he knows what "race" means; and today all but a very few individuals take it for granted that scientists have established the *facts* about *race*. So it is not hard to understand why most laymen believe with all sincerity that there "is" such a "thing" as *race*—that the word refers to something real, just as "sword" refers to a sharpened three-foot piece of steel with a handle on it. The truth is there is no referent for *race*; the word refers to nothing that exists. Its meaning now is so diffuse that "in popular use *race* can apply to any more or less clearly defined group thought of as a unit usually because of a common or presumed common past (the Anglo-Saxon *race*) . . . (the Hebrew *race*) . . ." (Webster III). Webster gives us here a blatant example of the obfuscating term, since there never were any such groups. Anglo-Saxon and Hebrew refer to languages, not people.

There's no harm in the word as long as we remember this looseness of application, and also that it refers to no real thing that distinguishes man from man. I see a Chinaman. I am in the habit of seeing his skin as yellow and his eyes as slanted. But his blood has the same composition as mine, and every organ in his body acts precisely like every parallel organ in my body, unless one of us is sick or abnormal or something. It is not "race" that distinguishes us one from the other.

Madame de Staël uttered the excellent observation, "I do not believe in ghosts. But I am afraid of them." Exactly: we do not need to fear the word *race* because we know that there is no referent to which it is a map; yet it can be *used*—usually emotionally—to set man against man. In an interview with Emil Ludwig Mussolini said, "Race! It is a feeling, not a reality."[72] And for once the incredible little man was right. And Hitler in a conversation with Hermann Rauschning said, "I know perfectly well, just as well as all those tremendously clever intellectuals, that in the scientific sense there is no such thing as race. But you as a farmer and cattle-breeder, cannot get your breeding successfully achieved without the conception of race. And I as a politician need a conception which enables the order which has hitherto existed on historic bases to be abolished and an entirely new and anti-historic order enforced and given an intellectual basis. . . . With the conception of race, National Socialism will carry its revolution abroad and recast the world."[73]

The reader may think we are beating a dead horse mercilessly; or, on the other hand, he may disagree with our statement entirely: he may be saying, "There is a black man, and here am I, a white man. Are you trying to say we are of the same race?" To which, with a sigh, it must be answered, "*Race* is the wrong word. The black he and the white you are of different physical types in regard to skin color, head shape, and in several other respects; but you are vastly more alike than you are unlike each other; and your cultural character and behavior are determined by your cultural experiences, not by color or shape. The concept of race is empty and explains nothing. The cells in his black skin grow precisely the same way as the cells in your white skin. The differences are quantitative not qualitative."[74] Pigmentation is the only major difference. If you want to call this "racial," go ahead. In terms of meaning, it's simple nonsense. A pigment of the imagination. As Dwight Dumond put it, "Only a fool would endorse the doctrine of racialism. It is a mythological concept, in its American origins a rationalization, in its survival a monstrous lie."[75]

6

Nonhistorical History, Heroes, and Hagiology

HISTORY REPEATS ITSELF?

The general reader who is not a specialist in history, sees great events outlined in a way which makes them comprehensible, more or less, to his understanding; and occasionally he sees among these silhouettes a profile which seems familiar. Leaping from his tub with a cry of "Eureka!" he charges into the drawing room without even bothering to dry himself off and proclaims the discovery that history repeats itself.

Thus World War II *repeated* World War I: a people, asserting that they needed more living space, set out to grab the needed territories by any means possible: Wilhelm was Hitler; it makes everything so simple. And if a person wanted to do a little digging he would see that Sparta of old was Germany of World Wars I and II: the state was militarized from top to bottom by "re-invigorating and adapting certain primitive social institutions" to the needs of the day.[1]

If this is what is meant by "history repeats itself," there is no denying that historical parallels abound and similar profiles are not hard to discover. There was a seer of sorts who shortly after the assassination of President Kennedy compiled a hatful of strange parallels which tied the assassination of Lincoln into the picture in a weird manner—Lincoln had a secretary named Kennedy, for instance; and

Kennedy had a secretary named Lincoln—there were dozens of such bits and pieces. To which one can only murmur, "Amazing," and watch the reverse parallels fall over each other's feet. But this is not history repeating itself, in any meaningful understanding of the words.

Others will point out examples from the Old Testament: where the people turned from the true God and worshiped idols—"just as we are doing today." Presumably the wrath visited upon the Children of Israel is therefore about to strike *us*. Or they will ask you to consider the fleshpots of Rome in the days of her decadence and tell you that the barbarian hordes are about to engulf *us* just as they did the depraved Romans, and for the same reason: *our* civilization is depraved.

It may be that here we have the key to the nonsense about history repeating itself. It may well be the same motivation which urged the early writers of bestiaries to explain moral and ethical principles through animal stories, many of them totally incorrect. "If you won't believe me, then believe history." Perhaps that's what it means.

But a moment's thought will convince one that a particular shipwreck is not all shipwrecks. In fact, it is no other shipwreck than the one it is. The action of crashing waves upon splintering wood may have been similar in both cases; the carrying power of water was perhaps exemplified in both; but each shipwreck was unique in thousands of details.

One indication of the fatuity of the "history repeats itself" fallacy is the fact that not a single character out of yesterday's event finds an exact duplicate among any of today's actors—nor among yesterday's, for that matter. It's a new cast every time.

Let us, by all means, learn what we can from history, lest we pull similar boners to those of old. But they won't be the *same*.

CAESAR BORN THROUGH ABDOMINAL SURGERY?

That Julius Caesar is the source of the medical term "caesarean section," meaning the incision in the belly and into the uterus to remove a child when ordinary birth seems dangerous or impossible, is beyond doubt. But whether Julius himself entered the world in this fashion remains a question. Partridge says, "Perhaps folk etymology, but probably correct, is the old Latin explanation of *Caesar: caesus matris utero*, cut from his mother's womb."[2] There are those who maintain that it was not possible for Caesar to have been born thus and for his mother to have lived—as Caesar's mother did—for many years afterwards. But the fact is that maternal survival after this operation was frequent in Roman times.[3] Another possible explanation is that the term is derived from the *lex caesarea*, as it came to be known, codified in Roman law by Numa Pompilius 715-672 B.C.), by which it was ordered that the operation be performed on women dying during the last few weeks of pregnancy, in the hope of saving the child.

The *idea* of a caesarean birth had long been common knowledge—enough so that Shakespeare could use it on the stage and be understood. ("No man born of woman shall have power to harm thee" —but in the final encounter it turns out that "Macduff was from his mother's womb untimely ripp'd," and therefore the big Scotsman, not having been born of woman in the common meaning, could and did kill Macbeth.)

Yet even as late as 1875, a famous British surgeon by the name of Sir John Eriksen was saying that there are "regions into which the surgeon could never enter with impunity—the brain, the chest and the abdomen."[4] The danger was largely from infection. City surgeons of the eighteenth and nineteenth centuries were really very dirty: they would handle fresh incisions with hands still germ-covered from autopsies, and it was not until Lister that any scientist even faintly understood about germs; Lister freely credited Pasteur with the germ theory and proceeded to develop aseptic surgery accordingly. Doctors would come to patients from the dissecting rooms, wearing the same old gown stiff with dried pus and blood; and of course all the windows were kept wide open to get rid of the unbearable stink of gangrenous tissue. . . . To open the peritoneum under such conditions was an effective sentence of death. But when Lister read his paper to the British Medical Association meeting at Dublin on March 16, 1867— "On the Antiseptic Principle of the Practice of Surgery"—he was openly laughed at by the witch doctors of the period. The medical fraternity dismissed the germ theory and sternly adhered to its own folk nonsense, as men still do.

Even so, we know that under fairly clean conditions, even without scientifically aseptic surgery, it was possible to enter the peritoneum without fatal results—both in Rome and in the Wild West. Even in city hospitals, when operating rooms were kept spotlessly clean and doctors scrubbed their hands prior to operating—possibly just on general principles or because of some personal fastidiousness—many patients lived through the ordeal of abdominal surgery. Dr. Spencer Wells in London had been excising diseased ovaries successfully for years; and on the frontier, the American Dr. Ephraim McDowell had removed an ovarian cyst in 1809 and later repeated the performance on several occasions. Since no anesthesia was possible, it must have been something of a strain on all concerned. In fact it makes the flesh crawl to consider it.

For such reasons, however, one cannot say that Caesar's alleged birth by surgery is an impossibility. Perhaps his mother, Aurelia, had a clean doctor.

In any case, the Latin verb "to cut" is *caedere,* and this gives us not only Caesar and Czar and Kaiser, but the term familiar in English verse, *caesura,* a cutting-off point, a pause in the meter, typical of Anglo-Saxon poetry.

More surprisingly the same Latin word gives us *Xeres* or *Jerez,* "Caesar's City" (Caesaris urbs) from which we have *sherry,* wine of Jerez, often combined with *sack* (seck, sec, dry, from *siccus*) so that dry sherry is sherry sack—one of Falstaff's favorite liquids, one recalls. It's a small world.

To those of our readers who are inclined to toss off the information about Jerez (actually *Jerez de la Frontera*) as being strictly in the Ivory Tower Department—too specialized to have any practical value —we are happy to point out that a lawsuit being argued in London's Royal Courts of Justice in the spring of 1967, just as this book was going into galleys, and already involving court costs estimated at close to a third of a million dollars (if that's practical enough for you) was to be determined by the "fact" that true sherry "comes only from the vineyards around the Spanish town of Jerez," and no other wine may be called sherry. The precedent is that the British courts have already restricted champagne to wine coming from the Champagne country of France. The complaint arose because cheap, non-Spanish "sherries" were capturing half the British market previously served by the Spanish product, claiming that the word *sherry* is nobody's private property. Four Spanish wine makers think otherwise.[5]

Meek as Moses?

Perhaps this phrase is less familiar these days than it was in the past, when the family Bible was on every living-room table, most of the children were given a name from the Old Testament, everybody inevitably went to Sunday school once a week—where the curriculum *was* the Bible—and communities were somewhat more ingrown (as in Lancaster County, the home of the Amish, where there are reputed to be only a score of family names in a population of about 30,000).[6] Now we have in America something like 350,000 different surnames, according to one authority, and our fashions in front names have changed.[7] But the ten commonest surnames ring with an old-fashioned tone: in order, they are Smith, Johnson, Brown, Williams, Jones, Miller, Davis, Anderson, Wilson, and Moore.[8]

All of which has little to do with "meek as Moses." It is true that in Numbers 12:3 the words occur: "Now the man Moses was very meek." But he appears far from meek in the Bible, and in the popular tradition is a hero-figure. So heroic that his reality has been doubted. Which brings up the question as to whether Moses was really a character in history, first of all. There are some scholars who believe that the evidence is in favor of his being a composite, no more historical than Siegfried, for instance (G. Holscher and E. Meyer have written to this effect).[9] Then there is the name itself, which may indeed derive from *mashah*, drawn (out of the water), as one tradition has it; or it may come from the Egyptian *mesu*, child—as we might say "junior." There is a familiar pattern to the stories surrounding his birth as set down in Exodus II—the escape from the butchers of Pharaoh, the discovery by the princess among the reeds at the riverbank—which reminds one of other legends. The Britannica suggests the parallels between Moses and Sargon, "the myths of Osiris and many others" (11th edition).

Finally there is no knowing; there are not any extant contemporary records to prove whether Moses was a single historic individual or the personification of an influence which made a nation of Israel and gave it the Law. Most of us in the Judeo-Christian tradition probably think of him as a real person—a great ethical hero and leader; and it is beyond doubt that the spirit of ethical leadership and statesmanlike government was there. If legends grew around him, we know that they grew around Washington also. It is worth recalling that some students of scholarly detection have come to the conclusion that William Shakespeare could not have been just one man. The writing, they believe, transcends the capacity of any single person. The plays must have been written by a committee: a secret society of learned men of letters; a group of Jesuits; a circle of poets.[10] In short, a man appears on earth every so often whose powers are so greatly beyond what we think of as human abilities that we have to assign some superhuman mystery to his case.

The question remains, why did "meek as Moses" gain currency? What has the adjective *meek* got to do with this gigantic figure whose miracles began in the basket discovered by the Princess Thermutis? (Her latent good looks were marred by sores on the face; but no sooner had she touched the basket with Moses in it than all the sores disappeared and her face grew radiant with beauty.)[11] One explanation is that the expression does not mean "meek" at all, but aggressive; it is a sarcastic remark like "light as an elephant." Another is that the splendid alliteration is appealing to the folk. "Meek as Mohammed" would have done just as well in this event; but somebody said "Meek as Moses" and it stuck. A third is that there is a type of humor in which a towering figure is brought into the local conversation of the humble artisan in a familiar, informal way, as if to say "I know him personally; we're pals," which the yeoman wit finds attractive. For example, the blacksmith is shoeing a horse and a nail breaks so that it cannot be pulled out of the horny hoof with the claw hammer —yet it must come out. The blacksmith scratches his head and says, "What would Napoleon do?" The circle around him laughs. The blacksmith makes a mental note to use Napoleon again sometime. A final explanation is that when God ordered Moses to go down to the court and demand of Pharaoh, "Let my people go," Moses was reluctant. If that is meekness, we should make the most of it, for Moses was never meek again. In every other adventure he seems to be the complete hero. One sample will show this:

There was a dispute one day in the field between a handsome Egyptian rascal who had been cuckolding one of the Jewish laborers, and lying about it when accused. Moses stood between the two, uttered the Ineffable Name, and prayed that God would show his wrath on whoever was lying. The Egyptian withered like a leaf and fell down dead. Moses was haled before the court and convicted of killing the Egyptian. He was condemned. The headsman aimed a muscular blow at the neck of Moses, but missed completely. As the judge tried to speak to order a second attempt, his tongue cleaved to the roof of his mouth. Moses started to run off, and the bailiffs yelled to the guards to stop him, but the latter had been struck deaf. The executioner jumped to his feet in pursuit, but suddenly he turned blind and couldn't see where he was going. And so, as we know, Moses got away.[12]

THE GUILLOTINE: CHILD OF THE REVOLUTION?

The first time the general reader hears about the guillotine is probably when he is following the course of the French Revolution or perhaps more specifically the Reign of Terror, through a novel, a movie, or perhaps even a formal history, if one dares hope so far. So the first myth that arises about the tall machine is that it originated during the French Revolution. Another myth is that the guillotine is a terrible and bloodthirsty instrument, leering at human necks and licking its chops. A third is that Dr. Joseph Ignace Guillotin invented it; and a fourth is that the doctor was put to death by the machine. They are all false.

There are legends of Chinese, Persian, Roman, German, and machines of other cultures for decapitating unwanted citizens mechanically, but "it is Ireland (as far as can be verified) which first bestowed on mankind the art of mechanised head-chopping."[13] The reference which impresses the author of our quote is no less an authority than Holinshed, in whose *Chronicles* (1578) is the woodcut of "an unmistakable 'guillotine' and the accompanying text proclaims flatly that it was used for the execution 'near to Merton' of Murcod Ballagh on April 1st, 1307. No earlier mechanical removal of heads is recounted with details as precise."[14]

There had been a Halifax gibbet in England which worked like a guillotine, and it is possible that the Irish derived theirs from it; the orderly Scots admit freely that it was the parent of their "Maiden" by means of which the Regent Morton was decapitated in 1581. (Attempts to locate the etymology of *Maiden* have produced some brightly imaginative thought: one is the suggestion that the machine went unused for a long time after it had been imported; another is that it derives from *mod-dun,* a place where justice is administered.) Visitors to the National Museum of Antiquities in Edinburgh have had the opportunity of seeing Herself: the Maiden is on exhibit there.

Thus, while we may not be able to spot the *first* guillotine or reasonable facsimile, we can say with assurance that the machine was in use hundreds of years before Dr. Guillotin proposed its use to the Assembly on October 10, 1789.

Which leads us to his reasons. The death penalty used to be carried out in many ways, depending on the nature of the crime for which death was the punishment. Treason, for instance, required the application of the most hideous torture. Damiens was arrested after a clumsy attempt on the life of Louis XV. When they led him out of the Conciergerie after two months of torture he was unrecognizable. "The hand which had struck so ineffectually at Louis XV was burnt away; molten lead and boiling oil were poured into his wounds. Four horses were set to dragging him apart, and when their strength proved inadequate—after sufficient time had been given them—the executioner used his knife to loosen the victim's joints a little and permit the horses to do their work before it grew too dark for the audience to see."[15]

Dr. Guillotin was a humanitarian in an Age of Reason, and he objected to the wheel, the rack, the pincers, and particularly to the clumsy use of the sword for beheading, where many times the scene became one of butchery before the head fell. It is not easy to strike a man's head from his neck, it appears.

So the good doctor presented resolutions doing away with torture in capital cases and insisted that decapitation be the sole and standard form of capital punishment. His first speech on this subject was met with applause, but final approval of the Assembly had to wait until June 3, 1791. Guillotin described an infallible machine for his purposes; and Dr. Antoine Louis, secretary of the Académie Chirurgicale, who had many surgical instruments to his credit, designed the machine. A German piano maker, Tobias Schmidt, built a working model from Dr. Louis's designs; and they were in business.

Any machine created for the purpose of causing death is an instrument of terror; and we do not mean to suggest that the guillotine was not a terrible sight to those under sentence of death; nor do we mean that the guillotine did not drink a great deal of blood, because it did. But ask yourself: if you had to die, would you prefer a quick, certain, one-stroke death, foolproof and absolute, or would you rather put your trust in the skill of some headsman whose aim might be bad? Also, don't forget the elimination of torture: one death for all when capital punishment is the judgment. It was a humanitarian advance. The culprit is strapped to the bascule which tips over on hinges so that the neck rests in a scooped hollow, where it is fastened (the lunette) by an upper half. The 13-inch blade, 10½ inches wide and slanting for maximum effectiveness, is set in an 80-pound metal *mouton*, which runs up and down in metal grooves on four wheels, two on each side; and this knife falls ten feet. It cannot miss its mark when the *bourreau* releases the *déclic*.

The final myth, that Dr. Guillotin was executed on the machine he had recommended, we owe, perhaps, to Thackeray, who wrote in *Philip* (chap. XVI): "Was not good Dr. Guillotin executed by his own neat invention?" The answer is, No, he was not. He died in his own bed in the Rue S.-Honoré of a very painful carbuncle in the shoulder, at the age of 76.[16] When an instrument is associated with shame and death and torture, something within us seems to be gratified by learning that the inventor also suffered through his invention. The carpenter who built the first stocks in Boston in 1634, chap named Palmer, was the first to occupy them. He submitted a bill for 1 pound, 13 shillings for his construction and "the town elders felt this to be excessive and haled Palmer before the court on a charge of profiteering. He was found guilty, fined one pound, and sentenced to spend a half-hour in the stocks—the elders wanted to try out the new apparatus without delay."[17]

There is one last myth about Guillotin which you probably have *not* heard. It is about his birth, which "was accompanied by an augury almost unbearably apropos." Just before his birth his mother, on a promenade, passed a place where a criminal was being tortured on the wheel. She was so stricken that labor pains began very shortly and little Joseph Ignace was born the next day, May 28, 1738, at Saintes.

Pasteur Made Us Safe from Rabies and Bad Milk?

Sir William Osler took for his own the words of a tribute in the *Spectator* about Louis Pasteur: "He was the most perfect man who has ever entered the Kingdom of Science." [18] It is difficult, after some hours spent in company with the man and his methods, not to hero-worship. He was tireless himself, and his last whispered words on that autumn afternoon in 1895 when death came quietly for him were, *"Il faut travailler"*—we must work. If the memory of the folk retains two important credits for the French genius after all these years, he may count himself fortunate—two is a high number in the recollections of

busy people, and most heroes (like Robert Koch, the German bacteri-
ologist, without whose work that of Pasteur might never have grown to
maturity) get none at all.

So we remember Louis Pasteur as the doctor who found a cure for
rabies in animals and hydrophobia in man; and through whose process
—pasteurization—the fermentation of milk is checked. The first is
attended by such highly sensational and fearful symptoms in both man
and beast that the popular mind could not very well forget it—frothing
at the mouth, spasms, and so forth. Through Pasteur's serum deaths
throughout the world from this cause have dropped to less than 1
percent.

But the contributions of Pasteur were of far greater reach than the
things he is popularly remembered for. Varro in the first century B.C.
and Fracastoro, the Italian physician, in 1546 had already suggested
that disease is spread by little animal or disease units too small to be
seen. But it remained for Pasteur to prove it scientifically, and to lay
the foundations for the science of bacteriology—thus revolutionizing
all medical practice and vastly benefiting every one of us. The Floren-
tine physician Francesco Redi had shown in 1668, by experiment, that
the belief in "spontaneous generation" was false. Up to the time of
Redi's experimental disproof it was generally believed that maggots
appeared in rotting meat by spontaneous generation. Since Redi, we
know that the flies put them there. Pasteur confirmed Redi's finding. It
was the same Frenchman who developed the beginnings of preventive
medicine and vaccines; he saved the French silk industry by providing
an immunity for the silkworm from a devastating disease; he found a
cure for chicken cholera; for anthrax in cattle and sheep—killer of
millions of animals. The list of his accomplishments fills a book; and
his wise observation as he gave his inaugural address as dean of the
Faculté des Sciences at Lille was this: "In the field of observation,
chance only favors those who are prepared."

What we do forget—and this is folly—is to give any space in our
folklore to East Prussia's Robert Koch, who, according to some authorities, deserves equal credit with Pasteur for the development of
bacteriology as a science. He was the popular young district physician
in Wollstein, delivering the babies, strapping up the sprained ankles,
and tending to the headaches of his people. Life changed for him when
his wife gave him a microscope for his birthday. Working on the
anthrax problem, he injected blood from an anthrax sheep into a

mouse (he couldn't afford sheep himself) and found the bacilli in the mouse's spleen and liver. Then, using the fluid in the eye of an ox (it sounds like something from the witches' formula in *Macbeth,* but it's the truth), he was able to culture the anthrax bacilli—and thus inoculate animals with a pure culture for the first time. Previously nobody had cultivated bacteria outside a body, in an incubator. When Koch demonstrated his discovery at the Botanical Institute in Breslau in the spring of 1876, many famous medical and scientific experts were there, watching and listening with the critical suspension of belief that marks the true scientist awaiting proof: there was Weigert, the first to use the technique of staining bacteria with dyes for better viewing; Cohn, chairman of the botany department at Breslau; Cohnheim, the world's most distinguished investigator of cellular pathology; Auerbach, the great anatomist; Traube, first to record a continuous fever chart; and others. And Koch took them by storm. . . . Later he identified the staphylococcus and the streptococcus, and the tubercle bacillus (1882).

The next time you get injections in preparation for your European vacation, remember both men—Pasteur and Koch.

Sir Isaac Newton Learned from an Apple?

In one story Isaac is hit upon the pate by a falling apple as he sits under the tree—indeed, as late as 1820 the very tree itself was pointed out to sightseers; and in another, he *sees* an apple fall and that suddenly clinches the matter of gravitation for him. Whatever actually happened, the combination of Isaac Newton and apple is a classic, and since it can never be proved or disproved, it is undoubtedly destined to remain. The part of the story which we can, with some certainty, regard as apocryphal is that the fall of the apple started the train of thought which led to everything else. We have Voltaire to thank for the apple story; he got it from Newton's niece, who kept house for the old scientist in those latter affluent days when he was master of the Mint. Possibly Newton had used a simple illustration to explain his theory to his relative, who knows?

The facts show that Newton, ever since his 24th year (1666), had tried to explain the motion of the moon by means of a hypothesis which assumed gravitation. Meanwhile some French geographers had been testing the spherical shape of the earth and had arrived at a new and more accurate triangulation. Comparing their data with his own theory that force varies inversely as the square of the distance, he saw that each set of data supported the other, and he was, according to witnesses, so overcome with emotion at having found the solution to so magnificent a problem that he couldn't bear to complete his calculations and asked a friend to finish up for him. The result, as we know, was that the new astronomy which had begun with Copernicus, Brahe, Kepler, and Galileo could be formulated mathematically by a single mechanical principle. One can imagine with what triumph he wrote (*Philosophiae Naturalis Principia Mathematica*):

The force which retains the celestial bodies in their orbits has been hitherto called centripetal force; but it being now made plain that it can be no other than a gravitating force, we shall hereafter call it gravity.

Isaac had always been an extremely imaginative person, and it was just as well, since he had to make his own way. His father died before he was born—incidentally he was born on Christmas Day, 1642—and left his mother on the farm to eke out her living as best she could. Young Isaac, however, made ingenious mechanical toys and through them earned his way to college. By the time he was twenty-seven he was professor of mathematics at Cambridge University. His accomplishments were many: he demonstrated the compound nature of the rays of the sun by use of a prism; he invented for his own use a reflecting telescope; he formulated a Second Law of Motion (force equals mass times acceleration) and a Third Law of Motion ("For every action there is an equal and opposite reaction"). In addition, he did much experimenting in chemistry, but somehow his papers were destroyed, and the legend is that he never got over the shock of their loss. At least his last three decades were years of affluence, we are happy to report. He could afford to keep plenty of apples in the cellar.

Did Little George Cut Down the Cherry Tree?

Famous last words and famous first actions of notable persons should always be taken with a soupçon of the salt that pours when it rains: they are usually somewhat too brilliant, too superior; and their occurrence is almost always surrounded by emotional circumstances of high color. You trace them back to the utterance or to the action and you discover that history has been depending upon the half-heard whisper of some faithful servitor or passer-by which gets picked up, without loss of content, for the next telling. Or else they are simply legitimate hyperboles intended to enhance the glory of the historical or mythical character under discussion, and not intended to be taken literally—like the statement that "he had a faith that could move mountains." We know perfectly well that it takes more than faith to move mountains: it requires either a great deal of hand labor or the presence of some large machines—but the *idea* of moving the mountain may have originated in a person of adamant will who could see the good that would be done if the mountain were moved, and refused to give up until the project was completed. Beware of metaphor. She dropped her eyes; he pierced her with a glance; she broke off in the middle of her speech. Probably not, what? Still, it makes for more colorful speech.

For years we heard that Nelson's dying words were, "Kiss me, Hardy." Something less than the tone of the tough sea dog there, hm? Now comes someone who suggests that what Nelson said really was, "Kismet, Hardy!" Fate, old man. More like it?

Which brings us to George Washington and the cherry tree. The first biography of the Father of his Country was the cheerful prose of Parson Weems, and it is very hard indeed to hold anything against that charming old gentleman. He was so enthusiastic about his subject; he so idolized his hero. So little George gets a nice sharp hatchet for his birthday—precisely the sort of toy to please an active young fellow on a large plantation where there were all kinds of things on which to test the blade. Ah, George was delighted. He chopped here and he chopped there. That his father was doing some experimental horticulture with a new breed of cherry trees was, at the moment, of no interest to him, although it became so shortly thereafter when his paternal ancestor demanded hoarsely the name of the vandal who had ruined one of his best specimens. Like a little man, however, he fessed right up; and his father opened his arms declaring that he had rather lose—we forget just how many trees Augustine ("Gus to his friends," says Columbia Encyclopedia) estimated—than have his son be a prevaricator. That's the way Parson Weems heard it, and that's the way we pass it along. The father, we might note, knew the ways of children: he had had four by his first wife, Jane Butler, before he married George's mother, Mary, by whom he had six more; and we know that he died when George was eleven.

History is full of instances in which legendary events, which may or may not be founded upon solid substance, come to be accepted without much question; and we would not have it otherwise. *Some* fantasy is needed in this prosaic existence. But for old Eusebius, for example, who was the Parson Weems for the Emperor Constantine, we would never have had the charming story about Constantine's fiery skyey vision thoughtfully captioned "In hoc signo vinces"—under this sign thou shalt conquer—just before the Battle of the Milvian Bridge (A.D. 311), the victory which put Constantine on the imperial throne. What does it matter whether the legend is literally true or not? *Something* moved Constantine to become a Christian, and his conversion changed the history of all Christendom.

And as for last words, we hear that Elizabeth the Great of England spoke for the last time in Latin and said, as she sank into unconsciousness, *"Ad inferos eat melancholia"*—To hell with grief. If it's not true, *Se non e vero, e ben trovato*—it should be; and that goes for the cherry tree, too.

Incidentally, Parson Weems was a man who warmed to his work, and when the excitement of historical reconstruction was high he was not above adding dialogue of his own invention to make the scene live again. His first edition of the Life of Washington was just an overgrown pamphlet of 80 pages; but his story proved to be very popular and by the time he was in his fifth edition Weems was using 250 pages. He was also referring to himself, we are sad to report, as the former rector of Mt. Vernon Parish, presumably to add an air of authenticity. This is rather too bad, because anybody can check the fact that there *was* no Mt. Vernon Parish. But in the main one has to forgive Parson Weems. He wanted to blow the dust off Clio's wan brow and cause the blood to course again; thus in his biography of William Penn he had at his command all the details of the famous—and mythical—treaty with the Indians, right down to the verbatim statement of the sachems, whom he quotes at length and without faltering, ending, "all brothers together, long as the sun and moon give light." At least it's not dull.

THE CALENDAR: DATED FROM THE BIRTH OF CHRIST?

When we say "the calendar" it is assumed in most places where English is spoken that we are referring to the system established by Pope Gregory XIII in 1582. Prior to that time the calendar in use was the Julian, which Julius Caesar had established in 46 B.C. The trouble with the Julian system was that the length of the years was not exactly calculated, although it was very close; but by A.D. 325 the error had added up enough to cause the vernal equinox to fall on March 21 instead of the 25th, thus fixing the 21st as the earliest date for the Paschal full moon. If Gregory had not made his reform, we would now be running on a calendar which would be 13 days behind where we are, as, indeed, the Eastern Orthodox Church is today—but more of that in a moment.

Gregory decreed that ten days should be dropped from the calendar for the year 1582 to balance the current error, and then he clinched the matter by altering the rules for leapyear to prevent a recurrence of the mistake. The new system made so much sense that even the English adopted it officially—170 years later. (Up to that time the English, as Voltaire put it, preferred to disagree with the sun rather than agree with the Pope.) After all, no system of measuring or calculating time is of any help unless those attempting to live a reasonably civilized life all mean the same thing when they say, "I'll meet you on June 19," or, "My ship will sail from Rome on the 21st: please be on it."

The belief that we are dating events a certain number of years before or after the birth of Christ is held more or less everywhere; and it is not this belief in itself which we are listing as nonsense or as an example of a popular error. The nonsense comes in when men pronounce uncertain facts as absolute truths and condemn anyone who will not accept their single "official" version as the one and only explanation. The nonsense appears when officials command us to defend a myth or a hypothesis with more loyalty than is considered appropriate in the defense of verifiable fact.

The uncertainty in this case is, of course, the precise year and day on which Jesus was born. We know that he was born before the death of Herod the Great, and we know that Herod the Great died in 4 B.C. What we do not know, and stand a very poor chance of ever finding out, is exactly how long before the death of Herod the birth of Jesus occurred. The authoritative *Oxford Dictionary of the Christian Church* contents itself with the statement, "Jesus was born before the death of King Herod . . . but probably not more than three or four years before."[19] According to Matthew, Jesus was born "in Bethlehem of Judea in the days of Herod the king" (Matt. 2:1). Luke says that Jesus was born at the time of the census of Quirinius, which was in A.D. 6.[20] Vincent Taylor suggests a date as early as 8 B.C.[21] But the writers of the Gospels were not in the least interested in the scholarship of dates; they were interested in the character and message of Jesus and the dates didn't matter to them. Since they are our only source, we fall into folly ourselves if we try, on the basis of insufficient data, to supply accurate dates ourselves. One scholar, Professor A. T. Olmstead, settled to his own satisfaction precisely the number of days covering the ministry of Jesus: from December 18, A.D. 28, to the crucifixion on April 7, A.D. 30—a total of 475 days.[22] As if that mattered.

At any rate, we have dated the world's events from the birth of Jesus ever since Dionysius Exiguus suggested it in the sixth century; and his date for the incarnation was (incorrectly) the Roman calendar year marking the 753rd since the founding of the city (*ab urbe condita*), which was the customary way of dating events at that time. We can blame that Scythian monk for whatever error exists, if we wish.

To Patriarch Benedictos of the Greek Orthodox Church, however, this is no laughing matter. The liberal voices reaching him from Vatican II sounded loud and clear—and dangerous. He sent out a pastoral letter to his people at Christmas, 1965, calling upon the clergy and the faithful to preserve "the hallowed traditions" of the Church and not be "led astray by propaganda for innovations." The ecumenical movement was tempting some Orthodox families into an intention to celebrate Christmas on December 25, as the Gregorian calendar marks it, instead of January 6, as the older Julian calendar and the older Christian usage had it. One only could be correct and the correct one, of course, was that held by the Patriarch.

JAPAN IS IN THE ORIENT?

Everybody knows that you have to travel eastward to reach Japan. But what everybody knows is very likely to prove to be a popular error; and a quick look at a Polar Projection, or even a Mercator, but especially at a globe, will be enough to indicate to the slowest eye that from any point on the North American continent, Japan is much closer if one travels *westward*. Or, better still, northwestward over Point Barrow, Alaska.

Of course this was not so in the days before Europeans knew there was a North American continent and a Pacific Ocean on the other side of it. The fabulous East with its peacocks and frankincense and spices and silks and monkeys—we had the word of Marco Polo for it—was located at the site of the rising sun. Zipangu, he called it. And so when the Turks cut off the caravans at Constantinople in 1453, the ships sailed eastward. It was a habit of thought.

Politically we are still Europe-minded; and to Europe-minded people Japan continues to be eastward. A certain subtlety lies in the fact that the Japanese think of themselves as the East, *also*: their flag is the Rising Sun. They are Europe-minded, too, those exceedingly industrious inhabitants of Hokkaido, Honshu, Shikoku, Kyushu, and a few other smaller islands. . . . Even the huge air freighters do not change a habit of thought rapidly; for, as Sir Thomas Browne said, "with the common people proverbs are more powerful than demonstrations."[23]

Robert Fulton's Boat Was the <u>Clermont</u>?

This is one of the most prevalent of popular errors. Part of its charm is the manner in which it illustrates the natural history of nonsense, showing how a bit of incorrect information can get started almost, as it were, through a process of spontaneous generation, and thereafter achieve acceptance among persons of repute and thus become firmly established as fact. The Muse Clio must wince from time to time as scholars pore over their history books, taking down notes on incorrect statements in order to pass them along in yet another book. But in this case, if you examine the Encyclopaedia Britannica, and dozens of other reputable reference works, including weighty tomes on the history of travel and the story of mechanical inventions, you will "learn" that when Fulton and Livingston put their first steamboat into operation on the Hudson River, it bore the name of *The Clermont*.

Gentlemen, hush: it did not.

We shall now proceed to rewrite history—this time correctly—in the full knowledge that, unless something extraordinary happens involving readership of these paragraphs, future generations will still salute Fulton for his *Clermont*. Heigh, as they say, ho.

We happened to notice in "Charlie Rice's Punch Bowl," a regular feature appearing in *This Week* magazine, a series of common mistakes that have become popular; and the case of the *Clermont* was given an idle mention. Failing to find any book that did *not* attribute such a steamboat to Fulton, we opened a correspondence with Mr.

Rice, and he suggested a close and steady look at the World Book Encyclopedia and also at what we will have to consider the supreme authority in this matter because of the detail and sources of its documentation.[24] The *Hudson River Day Line* begins with the steamboat *Robert Fulton* casting off her lines at Albany on September 13, 1948, and starting downstream for New York. That was the last fall trip of the boat, and it was the last trip sponsored by the Hudson River Day Line. "It was appropriate," says Mr. Ringwald, "that the *Robert Fulton* had ended it, since Robert Fulton began it in 1807 with his first Hudson River steamboat." It is then narrated how Fulton and Livingston (the latter had met the former in France when Livingston was the U.S. minister to that country) held "a twenty-year monopoly of steamboat operations on New York State waters." The book then describes the boat—a side-wheeler with an imported engine and fitted with sails for use when the wind favored. On her maiden trip upriver she lay over at Clermont, the name of Livingston's estate on the river, so that her actual running time was about 32 hours. She returned in 30.

Having thus proved that the trip was possible commercially—although there had been the usual hoots and catcalls of the idlers on the docks—Fulton set to work to make the boat suitable for passengers. He then proceeded to enroll her, on September 3, 1807, under the name of *North River Steam Boat*. Yes, that is the name Fulton used on the official register. He had obviously not given the matter any particular thought—he had been too much preoccupied with getting the bugs out of the machinery and making the boat comfortable enough so that the public would make use of it in crowds. His name for the vessel was merely practical—she *was* a Steam Boat, and she *did* ply the North River, which was another contemporary name for the Hudson. On the next day, September 4, the *North River Steam Boat* formally inaugurated commercial river transportation, making the run to Albany this time in 28 hours and 45 minutes. One could go to Newburgh for $3, to Poughkeepsie for $4, to Hudson for $5, and all the way to Albany for $7.

There were plenty of bugs still in the machinery. According to other accounts, the engine groaned and squeaked formidably, the boat shook and a chap with a pot of melted lead kept running about stopping up leaks in the steam system. Hence at the end of the season Fulton laid the boat up to enlarge and improve her. The wooden hull, for those interested in such details, was increased from 142 feet to 149 feet in length and from 14 feet in width to 17 feet 11 inches, while the hold grew from 4 feet to 7. She had one boiler and an engine cylinder with a 4-foot stroke and a diameter of 24 inches.

When the spring season opened the first hailing port, which had been New York, became Clermont, and the ship was newly enrolled there. She made her last trip in 1814, still under the name of *North River Steam Boat.* (The Hudson River Day Line did have a *Clermont,* but it was made with a steel hull and was built in 1911. Later it was renamed the *Bear Mountain* and ran as an excursion boat until 1947.)

Now we come to the manner in which the legend of the *Clermont* arose and continued in excellent health. It's another Parson Weems thing, in its own way:

Two years after the death of Robert Fulton, a lawyer by the immensely satisfactory name of Cadwallader D. Colden published a biography, *The Life of Robert Fulton* (1817). For reasons which nobody will ever know and on the basis of what considerations we can do no more than guess, this New York City author, who later became mayor of the city, chose to call the *North River Steam Boat* the *Clermont.* But he was a man of status, and he was known to be a close associate of both Livingston and Fulton; so his biography had the air of an official publication. Later writers, retelling the Robert Fulton story, came to Cadwallader's book and apparently felt that it was not necessary to go to any other source, although the government records listing the statutory dimensions of the boat were available then as they are now. Official documents and MVUS (the Government's annual *List of Merchant Vessels of the United States*) do not make especially exciting reading anyhow. The famous picture of the boat, painted by Richard Varick De Witt more than forty years after the steamboat went out of service, captions the boat, "the *North River* of *Clermont.*" But everybody had decided that the boat was the *Clermont* by that time and probably anybody who calls it by any name at all will keep right on doing the same from the kindergarten to the grave, from now until the Angel Gabriel, with one foot on the land and the other in the sea, blows the final Trumpet. We can almost see why Henry Ford felt the way he did about history. . . .

There is just one note of hope: In a book by Frank Donovan he has this to say:

During its construction, Fulton called the craft "the steamboat." Later it was advertised as *The North River Steam Boat*. After it was remodeled it was registered as *The North River Steam Boat of Clermont*. In all correspondence Fulton called it either *The North River Steam Boat* or *The North River*. The vessel was apparently first called *The Clermont*—the name of Livingston's upriver estate—in a biography of Fulton written two years after his death by his friend Cadwallader Colden. Since Colden's writing was considered "official," the name was picked up and the vessel has come down in history under that appellation.[25]

Thus it is possible that the day will come when even one or two school histories will begin to acknowledge the ancient wrong. But not before we are old and gray and full of sleep.

The Myth of "Silent Cal" Coolidge

Among the things which occupy the mind of that mythological beast known as Every Schoolboy is the utterly certain knowledge that President Calvin Coolidge was a man of few words. Taciturn. Yankee. But effective. This is probably the only thing that Every Schoolboy *does* know about Mr. Coolidge.

The idea is factually incorrect. Old Cal was far from silent. He was, instead, quite garrulous. But only when he was in a company where he felt at ease and in control of the situation. If he were to have been faced with the problems of a White House conference in the F.D.R. tradition, with two hundred or more reporters asking uncensored questions, or in the J.F.K. tradition, with the rapid-fire and quick rebuttal tempo, he would infallibly have withdrawn into his shell and become the "Silent Cal" that his reputation still acclaims him.

The "Silent Cal" myth would still be intact, actually, had it not been for a stroke of luck through which two researchers discovered, in the Forbes Library at Northampton, a wooden box which nobody had bothered to investigate, and which bore labels showing that it had been shipped from the White House in March, 1929. They opened it and found a goldmine. "It held the typed ribbon-copy verbatim transcripts of all the Coolidge press conferences."[26] In these pages was revealed the character of a shrewd politician who showed a wide comprehension of public issues; more than that, they showed a man who, at his relaxed best, had a Buster Keaton style of wit: with a stone face, Coolidge would remark, for instance, that he had been up at the Lodge, fishing—and that there are "45,000 fish up there. I haven't caught them all yet, but I've got them all pretty well intimidated." The reporters asked him if he'd had any reports from Minnesota, where the rumors were that the Republicans would carry the state (October 24, 1924), and Coolidge shook his head. "I haven't any specific reports about any states. My reports indicate that I shall probably carry Northampton."

It was Coolidge who "was the contriver of the most persistent and transparent political hoax of twentieth-century America . . . through the medium of 'the White House Spokesman.' "[27] ". . . All questions had to be submitted in advance, and the correspondents were forbidden to quote the President's answers."[28] His conferences involved only about a dozen newsmen, who could quote only the "Spokesman" and Coolidge was in complete control of the meetings. Here he often waxed garrulous, as well as sharp-witted, informed, and anecdotal.

First Armored Ships Were <u>Monitor</u> and <u>Merrimac</u>?

It is accepted as basic doctrine by many Americans that the first practical armored craft were the Confederate *Merrimac* and the Federal *Monitor*; and the effectiveness of the armor is attested to by the fact that these two ships fought each other to a draw in a five-hour battle on March 9, 1862. Later the *Merrimac* was destroyed by the Confederates to prevent her being captured and her secrets exposed.

These two ironclads, however, were far from being the first metal-sheathed ships.

We take you now to the era of the great merchant days of the Hellenistic Age (323-146 B.C.):

The *Syracusa*, built by Hiero II of Sicily to run between Syracuse and Alexandria, had a cargo capacity of nearly 4,000 tons besides room for passengers, seamen and marines. The ship had cabins for passengers, luxuriously furnished saloons, a gymnasium, gardens, a temple, a bathroom, and a pool. It was covered with plates of lead, and had eight towers equipped with catapults which could hurl against an enemy stones of three talents' weight [a talent was at least 58 pounds, although the weight differed in times and places] or long arrows. By means of the new system of pulleys and the automatic pump of Archimedes, the water could be pumped from the hold by one man. The great scientist had superintended the building of this "Leviathan" and was able to launch it by his new principle of the screw. But the ship proved too large for most Hellenistic harbors, and was presented by Hiero to Ptolemy as a curiosity.[29]

They were way ahead of us. Neither the *Monitor* nor the *Merrimac* had a fish pool; and gardens were the furthest things from the imaginations of their architects. It's an idea, though: if you're going to war, why not go with music and flowers?

CICERO CONSIDERED THE BRITONS STUPID?

For many years it was a learned tradition, which for some reason was allowed to pass without questioning, that the ancient Britons were hopelessly primitive, the hayseed thick in their unkempt hair, quaking with superstition, and bloodthirsty for human sacrifice. That they had no aptitudes in the arts, except of killing, and that they were too stupid to be taught anything. It is easy for some people to be anti-British, but that was carrying it a little too far: because no people is as brainless as all *that*. A tribe may have cretins and morons within bowshot of the long house, but the whole group is not imbecile. Nevertheless, that scholarly myth had enough survival value so that it seeped down to the folk—of countries other than Britain—and continues to be repeated. The chief authority for the learned error has been given as Cicero, to whom have been attributed certain words allegedly written by the great orator to his friend Atticus. It is rather too bad that somebody has not checked up on the original before repeating the ancient canard. Cicero never said it.

What Cicero is *quoted* as saying in the famous letter to Atticus is this Consumer's Report on the purchase of slaves in the open market: "Do not let anybody sell you slaves from Britain, because they are so unintelligent and so utterly incapable of being taught anything that they are not fit to be any part of an Athenian household." In other words, these blond and muscular blue-eyed savages (Pope Gregory, one remembers, punned that they were not Angles but angels, a few centuries later) may *look* like good models on the slave blocks but their performance is inferior because they are a race without brains.

The distinguished anthropologist, the late Ruth Benedict of Columbia University, referred to the Cicero statement in her excellent 1943 text to illustrate the phenomenon of a people improving and changing over the years;[30] and the misquotation has been many times repeated, most recently in an anthropology text.[31]

Cicero did not think highly of Britain as an investment for conquest; and he thought the natives of the islands showed little or no training in literature and music, skills which were highly valued in sophisticated Athenian homes, where the most brilliant slaves were the musicians and the tale spinners and entertainers. But he never wrote that the Britons were stupid, untrainable, or unfit to serve in the household. What he *did* write to Atticus (July 27, 54 B.C., as Caesar was in the first stage of his second invasion of Britain) was this. Listen closely: *"Etiam illud iam cognitum est, neque argenti scripulum esse ullum ab illa insula neque ullam spem praedae nisi ex mancipiis; ex quibus nullos puto te litteris aut musicis* [get it?] *eruditos expectare."*[32] Which, quite simply, of course, is, "From all evidence, there's not a scrap of silver in the island, and no hope of booty except in terms of slaves. And I doubt if you'll find any literary or musical talents among them."

They developed something in these fields later, from what we hear; but there is no reason for anyone to continue to quote old Silvertongue incorrectly on this question in the future, and let's hear no more of it.

ROMAN AQUEDUCTS RESEMBLED ARCHED STONE BRIDGES?

The tourist, seeing the great triple arches that remain from the aqueducts, is impressed with the dramatic magnificence of the Roman Water Department and comes home with the idea that he has seen the heart of the system. Forever afterwards he thinks of the aqueducts in terms of these stone bridges. Which is not unnatural, since they are impressive; but it is not at all true that the tourist has seen the heart of the system. He has, in fact, seen about one seventh of the system. These bridges running water into the city from the hills have one thing in common with the floating iceberg: only one seventh of the whole thing is seen.

"The course of the Roman aqueducts was mainly underground. About A.D. 52 the total length of the eight main aqueducts was about 220 miles, of which only about 30 miles ran above the ground."[33]

Hence, while the ruins which the tourist sees are impressive, what he does *not* see is still more impressive; and capping the visible in impressiveness is an unseen fact which is more amazing than any spectacle: at peak, the Roman water system supplied almost six times as much water per day per person as does the London (England) water system. The output in Rome, fourth century A.D., 300 gallons

per person per day; London, 1960, 51 gallons per person per day, "of
which 34 are for domestic and 17 for trade use."[34]

Pocahontas Saved Captain John Smith from Death?

Unless new evidence comes to us from some unassailable source, it
is probable that we shall all go to our graves without being absolutely
sure whether the Pocahontas story is a fabrication or not. It is certainly one of the best-known and most romantic legends in American
history, and it is more than likely that by this time the tale has become
an artifact in its own right, obeying its own laws, as happens to a
painting at some time during its growth, so that what is "out there" no
longer matters, but only what is on the canvas.

Thus when the name of Captain John Smith is spoken, the dramatic
associations crowd in and we hear the beating of the drums and the
chanting of the red-skinned priests as they howl their barbaric litany
while the smoke hovers and circles over the great fire. Suddenly dozens
of hands seize the Englishman and he is dragged over the stamped-
earth floor to an improvised stone altar, where his head is forced down
while certain braves stand over him with uplifted clubs. At this point
Pocahontas cries out; and when the rite continues the 11 (some say
13)-year-old maiden breaks out of the ranks of the women, runs to
the altar, and places her own royal head on the block beside that of
the diminutive bearded paleface.

She "defied the priests and the ministerial executioners. She was
only a little girl, but she was the favorite daughter of the absolute Lord
of Tidewater Virginia. Clearly this was the will of the gods."[35]

Such is the one event in the life of Captain John Smith which is
known to everybody. The other things in his life don't matter—being
forced into slavery in the wars with the Turks, for instance, and escaping from a prison camp near the Don, after which he worked his
fugitive way through Russia, Poland, Hungary, Germany, France,
Spain, and Morocco—home to England. "Everyone who has heard of
Virginia has heard of Captain John Smith, usually in the company of
an Indian maiden named Pocahontas. In popular history, Virginia is
unthinkable without Captain Smith."[36]

We are not saying here that it is a popular error, a piece of nonsense, to believe in the Pocahontas story; but we are saying it is

nonsense to assume that anybody *knows* for a fact that (*a*) the story is true or that (*b*) the story is fiction.

Smith's first book (1608), *A True Relation,* does not mention Pocahontas. Neither does Edward Wingfield's *A Discourse of Virginia* (1608); nor do any of the other contemporary diarists. In fact, Pocahontas appears first on the pages of history when she comes to London in 1617, a Christian convert, the first Indian girl to visit the town. She is now the wife of John Rolfe. And she charms the English with her beauty, her dignity, her wit, and her intelligence—to the point where Queen Anne becomes her patroness and the whole court goes mad about her. She has soirées with the theologians and the dons and the scholars, who are overwhelmed by this representative of New World royalty.

Now, while all this is going on, a new edition of Smith's book comes out; and here, for the first time, the famous story is told of the little Indian princess and the famous soldier—with the obvious implication of the latter's deserved credit for her conversion.[37]

Philip Barbour answers these doubts (although he was writing two years *before* Paul Lewis) by saying that, since Smith's first account "is known to have been subjected to editing 'to make it suitable,' the absence of the rescue story means nothing" (*Three Worlds,* p. 483).

Lewis asks why Powhatan should have been so angry with Smith on this occasion, and demand the death penalty, when he had been outstandingly friendly on previous occasions? Barbour answers that "Smith did not correctly interpret what he saw and thought was going to happen to him," and that actually it is probable that Powhatan was putting him through initiation rites which would make him a member of the tribe, and not preparing to kill him at all.

And so, alas, we may never know the whole truth. But we will continue to swallow the whole story, you may depend upon that. After all, when the minnesingers have taken up the matter and when the poets talk about "Pocahontas' body, lovely as a poplar, sweet as a red haw in November,"[38] and so forth, you can put your money on the proposition that Pocahontas is here to stay.

THE MYTHS ABOUT GALILEO

It is well "known" that Galileo Galilei invented the telescope, was subjected to torture by the Inquisition for having asserted that the earth is not the center of the universe, and that he was finally forced to recant. But in the midst of his recantation, noticing that the chandelier above the heads of his inquisitors moved slightly, owing to the motion of the earth, exclaimed *"Eppur si muove"*—Nevertheless, it does move.

Galileo did not invent the telescope. It was invented, according to the best authorities, in 1608 by a Dutch optician Hans Lippershey. However, it was indeed Galileo who developed the instrument as a tool for studying the heavens. He made his own first telescope in 1609 and the next year improved it by constructing a refracting instrument with a magnifying power of 33 diameters. It was a tube with a convex object glass and a concave eyepiece.[39]

There is a nice point here: in March, 1610, Galileo published the *Nuncius siderius,* a Latin pamphlet whose title means "Message from the Stars." In it he announced the discovery of the telescope and spoke of "that universe that I enlarged a hundred and a thousand times from what the wise men of all past ages had thought."[40] Based on this statement, many scholars previously accredited Galileo with the *invention* of the telescope, and it is easy to see why. But Galileo is not saying *he* invented it. He *perfected* it.[40]

Second, Galileo was not tortured by the Inquisition or by anybody else, in the physical sense of the word. His torture was entirely a punishment of the mind, and his trial "was based on a judicial forgery" and on the most complicated intrigue within the hierarchy involving Jesuits and "an extremely capable outfit of 'hypocrites without Nature and without God,' as Micanzio calls them." He was attacked by Protestant interests as well as Catholic—although this is seldom reported.[41] In fact, some of the most irresponsible charges were made by Protestants, notably Mallet du Pan and Sir David Brewster.

Moreover, his forced recantation "is not at all the surrender and moral disgrace that self-appointed judges have made it out to be." He stood firm, even at the risk of the stake, on two major points involving his free will: he never admitted that he had deceived anyone deliberately; and he maintained that he had never deviated from Catholic orthodoxy. "His real statement then amounted to this: 'If the Vicar of Christ insists that I must not *affirm* what I happen to *know*, I have to obey. . . . Not even God can prevent my reason from seeing what it sees, but by His Vicar's explicit command I can withdraw my public adhesion from it to avoid scandal among the faithful.' "[42]

In short, according to Santillana, what Galileo was in fact saying was, "It's your lie and not mine which you force me to repeat." When he had fulfilled the technicality of a recantation, Galileo was allowed to go back to the little farm in Arcetri for the rest of his life, albeit under technical "house arrest."

There are two other myths about Galileo, familiar to students of general science: one, that he observed a lamp swinging on a long chain in the cathedral at Pisa, noticed that it made an arc to the left which was about equal to its arc to the right and thus, as the Britannica puts it, discovered the "isochronism of the pendulum." But Einbinder, in his survey of the errors in that encyclopedia, points out that Professor Lane Cooper of Cornell had written a biography of Galileo in 1935 exposing this myth and also the famous legend of Galileo's dropping weights from the Leaning Tower to prove that objects of different weights fall at the same velocity (which they do not). The corrections had not been made, he reports, in the 1958 edition of the Britannica. Galileo never mentioned either one of these discoveries in his own writings, and they were not even attributed to him until many years later. No contemporaries of Galileo mention either one.[43]

BATHTUB AND WATER CLOSET—MODERN INVENTIONS?

Not only are our "modern" bathrooms not new, they are not even improved much beyond the primitive,[44] and are not essentially any better than similar accommodations available a couple of thousand years before Christ. The ancient civilizations all around the Mediterranean Basin were, to all intents and purposes, as well served as we. In the houses of the well-to-do, that is. We outstrip them only in quantity, not in quality. One study of the subject points out that "In the ancient cities of the Indus Valley, flourishing from about 2500 to 1500 B.C., many houses had bathrooms and water-flushed latrines."[45] The waste went through drains in the streets. In Mesopotamia, according to Wright, there are some which date from 1500 B.C. and are still in working order, which is considerably more than the historians will be able to say of any plumbing now in use in American cities. We have already shown that there was more water available per person in fourth-century Rome than in twentieth-century London.

So there goes our much-touted symbol of opulence, our overvalued Bathtub Civilization. Some private houses in old Pompeii had as many as thirty outlets; and there were plenty of public comfort stations as well—Rome in A.D. 315 had 144 water-flushed public latrines.[46] Not to speak of enormous public baths (some of them six times the area of St. Paul's Cathedral in London) and hundreds of public fountains and cisterns.

It is amusing how bathing habits change from time to time. "The monk of 1350 enjoyed more orderly plumbing and had sweeter habits, than the Londoner of 1850,"[47] and a twentieth-century Englishman who had been educated under the established Spartan conditions at Oxford, complained that the institution had denied him the ordinary everyday sanitary conveniences which were familiar in Minoan Crete.

Of course we must remember that in some circles dirtiness was associated with holiness, as in the cases of the desert hermits who apparently *wanted* to suffer from lice and what not on behalf of their souls. Francis of Assisi abstained from the bath; St. Agnes died at the age of thirteen without ever having taken a bath; the tenth-century archbishop of Cologne, one Bruno, and Archbishop Adalbert of Bremen in the eleventh century, did not bathe; while "St. Catherine of Siena not only avoided washing, but practiced another and very costive form of self-denial."[48]

The Romans even had insulated hot-water cylinders; and Westminster Palace had both hot and cold taps in 1351. Louis XIV had cushions in *his* bathtub, but we find no record of any such softness in England, where King John took a bath about once every three weeks. His tub, like those of the monasteries, was a round wooden form in which the bather stood up. In fact, when the tubs were lengthened out more after the fashion of today's bathtubs, it was not to let the washer lie down but to fit in more people standing up—because most of these tubs were not connected with running water and somebody had to lug the hot water in buckets. Heating water was not accomplished by turning a switch, we must remember. One had to make the most of the hot water available. Six can live as cheaply as one.

Mixed bathing had its ins and outs. In the thirteenth to the fifteenth century, it was the custom for girls to serve the knights in the bath; and "through the Middle Ages the sexes bathed together, and not innocently," as contemporary fables indicate, indeed, in their cheerful, carefree way.[49] The Council of Trullanum as early as 692 forbade the sexes to bathe together and ecclesiastical authorities from the eighth century on did what they could to suppress the custom, "but never could control it."

Perhaps we are preparing today for a new era in which the daily bath will be discouraged again. Some pediatricians are proclaiming, much to the delight of the very young, that we are bathing too much, that soap is too strong, that a daily bath can be harmful, that we should wash only the parts that are dirty, and that "otherwise our skin should be left alone."[50] The 10-year-olds will be delighted.

MATRIARCHY IN SOCIAL ORGANIZATIONS?

In a society like that of the United States at the beginning of the last third of the twentieth century, where persons under 21 years of age have committed, within one calendar year, more than 4,600 *recorded* crimes of forcible rape[51] the obvious fact is that one can usually identify the mother of a child, but often not the father. This would of course be true for any society which permitted sexual promiscuity without sophisticated methods of birth control available. This comparative ease in spotting the mother led some anthropologists and sociologists in the old days into theorizing that early societies were probably matriarchal (Greek "mother" plus "to rule") so that property could descend to the offspring from the mother with some assurance that it was being kept in the family. Such scholars as Bachofen, McLennan, and Briffault were quite certain that early human societies were matriarchal, and the belief that this was indeed the case became widespread and was readily accepted as fact in many circles. Today such a view is regarded as erroneous.

There are no matriarchal societies in the world today, and it seems highly unlikely that there ever were. In fact, anthropologists today are ready to declare that they know of no human society within recorded history that was sexually promiscuous. This is not to say that there has not been sexual promiscuity, usually among the highest and lowest of the social classes within a society; but the *society* was not so. Thus the presupposition on which the theory was built is down, and the theory falls with it.

In real life, the argument about assigning the right child to the right family through the mother is without basis; because the father of the child in almost all nonliterate societies is the husband of the woman who bears it. Moreover, the theoreticians confused *descent* in the

female line—matriliny—with *government* by females—matriarchy.
The first is a very real phenomenon, the other a creation of the
imagination.

Many societies allow special prerogatives to women. Among the
Hopi Indians, for example, only the women own homes. Among the
Iroquois the women nominate the chief—but the women play no part
in the government. Among the natives of French Equatorial Africa, a
wife is a valuable commodity and must be paid for; and if the bride
comes howling back to mother complaining that she has been cruelly
treated, she is accepted back into the home tribe and the lonely husband cannot claim back his payment but has to start all over again.
And so forth. But special privilege does not make a matriarchate.

DID VOLTAIRE REALLY SAY IT?

A beautifully turned remark tends to be repeated by people who
like beautifully turned remarks; but one is under the compulsion to
attribute such comments to someone important, otherwise the cogency
of the beautifully turned remark might be lost on people. This somewhat circular process is responsible for some of the least likely statements in our historical accounts, like the one on the stone at Lexington
Green, where Captain John Parker of the Minutemen is quoted as
having said, "Stand your ground. Don't fire unless fired upon; but if
they mean to have a war, let it begin here!" He must have shouted
some sort of encouragement to his men as they straggled up to the
muster on that pre-dawn scene of April 19; but at that moment and
in that place, it seems fairly certain, nobody—British or American—was
thinking in terms of starting a war. However, it's a fine statement; and
there it stands, carved in stone, awaiting the sounding of the final
trumpet.

In the same tradition, the remark, "I disapprove of what you say,
but I will defend to the death your right to say it," which has been
assigned to Voltaire, is a splendid statement. Bartlett in giving the
citation, points out that it is taken from a letter to Madame du Deffand
appearing in *Voltaire in His Letters* by S. G. Tallentyre, 1919. In a
second footnote is given the Will Durant variation ("I do not agree
with a word that you say, but—" etc.). Then the editor explains more
fully, "This quotation is not found *verbatim* in Voltaire's works. It
seems to originate in S. G. Tallentyre (E. Beatrice Hall): *The Friends
of Voltaire* (1907), where she employed it as a paraphrase of Voltaire's

words in the *Essay on Tolerance*: 'Think for yourselves and let others enjoy the privilege to do so too.' The editors are under obligation to Mr. Harry Weinberger for establishing this point."[52]

Bartlett is correct. *The Friends of Voltaire* was published in London in 1907 and the quote is found on page 199. Voltaire's original admonition was a great piece of advice; but it cannot compare in éclat with the translation or paraphrase which E. Beatrice gave it. Her rewrite may possibly constitute poetic license at its apogee; but it certainly gives us a beautifully turned remark, even if Voltaire never said it. Incidentally, Mme. du Deffand did pretty well, too. She said, "Voltaire has invented history."

This particular misquotation is given additional illumination in a book published in 1967. It is *Quotemanship* by Paul F. Boller, Jr., containing a chapter entitled "Spurious Quotes," in which Mr. Boller explains that Miss Evelyn Beatrice Hall (pen name, S. G. Tallentyre) was questioned about the Voltaire quote in 1935, and said at that time: "I did not intend to imply that Voltaire used these words verbatim, and should be much surprised if they are found in any of his works."[53]

As Mr. Boller reconstructs events, the encyclopedist Claude Adrien Helvétius published his book *De L'Esprit* in 1758. Here he set forth the views which disturbed the Church and others so deeply: that self-interest is the only true motivator and that good and evil are inventions. "The book was condemned by the Parliament of Paris, attacked by the Pope, censured by the Sorbonne, publicly burned by the hangman." To all of which Voltaire exclaimed, "What a fuss about an omelette." And the conclusion of Miss Hall's account said: " 'I disapprove of what you say, but I will defend to the death your right to say it' was his attitude now." In short, Miss Hall herself didn't mean Voltaire said or wrote those words; she simply reported that those words reflected his attitude. We do this constantly as in the sentence, "The Colonists said, 'If you tax us without giving us representation in the government, we will fight it.' " Perfectly acceptable rhetorical usage. Anyhow, it's sort of a relief to see the whole thing explained.

Vicisti, Galilaee!

Learned errors get passed around among the academicians and the intelligentsia for a time, but sooner or later they tend to seep down and become folk errors. The famous last words of Julian the Apostate, "Thou hast conquered, Galilean!" must be counted among such improbabilities, although it cannot be proved absolutely at this point that it *is* an error to attribute these words to him on his death bed. What we do know is that the early historians of the Christian Church were delighted to keep in circulation the story that when Julian left the safety of Antioch to join in the battle against the Persians, he received a spear thrust which proved to be lethal on June 25, A.D. 363. He had been spending the winter in the city writing a literary polemic against Christianity, criticizing the anthropomorphic elements of the Old Testament, objecting to Christianity as a mere novelty, and arbitrarily denying the divinity of Jesus. The spear wound stopped him from completing the work; he was cut down just at the moment of a military victory also in the battle against the Persians. Thus, when he lay on his bed in the camp and his physicians told him that he could not live, he is reputed to have "caught some of the blood from his wound in the uninjured hand, and, casting it towards heaven, to have exclaimed, 'Thou hast conquered, Galilean!' "[54]

The trouble is that Ammianus was an on-the-spot witness and a credible reporter, and *he* mentions no such words or gesture, but he does describe the long night by the bedside where Julian lay dying, and he says the warrior-author received the information about approaching death calmly and even thanked the gods for taking him early in life—a sign that they were fond of him. Apparently he talked in this vein to his friends all night, and then died at dawn. There was no "death bed" statement.[55]

Swinburne, as is well known, did for Julian what Longfellow did for Revere, in the mournful quatrain from *The Last Oracle*, where the gallant captain bows his hopeless head,

> And, dying, *Thou hast conquered*, he said
> *Galilean*, he said it and died. . . .

More than that: the situation captivated Swinburne, apparently; in the *Hymn to Proserpine* he keens,

> Thou hast conquered, O pale Galilean;
> The world has grown grey from thy breath. . . .

However, we must sternly set our lips and state the judgment that it makes better poetry than fact—which doesn't mean we cannot *enjoy* the poetry.

7

❦

Fallibilities of the Law

Law Must Be Consistent?

Perhaps in no country more than the United States is the myth more popular that (*a*) the law means what it says but (*b*) there is no need to take laws too seriously because legislators often propose bills for no other reason than to attain popularity and votes, and (*c*) the only real crime is in getting caught *flagrante delicto*, while the sin is flaming. The Prohibition era in particular was rich with illustrations: the law said spirituous liquors were not to be manufactured, transported, nor sold, but judges and clergymen had their bootleggers. Many a small town announces a traffic law that in the congested area ahead the speed limit is 20 miles per hour; but if anybody really obeyed that law, the cars would back up behind him and other drivers would yell, "Get a horse!" Until May 4, 1966, it was illegal in Massachusetts (alone among the fifty states) for anyone to sell, distribute, or advertise a contraceptive, and it was generally understood that Catholic pressure stood behind the prohibition. Yet population figures made it perfectly plain that citizens of the state, and Catholics among them, were practicing birth control. Indeed the National Council of the Churches of Christ in America had endorsed birth control as long ago as March 20, 1931,[1] and it was a Catholic, Dr. John Rock, who had helped develop Enovid, the first commercial oral contraceptive.[2]

In short, a person is regarded, consistently with the American myth, as a law-abiding person if he goes his own way quietly stretching the law a little here and there—as long as he doesn't get caught.

Rarely, however, do we find the law itself supporting a deliberate infraction of the local corpus juris. That would be almost too much to expect—except, perhaps, in Mississippi. And it was in the Magnolia State indeed that the legislature passed a law in 1964 requiring that illegal (i.e., bootleg) liquor must carry a state tax stamp. Which means that Mississippi has two kinds of illegal liquor: unlawful illegal booze and acceptable illegal liquor. Men of the Mississippi Tax Commission "pay no attention to the fact that the State still has prohibition" as long as the container has the proper stamp affixed, the Associated Press reported.

A not dissimilar instance was observed a couple of years later in Washington, D.C., that happy hunting ground for the curiosity enthusiast, when the United States Tax Court ruled that "an embezzler must pay income tax on the funds he embezzled and that his wife, in the case of a joint return, is also liable for the tax." The specific case at issue was that of Mr. and Mrs. Richard M. Horn of Birmingham, Alabama. In twenty years as treasurer of a credit union he managed to get away with $51,000. When he was indicted he pleaded guilty. The judgment finally rendered against him came to something over $61,000; and in addition, the court ruled that he owed more than $7,000 in taxes for the years in which the funds were embezzled. So when you're making out your forms this year, be sure to declare *everything*, understand?

No Conviction for Murder Unless Dead Body Is Produced?

In the popular mind it is widely believed that there cannot be a conviction for murder unless the body of the murdered person can be produced. Thus in the detective stories we see the creative imagination grappling with the problem of disposing of the body. Once get *that* out of the way, and your murderer is as safe as your king in his castle. All kinds of gruesome and inventive means have been employed—right up to cannibalism as in a short story entitled "Two Bottles of Relish," which some readers may remember with a shudder. And nine chances out of ten, the popular mind considers the murdered man "the corpus delicti."

Let's take these one at a time. It is *not* necessary to produce any part of the body of the murdered person to secure a conviction of murder. What must be produced is evidence which shows beyond a reasonable doubt that the death was caused by the prisoner with malice aforethought.

And "the corpus delicti" is not the body of the murdered person at all. *Corpus delicti* means literally "the body of the *crime*," not the body of the *victim*. As Roy Copperud puts it, "It is the evidence necessary to establish that a crime—not necessarily murder—has been committed."[3]

IF A HANGED MAN REVIVES, HE GOES FREE?

Perhaps to remove part of the horror—and the guilt—of terminating the life of a fellow man, the notion survives that if by some chance the hanged man lives after the trap doors have been sprung, he cannot again be forced to mount the platform. He has paid his debt with the single experience. That the rope broke or that a physician was able to resuscitate him after he had dangled for a required period of time— these were 100-to-1 chances, not of his doing, and he should go free. It is simply not sporting to hang him all over again.

But alas for romance, there is no truth in the popular belief. It is not the prisoner who is "executed" but the sentence of the court; and the sentence of the court is "hanged by the neck until you are dead." The condition of death is an inseparable part of the sentence that is being executed. We hear of cases of frontier justice in which a rope snaps and the prisoner is hailed as something of a hero for having survived, the drinks being on the house as one and all repair to the nearby saloon; but one fears that this is a reflection of western romance. It certainly is not law. In law the malefactor would inevitably be strung up again and the sentence of the court carried out as ordered.

Even so, tales of escape from the noose continue to be heard, one of the most famous being that of the Rev. Dr. Dodd, the eighteenth-century forger, whose expressions of piety and repentance aroused immense public feelings of pity and horror so that a plan was formed to rush him to a waiting doctor at the expiration of the legal minimum of suspension. But the crowd witnessing the event was so thick the friends couldn't carry the body through in time. This is close to being hoist by one's own petar—the crowd was in *sympathy* with the hanged man and wanted to see him rescued. Dr. Dodd's popularity was the death of him.

And, incidentally, if anybody wants to argue about that "petar" back there, we can only urge caution. It was good enough for Shakespeare in his most famous play.

A WILL MUST BE NOTARIZED TO BE LEGAL?

Not everybody acts in time to get his will duly dictated, transcribed, bound in a folder with a blue back, and signed by witnesses in the presence of a notary public. Nor is it necessary to do so, despite the folklore to the contrary. A perfectly valid will can be scribbled on a scrap of paper with neither lawyer nor notary within miles; and if the signature is witnessed by two persons, the will holds. Even the two witnesses are not always necessary, but they improve the chances.

THE TEN COMMANDMENTS ARE THE BASIS OF ALL LAW?

To the person whose cultural resources are limited to the Bible and whose literary world goes no further than that, it may appear that the Ten Commandments are the basis of all the law he is conscious of; and since there are still large numbers of such people, this popular error remains widely current. With the belief goes a dark and bloody tale, for one recalls that when Moses came down from the mountain he found that Aaron had made a golden calf at the behest of the people; and he broke the tablets on which the Lord had written with his own hand and cried out against that stiffnecked generation. That night he and the sons of Levi murdered three thousand men in the camp by way of correction, reminder, and retribution. After which Moses went into the mountain again for forty days and nights during which he neither ate nor drank, and the Lord gave him "the words of the covenant, the ten commandments."[4]

Of the ten, the command to observe the Sabbath is law in some American and British localities; the only other four remotely associated with American or English law are those against murder, adultery, theft, and perjury. The final commandment forbids men to covet. Since 1611 (date of the King James Version) that word has ordinarily meant "to desire culpably; to want what is another's," although it can be used to mean a passionate yearning. A good part of our economic structure appears to be based upon our evasion of *that* law.

But now that the subject is on the table, we might remind ourselves that the basis of contemporary law is richer and wider than one culture: there was Hammurabi and his Code in Babylon; Manu in India; Moses in Palestine; Solon and Lycurgus in the classical era; Roman Law and the Law of the Twelve Tables leading up to Justinian's *Corpus Juris Civilis* and the Canon Law—all influential in our contemporary legal structure.

You Can't Hang a Man on Circumstantial Evidence?

It is widely believed that a man cannot legally be put to death on what is called "circumstantial evidence." Often this is intended to imply that a man can't be convicted and sentenced to death unless a reasonable motive for the crime has been established—this is particularly true in the crime fiction field.

Conversely, one is tempted to ask, "What sort of evidence is there *except* 'circumstantial' evidence?" Do we have anything but circumstantial evidence to convince us that the earth moves around the sun or that the world is not flat and carried on the back of a great turtle? Of course there are those cheerfully mystical souls who are in direct contact with Infinity and hear Voices or receive Revelations direct from the Throne—but that kind of evidence relates more to the mental condition of the witness than to the facts we seek to establish, perhaps.

The person who holds that circumstantial evidence is not enough is very likely to have a denigrating understanding of "circumstantial"—he thinks, perhaps, it means "incidental but not essential," and indeed this is one of the current usages listed in Webster III. This authority, however, fortunately has a separate entry on *circumstantial evidence*:

Evidence that tends to prove a fact in issue by proving other events or circumstances which according to the common experience of mankind are usu. or always attended by the fact in issue and that therefore affords a basis for a reasonable inference by the jury or court of the occurrence of the fact in issue.

Here the key phrase is "reasonable inference." If this is the same as "beyond reasonable doubt," one can understand why history records that most executions have indeed been based upon pure circumstantial evidence. In fact in today's legal usage a person could not be condemned to death *without* circumstantial evidence. A full and willing confession, for example, would not be enough. Positive identification of the accused by an eyewitness would not be enough: too many positive identifications by eyewitnesses have proved incorrect; in fact, the testimony of eyewitnesses is notoriously colored by all kinds of emotional drives, as dozens of classes in law and psychology have seen demonstrated.

In short, circumstantial evidence should not be viewed as a pejorative characterization. We can safely rely on it as long as it appears in abundance, not in the form of a single condition but as a total complex. Besides, we are forced to admit with a shrug that we have nothing else.

You Can Be Sued for Libel Even if You Speak the Truth?

The nonsense in this case is not that you are not liable to be charged with libel and sued therefor, but that no suit for libel can be won against you if you can prove that you spoke the truth. In other words, the happy routine of your life can be interrupted and you can be forced to appear in court at such time or times as are deemed necessary; but to do so would be nonsensical because no court will punish you if you can prove the truth of your libel.

"There is but one complete, entire defense to every libel. That is the truth of the libelous accusation . . . the truth of the accusation is a complete bar to the action; an absolute, unqualified; entire defense."[5]

By way of *pourboire* in the case of *libel* we have a fascinating bit of detective work to report. Probably you never saw the word *bast*. One of us, at any rate, never did before this. It means the fiber between the wood and the outer bark of a tree; and before the use of papyrus, men made a sort of crude paper from it. The Latin word for *bast* is *liber*, from Old Latin *leber*; so *liber* comes to mean "that on which something can be written" and then "paper" and thus "book." The diminutive "little book" or "memorandum," etc., was *libelle* in Old French, and they used it to mean a legal document; and then in Middle French we find *libelle diffamatoire*, which quickly brings us to our own word *libel*. It is cognate with *leaf*.[6] Ho-hum. Either you enjoy etymologies or you think they're silly.

SEVEN YEARS OF SILENT ABSENCE MAKES YOU LEGALLY DEAD?

Most of us have read stories in which an important support of the plot is hinged on a remarriage or an inheritance which depends upon some absent person's being dead—and the idea that his death may be legally assumed if he has been totally out of contact for seven years. Seven, of course, is a magic number in many contexts.

Unhappily for the narrators of such tales, the presumed death *because* of a seven-year silence would not be enough to satisfy a court of law, especially if the benefits accruing happened to be very large and important. Any person asserting that a death has occurred on the basis of this presumption would have the burden of providing factual evidence enough to make the court accept the presumption.[7]

That a search and inquiry had been made after an absence of seven years would have to be shown. The mere absence, even for more years than seven, unless supported by what the lawyers call "probative evidence," is not enough to establish a presumption of death.[8]

For remarriage—at least in New York State (state laws are scandalously inconsistent in this area)—a person must allege that the spouse has been absent for five consecutive years without being known to be alive to the petitioner during that time; that the petitioner believes the spouse to be dead; and that a diligent search has been made seeking for evidence to show that the husband or wife was dead, without success. Then the petition has to be published for a period of weeks in a newspaper. After that, there is a court hearing and proof of publication of the petition is presented and then, if the court is satisfied, it may make an interlocutory order dissolving the marriage. That becomes final only after three months. After that the person would be free to remarry. We take our monogamy seriously in the United States: while it lasts.

8

❦

Literary and Language Legends

The accuracy with which myth, fable, tradition, doctrine, and even biography and history have been passed along without a written record from generation to generation is a matter few people have examined; when a serious investigation of early manuscripts is undertaken, scholars are amazed at the purity with which a narrative is preserved under the largely verbal transmission which preceded the art of printing prior to the fifteenth century. In the Christian tradition the various manuscripts narrating the events in the life of Jesus, the acts of the apostles, the lives of the saints, show a quite wonderful uniformity; and so it is with many epics from Homer to *Beowulf* and the *Song of Roland*. Clearly there were artists in the old days who could repeat a story, evening after evening beside the great hearth, and hardly miss a syllable, as they sang or chanted the magnificent tales. All of which preceded the art of literary criticism. . . .

Undoubtedly there were many follies and discrepancies in the ancient legends—as there are in the printed versions of the Old Testament and the New. But not until the invention of movable type and the wide use of paper did the world really get a chance to examine them. Now they are part of our heritage, and literary criticism has become a specialty in its own right. It is no derogation of a legend to point out its innocent follies, and we do so lovingly, with no intention of detracting from the great tales.

GOOD-BY, PLEASE . . .

Rudyard Kipling, whose imagination was capable of the widest range of subject matter, gave his thought at one point to a life of the fighting Danes, the famous marauders of the sea who would make a quick, unannounced invasion of an unprotected coast, burn and slaughter, and beat out to sea again with captive women and anything else worth lugging away. The wild, rugged life came alive in his mind and he composed "The Harp Song of the Dane Women," written in a style highly reminiscent of the Norse sagas, with the customary caesura in the middle of each line. Sang he:

> What is a woman, that you forsake her,
> And the hearth-fire, and the home-acre,
> To go with the old, grey widow-maker?"

The widow-maker, of course, was the sea. The poem is a lament by the women because spring has come again, the ice is broken up, and the men are repairing their ships and gear, preparing for the wild and bloody days ahead. It's a great old poem.

But let's see, now. How much fun was it, truthfully, in a typical Danish household—even in a noble household—during the long, cold winter days—and nights? With the menfolk underfoot all the time, sharpening up their damned old battle-axes, getting oiled up and boasting about how big and strong they were and what fun they were going to have with the native girls when they sailed up the Rhine. . . . Every night they stalked off to the Long House to make wassail with their Fearless Leader, and half the time most of them never came home until sometime next day, when they'd show up bleary-eyed and hardly able to walk. Remember, the days were short and the winters were long, and there was no central heating, and the fireplace smoked. After four or five months of this domestic bliss one might imagine the Dane women plucking at the old harp with a somewhat more realistic tune, to this effect, "So long, fellahs; have a good summer and don't take any wooden kronen. Come on, girls, let's get a good rest."

PAULDRON, BREASTPLATE, AND GREAVES

In the days when Lancelot and the rest of the lads went about on their sturdy Percherons (and it required a Percheron to hold one of them up—it has been estimated that a knight in full armor might weigh 24 stone, which is 336 pounds) romance was in the land, true love was paramount among the values, and physical comfort was at a minimum. But we think of the Table Round, of gay banners flying, and of dragons losing their heads to the unconquerable swords of the invincible heroes, and we speak lyrically of the era when knighthood was in flower. This romantic mood reaches some sort of an apogee with Tennyson's immortal line:

> "Tirra lirra" by the river
> Sang Sir Lancelot.

BETWEEN THE FOUR OF US?

Many persons who aspire to purity in speech and writing will tell you soberly that the proper preposition to use in referring to the relationship existing between more than two things is *among* and that *between* is allowable in formal usage only where there are two things and no more. This widespread tenet is clung to with great tenacity by many people who in most of their ways are pleasant enough company and tolerant in their thinking, but who will *not* budge from this passionate belief, and become charging elephants driven by wildfire. They are wrong, as it happens.

The law and the prophets on this subject are the Oxford English Dictionary and Fowler's *Modern English Usage*, for the British; and Merriam Webster's Third Edition for the American. The OED says that from the earliest appearance of the word, *between* has been in all senses "extended to more than two." Fowler calls it a superstition that the word "can be used only of the relationship between two things." Webster gives several examples of good American usage, citing F. A. Swinnerton ("There is no continuity of mood between the three books"), *Time* magazine, J. B. Carroll, and others. Copperud says, "There is a misguided though prevalent idea that *between* cannot be correctly used with more than two,[1] and the great Bernstein adds, "To speak of a treaty *between* nine powers would be completely proper and exact."[2] The Evanses agree.[3]

CINDERELLA HAD GLASS SLIPPERS?

It is quite possible that one could canvass the graduates of every kindergarten in America and not find one person who would question the fact that when Cinderella's godmother provided her with magic slippers, they were made of glass. Glass slippers go with Cinderella as naturally as ham goes with eggs: something in the logic of the universe appears to ordain that one is "right" for the other. Besides, we never heard anything *else*.

In this book we set out to expose certain popular errors, but we had no idea that the investigations would lead us to anything as drastic as this, and we are a little timid about being considered old spoilsports and bitter disillusionists. But the fact is there is a very serious doubt about that glass. Very serious. The whole thing may be just a trick of the language. The story of Cinderella, of course, is the property of all children everywhere in all languages; and those slippers are glass only in French language versions and those influenced by the French. Indeed, as Robert G. Davis points out, "it is only in French that this error could have occurred."[4] He cites in detail the exhaustive study by Marian Roalfe Cox of 345 variants of the Cinderella story, and also Paul Robert's *Dictionnaire*.

In a word, it is believed by many learned authorities that those slippers in the earliest—and verbal—tradition were "pantoufles en vair" meaning slippers of gray and white squirrel; or perhaps "en menu vair," ermine (*little* squirrel)—whence our *miniver*. But the word *vair*, familiar in heraldry, where the fur is represented by rows of small bells, one row upright and the next turned down, went out of use about the fourteenth century, and by the time Charles Perrault published his eight stories comprising one of the earliest "Mother Goose" collections (1697) *vair* was obsolete; and Perrault therefore wrote *verre*, glass.

Thus the Cinderwench (as the wicked stepsisters called her, because she huddled in the chimney corner with the ashes) was presented by her fairy godmother with glass slippers; and of course, being magic, they could be adapted to no feet but those of Cendrillon herself.

Seen from the point of view of a scholar who has become familiar with all, or certainly nearly all, the versions of Cinderella in the world, the glass slipper gets very few votes (Scotland, the Netherlands, Chile, Catalonia, France, and England). Elsewhere the slippers are of gold, of silver, satin, pearl-embroidered, spangled with jewels, and, as we have seen, white ermine.[5]

But in English it's going to remain glass. Wait and see.

Very familiar indeed is the folk belief that some bright new idea is a brilliant conception but cannot be brought to a practical application. "It's all right in theory, but it won't work in practice." That is the saying and, so far as we have been able to determine, it has seldom been questioned before as a statement of fact. It should have been, of course, because it must be obvious that a thing cannot possibly be "right" in theory if it is "wrong" in practice.

During the sugar shortage at the time of World War I, an inventive chemistry student at the old Roxbury Latin School ("the oldest endowed school in the United States" and supposedly founded by the Apostle Eliot, translator of the Indian Bible) suggested manufacturing sugar by hanging an apparatus on the exhaust pipe of the Model T and thus making sugar out of the carbon, hydrogen, and oxygen present. He figured this would at least create monosaccharides in some such simple form as glucose; and by refining the apparatus a little further, make shift to remove one molecule of water from two monosaccharides in union and thus produce such disaccharides as lactose and sucrose. He wrote an enthusiastic paper on the subject, and everybody cheered and said it was a marvelous idea *in theory,* but that it could never be made to work *in practice.* They managed to convince the student, and he dropped the matter, with what loss to civilization one will probably never know. We've just had to get our carbohydrates in other places.

"MISCEGENATION" IS A BAD WORD?

Although *miscegenation* is a very recent addition to the language (it is barely a hundred years old, having been used in print for the first time in 1864), it is loaded with pejorative sentiments and bowed down with fierce prejudices. In its brief century it has gathered to itself—or had attached to it by others, to be more accurate—all kinds of dark, dismal, and bloody associations. What kind of nonsense is this? Here is a substantive given the noun ending "-ation," a prefix which is the past participle of a Greek and Sanskrit word meaning "to mix," and combined with *genus,* race. One must admit such artful selection of ingredients brought together with such euphonious éclat to make a quite unambiguous and very descriptive term. It's as good as "telephone," from *tele,* distant, and *phonus,* sound. Beautiful! The applause should bring down the house: it was a stirring performance.

But from the outset the neologism was doomed. The word was dressed in such costumes that it was never allowed to stand alone, by its own merits, as a lovely piece of objective identification. It always had to wear the mask of lust, of terror, of sexual license, of threat to the great white master. Thus we find the Oxford English Dictionary giving the meaning, "*Esp*. the sexual union of whites with negroes," and Webster III, "*Esp:* marriage *or cohabitation* [italics supplied] between a white person and a member of another race." And the lexicographer John Opdycke, heads his paragraph on the subject, " 'Mixed marriage is one thing,' said the preacher; 'miscegenation is quite another.' "[6]

The writer who coined the word had, if we may adopt a fairly lofty attitude, an impure motive. David Goodman Croly, an editor on the New York *World*, was the creator of *miscegenation*. With one of the staff writers, George Wakeman, he produced a pamphlet which he copyrighted in 1863 and published in 1864, anonymously, which had the political intention of ascribing to the Republicans and the anti-slavery interests the basic desire to mingle the blood of white and black; and to argue that the Republicans were looking upon this objective as "indispensable to a progressive humanity." They had to believe this, the pamphlet said; their own logic required it. Since they believed that all men were "children of the common father," and therefore equal—a doctrine too difficult for most people to accept in this country —it followed that they must have in mind the mixture of the races. "This involves," the pamphlet said, "what is vulgarly known as amalgamation, and those who dread that name, and the thought and fact it implies, are warned against reading these pages."[7]

Thus the pamphlet, *Miscegenation*, was intended from the first as a campaign document in the presidential free-for-all of 1864. Its intent was satirical: to produce a phony "learned" word to replace *amalgamation*—something that might be sneered at, something to ridicule the objectives of the Republicans and to ridicule the Emancipation Proclamation which Lincoln had published a few months before. We must not forget how high the feelings had risen at this juncture, with the Civil War still in progress, and how bitter the differences were between brother and brother. The satire behind the pamphlet was equally bitter; the calling of Christians to the practice of true equality through miscegenation was chokingly vitriolic. The blood was high. And the word was apt—dreadfully apt.

We have evidence that it worked. On March 18, 1864, the Chicago *Tribune* commented: "Miscegenation. Such is the newly invented term to express the mingling of races generally, and specially the mingling of the white and black races on the continent as a consequence of the freedom of the latter."[8]

An English philologist explaining the American language to his people seven years later (1871) used this example to clarify "miscegenationist": "A miscegenationist named Williams was tarred and feathered."[9]

In 1885 it was clear that the word had settled in as a pejorative when the *Century Magazine* for September noted that antislave citizens are beginning to be called "negrophiles, negro worshipers and miscegenationists."[10]

Some words degenerate ("hussy" was once just a quickie for "housewife") as Greenough and Kittredge so eloquently demonstrated in their classic *Words and Their Ways in English Speech*, published in the first year of this century and still one of the most readable books available.[11] But *miscegenation* was born in the slums, grew up in the slums, and, not chancing to have the extraordinary good luck of Eliza Doolittle, remained slum-bound. One reason may be, as has been suggested, that beginning with a prefix that sounds like the "mis-" which precedes so many words to give them a "wrongly" twist (misplaced, wrongly placed; mis-named, wrongly named, etc.), miscegenation takes on the shadings of error or wrong behavior.[12]

LANGUAGE AND LUNACY

Some of the merriest lunacies on record originate among the highly literate, the well-read cognoscenti who have managed to attain eminence among the learned and therefore have no hesitation in using that reputation to support judgments in fields where they are complete strangers. Lord knows why they do it; and Lord knows they do it. Perhaps they are encouraged by the assurance that nobody will have the temerity to challenge one so highly regarded. And perhaps they're right about that.

Samuel Johnson, for instance, became The "Great Cham" in his own day, and pronounced on all sorts of things which cause the wrinkles of laughter to appear upon the face of the judicious of a later day; but his average was much too high for us to adopt a supercilious attitude—after all, he exposed himself most recklessly with that dictionary. A man must speak out of his own milieu, and much of what the good Doctor reported was simply the widely accepted nonsense of his time. Besides, he could be charming. For example, he defines *puberty* as "the time of life in which the two sexes begin first to be acquainted," and then proceeds to cite Bacon on the mechanism of voice change in the male:

The cause of changing the voice at the years of *puberty* seemeth to be, for that when much of the moisture of the body, which did before irrigate the parts, is drawn down to the spermatical vessels, it leaveth the body more hot than it was, whence cometh the dilation of the pipes.[13]

It was Johnson also who reported that *sirloin* derived from a loin of beef "which one of our kings knighted in a fit of good humor," and he cites Addison about a gentleman who was "not able to touch a *sir*-loin when it was served up." Eric Partridge, however, shows that the word derives from Middle French *surloigne*, with the literal meaning of "overloin," the section of the animal from which the cut was made.[14] But if you're going to mix it up with a man like Partridge, you should come prepared for many sudden and unexpected curtain raisings; for instance, *loin* and *sirloin* are associated etymologically with *lumber* and *lumbago*; with *numbles* and *umbles* (from which we have the folk etymology *humble*, as in "eating humble pie"), and *sir* comes from *senex* (Latin, *old*) which originates a whole group of words including *senior, monsieur, senator,* and even *surly*. And then along comes the Oxford English Dictionary with the information that *humbles* means "the inwards of a deer" and dates to 1460, whereas "humble pie" had to wait until 1830 to enter the literature. So we start off with a harmless jest by Johnson about a cut of beef and end up eating gut stew and acting submissive. Nothing is simple. Even the word *pie*, which goes back to *pica*, magpie, later shortened to pie; magpies were used in dishes covered with pastry crust, as were also, later, meat and fish. Such a dish has miscellaneous contents, however, so that the association with the printers' *pie*, meaning type in confusion, is an obvious possibility. When one considers that the common, ordinary culinary *pie* is a member of the *pick* family of words and therefore related to such words as *pique, piquant, picnic, picric,* and *pickle* and also with the proper name *Margaret* through the French diminutive *Margot*, which gives the English nickname *Maggot*, shortened to *Mag*, which was commonly in use to identify the magpie (although "the true base" of the name is the Latin *margarita, pearl*)—when all these things are tossed into the salad together, one can see what a complicated business it is to use the sober, homely, folk expression, "to eat humble pie," and what a long journey we have made from old Sam Johnson's knighting of the steak.

That there is much nonsense connected with language makes the study no less fascinating, however. Though this be madness, yet there's method in't. And as Bertrand Russell said in that charming little collection of essays *In Praise of Idleness*, there is much pleasure to be gained from "useless" knowledge. As an example he cited his own pleasure in preparing to eat an apricot: he was aware that the fruit had been developed in China during the Han dynasty long ago and that it had worked its way into the Roman Empire, where it was named, to all intents and purposes, "the precocious one," because it grew so fast. He said the prefix "a" was just a mistake. And sure enough, even the desk dictionaries show that *apricot* comes from *prae*, beforehand, and *coquere*, to cook. Same as precocious.

9

The Mythical World of Nature

Everybody knows—that is to say, it is a common error of the folk, supported by generations of verbal and written depositions of witnesses—that you can tell the age of a tree by counting its rings; and that you can tell which years had lots of rain (because the growth ring is wider in rainy years); and that a tree grows faster in warm, sunny weather than it does on cool, cloudy days.

Every one of the above assertions is inaccurate, as a matter of fact. This was established by Dr. Harold C. Fritts, associate professor of the Tree-Ring Research Laboratory at the University of Arizona, whose researches, reported in March, 1966, were based largely on his own investigations made over a three-year period in Arizona and Colorado.[1]

It is true that ring counting is probably the most accurate way of dating a tree; but in a season when moisture is scarce and the temperature exceedingly unfavorable, transpiration may be so rapid that a tree uses all its food reserves just staying alive, and may not form any growth ring at all. Ponderosas found by Dr. Fritts near Flagstaff had gone as long as three successive years without making the ghost of a ring. But this is very unusual; and ring counting is better than Carbon 14 dating, according to Dr. Fritts; the carbon method is accurate only for 1,500 years back and it can be as much as 60 years off in dating wood 4,000 years old.

As for growth: this year's rainfall will not be reflected in the development of the tree this year, but *next* year. So a thick ring shows that the year before that ring was grown was a relatively wet one. And trees such as pines and firs—the conifers—grow most actively on cool, cloudy days. Photosynthesis can almost come to a halt in a warm, dry atmosphere.

Incidentally, the redwoods are not the oldest trees: the late Dr. Edmund Schulmann, also of the Arizona Tree-Ring Research Laboratory, proved in 1956 that some of the bristlecone pines, surviving at elevations up to 12,000 feet in eastern California's mountains, were 4,360 years old—which makes them, it is claimed, the oldest living things on earth.

QUICKSAND: IT SUCKS YOU UNDER?

As every veteran of *Lorna Doone* knows, any living thing that steps into quicksand is gradually sucked beneath the surface to a horrible death. And a cold and clammy finish it is in the foul slime. Even the gigantic John Ridd, we remember with a shudder, was not able with all his enormous strength to pull the wretched outlaw, Carver Doone, from the jaws of death. One step and you're a goner.

Actually, no. The alleged sucking action of quicksand is totally imaginary, compounded of man's fears of mysterious dark pools and murky fens and the evil of darkness. All the folklores have this symbolism in one form or another, from the misty swamps whence Grendel emerged upon bewildered travelers to the frightful Maelstrom which sucked ships down into the sea.

Quicksand, of course, simply means sand that is alive. The word "quick" was attached to other inanimate things in the fifteenth century —a quick fence, for instance, was a hedge constructed out of living plants, such as hawthorn. In Psalm 124:3 we read, "they had swallowed us up quick," which is corrected in the Revised Standard Version to the more comprehensible "they would have swallowed us up alive." The speech habit persists: one has seen in the subways of large cities, "Danger: Third Rail Alive."

The composition of quicksand is a loose mixture of sand and water; it supports the human body about twice as easily as water, and a person who has stumbled in will not sink much farther than his armpits if he will remember not to thrash around and wriggle himself into a deeper burial. In reality, John Ridd should have been able to pull the villain out, since Ridd was standing on firm ground. But the trouble is that an animal or a man who suddenly finds himself caught in quicksand is liable to act hysterically, to beat about frantically in an effort to free himself quickly. Such action allows the body to work its way into the muck beyond the reach of any help.[2]

WEATHER PROPORTIONATELY COLDER AS YOU TRAVEL NORTH?

It would be convenient if our world were simple and followed certain basic, understandable rules, such as we might wish to set up for it—like the rule that it shall cool off in direct proportion to one's distance north from the equator. But there are ocean currents, mountains, prevailing winds, and other things that influence the climate, and every one of these other factors has to be taken into account. What a pity.

Thus we must record as a part of folk nonsense the belief that the weather is colder proportionately to the distance north. There are palm trees in Cornwall. At Fort Yukon the temperature reaches above 90 degrees in the shade sometime every summer. The mean January temperature at Reykjavik over a recent decade has been about the same as that of Milan. Mt. Kenia, about seven miles from the equator in Africa, is capped with a glacier. Montreal and Chicago get more snow than do the Canadian arctic islands. Stefansson stated that there are places in Montana where it gets colder, by as much as 10 degrees, than it ever does at the North Pole.[3]

IN THE OLD DAYS WINTERS WERE COLDER THAN NOW?

Central heating and apartment-house living, both of which provide comfortable shirt-sleeve warmth in every room occupied, tend to make us forget that a hundred years ago houses depended for their heat entirely on the fireplace and the kitchen stove, with the occasional use of supplementary space heaters such as Franklin developed. With the coming of kerosene, the portable stove became more familiar; but there was no attempt to heat the bedrooms and hallways, where the inside temperature was not drastically different from that outside the house. Often the toilet facilities were separate from the house, and completely without heat. Beds were warmed with heated soapstone or with warming pans, but only on the spot where the heater rested—the other areas of the bed were stone-cold. So it is not at all surprising that we hear from the old folks that the winters used to be more rugged "when I was a boy." Perhaps they really were; but available statistics do not bear this out; and everything else is guesswork. Obviously if we want to go back to the days of the glaciers, the climate has changed indeed. But within the memories of living men and their written records the yearly averages stay very much the same.

EVOLUTION FAVORS THE "SURVIVAL OF THE FITTEST"?

The idea that there is a never-ending struggle for existence affecting all life—plant, animal, and social—a struggle which inevitably sees the weaker being trodden under by the stronger in a process of natural selection which tends to improve species and society by eliminating the unfit—is one so thoroughly ingrained in Western thought since the age of steel and steam flourished in the nineteenth century that it seems sheer heresy to question it. And yet, closely examined, that idea is a perfect example of what might be called the Higher Nonsense.

The phrase "survival of the fittest" was coined by Herbert Spencer.[4] His system of thought was developed under the factory system in a milieu of competition, exploitation, and struggle: the environment in which he wrote was keenly and sharply aware of Lyell's new study of geology, Lamarck's developmental theory, Coleridge's notion of a universal evolutionary pattern, Hodgkin's anarchism, laissez-faire principles of the Anti-Corn Law League, the pessimistic predictions of Malthus, and the established principle of the conservation of energy. He was particularly concerned with mental evolution, and he accepted the Lamarckian idea that acquired characteristics can be inherited; therefore it would follow, he believed, that if a premium were placed upon human intelligence, skill, self-control, and the ability to adapt as technology advanced, these traits would be transmitted to progeny and one of these days we would have a race of ideal men proudly and nobly occupying the Sun's third planet. Human perfection, under the operation of such natural laws, was not only a possibility—it was an inevitable outcome. Progress is no accident. And the state has no right to interfere with the natural evolution of society where the unfit are automatically eliminated. Like many of our contemporary twentieth-century extremists of the far right, he opposed governmental aid to the poor, state-supported education, housing control, and so forth. Under nature's laws, anyone unable by his own efforts to survive should die; and it was best for the race that he should. Spencer's thought was widely popularized by Yale's great Puritan preacher and sociologist, William Graham Sumner, who held that in the struggle for existence money is the token of success; and the colonial notions of equality and inherent rights that we heard so loud and clear at the time of the Declaration of Independence were overruled by evolutionary realism. Millionaires, representing efficiency in management, were the flowers of an advancing and necessarily competitive society. The idea of equality has to be wrong; because without inequality the law of the fittest surviving would have no meaning. This hard-boiled philosophy could view with equanimity the vision of women in sweatshops, stitching corsets for 50 cents a day, and forced to pay a tariff on the thread they used.[5]

Such, certainly, was the thought of industrialized America prior to the enactment of child labor laws, labor unions, and minimum-wage scales. And even in today's England and America, in what some people refer to as the Welfare State and the Great Society, where starvation is supposed to be impossible and basic needs are supposedly guaranteed more or less from cradle to grave, the idea of the survival of the fittest rings with the tones of truth. But it shouldn't. Because it is nonsense.

It is nonsense because in reality evolution doesn't work that way at all. When the conditions to which the "fittest" are thoroughly adapted undergo sudden radical changes, those who were previously the best adapted are at a great disadvantage. They are too "fit," too specialized in their adaptation, and they are caught in the trap of their own fitness. They lack the general adaptability of those who have not overspecialized in suiting themselves to a particular ecological niche. At such times those who have retained a generalized plasticity for adaptation go to the head of the class. In short, it is the *adaptable,* not the *adapted,* who are most likely to survive: the "fit" and not the "fittest." To reflect the truth, the phrase should be revised to read "the survival of the fit," of the most plastic, most malleable, most adaptable. The millions of years of evolution have seen scores of well-adapted species die out and their places taken by the more adaptable forms of life under conditions of rapid and radical change, exactly as the workers on an assembly line are no longer employable when the line is automated. If all they can do is to adjust screw number 356 properly, they are out of a job when the machine does it in their place.

The "Impenetrable Jungles" of Malaya?

The mental picture entertained by the people of Western Europe and the Americas representing the jungles of Malaya is one showing trees and brush and vines and creepers all mixed up together in a brambled confusion which, as far as its passage by such a creature as man is concerned, can only be described as "impenetrable." Maybe something like a rat or other quadruped who runs close to the ground can get through; maybe snakes can make their way easily enough; but a large animal, no—and as for man, he has to toil away with a machete for three hours to travel 200 feet.

Even a book as respectable as the Rand McNally World Guide says of Malaya: "Covered in four-fifths of its surface by dense tropical jungle."[6]

The picture remains one of impermeable consolidation of bough and tendril. The defenders of Singapore in World War II relied upon this supposed character of the jungles to the north to protect the city, but these jungles turned out to be something that the Japanese penetrated at a jog trot. If the wild jungles of Malaya in a country annually receiving from 100 to 200 inches of rain, with high humidity and a uniform high temperature (71°-90°) are not impenetrable, then it may be wondered where a large area of impenetrable jungle can be found. Even in Brazil's enormous rain forest the precipitation is only 80 inches per year, according to the World Guide.

An interesting substantiation for the assertion that jungles are not impenetrable turned up in the story of a tiger hunt by S. Suydam Cutting, where the author remarks: "Shooting was, of course, out of the question till the tigers could be driven out of the grass and into the bordering jungle *where a proper view could be obtained*."[7]

Since creepers and vines and other similar entanglements need sunlight, they are never found in abundance in thick jungles where treetops interweave and create a gloomy twilight below.

Snake-Infested Tropical Jungles?

Any self-respecting tropical jungle expects to be characterized as snake-infested, and if one omits this elementary courtesy there is no telling what will happen. It's all part of an international plot to keep people away from the jungle. But snake-infested is just plain nonsense applied to tropical jungles. "There is infinitely less chance of being bitten by a poisonous snake in tropical forests and jungles than in any part of the United States," says Dr. E. D. Merrill in an article in *Science*. "In no part of the Old World tropics with which I am personally familiar are poisonous snakes either common or numerous," he states. In agreement is Dr. Franz Verdoorn, who says such creatures are rare in the Malay Peninsula, Sumatra, and Java; and Colonel Arthur S. Fisher, who in three months on Bataan saw a total of four snakes. Probably the creepers and columns of vine trunks give the appearance of being snaky; and of course the person who goes looking for and expecting to see snakes—he usually sees them. Whether they're present or not.

LIGHTNING NEVER STRIKES THE SAME PLACE TWICE?

Understandably, lightning is feared in all cultures. In fact, one of the few passages in the written or oral traditions of primitive or ancient societies in which thunder and lightning are represented as exhilarating and wonderful as well as fearful is Job 37:2-5: "Hearken ye unto the noise of his voice, and the sound that goeth out of his mouth. He sendeth it forth under the whole heaven, and his lightning unto the ends of the earth. After it a voice roareth . . . God thundereth marvelously with his voice; great things doeth he which we cannot comprehend."

It is therefore not difficult to understand why men should hope most fervently that lightning, having struck once, would not again hit the same place. The proverb, however, seems to appear only among the folk of Europe and America.[8] And unfortunately there is no truth in it. If lightning occurs once at a certain place and strikes, it is likely to strike again if it happens to be in the same locality in the future. The mast on top of the Empire State Building was hit 68 times within the first ten years of its erection. A moment's thought will indicate how reasonable and logical this is: the lightning is properly located; and something attracts it. If it happens once, it will happen again.

As Forrester points out, "Lightning is not limited to a one-bolt action. Many lightning flashes are of the multiple variety and may strike repeatedly in the space of a few seconds."[9]

Further, an Englishman by the name of John Pointer wrote a book called *A Rational Account of the Weather* more than two hundred years ago (in 1723) in which he pointed out that "various flashes of lightning followed the same track," and he says the reason is "that the first flash rarefies the air and makes a path for the succeeding ones."[10] Inwards says that many photographs have confirmed "this sagacious observation." And he refers to the church at Week St. Mary in north Cornwall, "known to have been damaged by lightning on at least six occasions since 1688, and St. Botolph's Church, Boston, Lincolnshire (the 'Boston Stump'), was struck four times between 1865 and 1908."

The proverb or belief, then, represents wishful thinking inspired by fear. The same fear has inspired dozens of curious beliefs. In many cultures lightning has been personified as a deity or seen as a manifestation of that god's wrath. Ancient Babylonian cylinders showed Adad with a boomerang in one hand (thunder) and a spear in the other (lightning). The Persians saw lightning as an indication of divine anger. Rudra, the storm-god with his bow and arrows, and the two Maruts, his sons, in their chariots of lightning, used to strike down cattle, men, and whole forests.

In Greece the spot struck by lightning was sacred forever. The Greeks had a belief that thunder on the right, heard before a battle, would bring them good luck—because of course the enemy would be hearing the thunder on the left, an ill omen. In Rome this was turned around, and thunder on the left was considered a good augury.

The Chinese have a legend of a spritely young goddess of lightning who travels with the thunder-god, carrying a mirror in each hand and flashing light on his path so that he will not make any misstep.

There are various protections against lightning. In Scandinavia burning the Yule log at Christmas protects the house against lightning for a year. In Shropshire a piece of hawthorn cut on Holy Thursday protects both house and person. Best of all, however, would be the discovery of a magic coal dug up from under a mugwort plant at precisely noon on Midsummer Day: this, carried on the person, gives him permanent protection against lightning. Incidentally, if lightning happens to be playing about, according to some European experts, the best thing to do is hide all scissors, cover all mirrors, keep away from wet dogs and horses, and lie on a feather bed.

Thunder produces some positive effects, also. It makes turtles come out of the water and lay their eggs (Australia); and it makes lizard and crocodile eggs hatch out (Dahomey, West Africa). In Dahomey lightning is the weapon of Gbadĕ, youngest son of Sogbo, and he uses it for killing. American Indians know, of course, that thunder is caused by the wings of great birds added to the drumming of their beaks against hollow trees; and it is the eyes of these thunderbirds flashing that you see when it lightens. Among some Negroes of the American South, if there is lightning while a man is dying, this is a sign that the devil has come for his soul.

But the best thing about lightning is this: you get a splinter of a tree that has been struck, a Maryland tradition holds, and you shape it into a toothpick—and you can cure the worst toothache in jig time.

Bullets Get Red-Hot as They Bore Through the Air?

We hear of meteors burning because of friction as they fall and we know that the barrel of a gun gets hot as bullets are fired through it; so why is it hard to believe that a bullet gets hot as it travels through air? Answer: it is not hard to believe. It *is* believed. But the parallel doesn't hold. The bullet does not get red-hot. If anything, it is cooler upon impact than it was when it left the muzzle, because of dispersion of its heat by the air itself. No bullet goes far enough to work up a friction heat of any account. There is heat as the gases explode after the ignition of the powder; and in a rifle barrel where the bore closes a little the friction is more intense and the heat rises quickly. But thereafter the bullet cools.

The friction of the impact causes heat; and anyone who has been hit with a bullet will tell you that there is a sort of sting. This may or may not be true; we refuse to test it. But we know that it is not from being red-hot, if there is a stinging sensation.

Ordinarily a lead- or steel-jacketed bullet will not cause a fire if shot through a gas tank. Incendiary bullets would not be required if the ordinary bullet would do it. Sir Thomas Browne found that a bullet of wax will penetrate some things without melting. (*Works*, I.276).

It's easy enough to test the red-hot bullet thesis: if you shoot a .38 into a sawdust pile and then dig quickly for the bullet, you find it warm but not uncomfortable to handle.

Plants in the Bedroom Where You Sleep—Dangerous?

To be able to sleep completely at ease and with more or less perfect safety seems to be a gift enjoyed by few people. Among popular myths has been the belief that our distant ancestors slept only a few seconds at a time, because of the need for alertness against enemies; and we have seen for ourselves that a person in a deep sleep is utterly helpless. Fantasies have been passed along in the oral tradition, and also in written form, of plants that attack sleeping people. Sometimes the vines wind themselves around the sleeper and eventually choke the life out of him; sometimes the plant has actually devoured the person, as in John Collier's short story, "Green Thoughts." Whether the idea that sleeping with plants in the room has its origins in some dark backward abysm of time from the world of fantasy or whether it comes from some half-knowledge about plants giving off carbon dioxide, the fear is there in the minds of many people.

It doesn't need to be. The fantasies are not based on truth; and as for the chemical process, plants give off such a miniscule amount of carbon dioxide that it would make no appreciable difference to a person sleeping all night in a room crammed with plants. One could even sleep *in* the plants if one's taste ran that way.

Rain Making Through the Use of Heavy Guns?

Ways and means of controlling the weather have been of intense interest to mankind from the beginnings of recorded history and are especially important in an age of flight, when fog and ice storms make flying hazardous. In the days of ancient Greece, as we know, the gods would whip up a serious storm whenever the plot called for it, or would becalm a sailor who was in a hurry but had in one way or another displeased the Olympian in question. Even after the discovery of the laws of planetary motion, the weather was believed to be in the hands of deity, and the purpose of man's maneuvering was to induce action on the part of the deity rather than to affect the weather directly. One of the main objectives of man in attempting to influence the weather has been to produce rain when it was needed. During the disastrous drought on the eastern seaboard of the United States in the summer of 1965, when the New York water supply was lower than it had ever been before, many news stories reported that afflicted people were resorting to prayer, just as in the prescientific days.

In vine-growing districts, the peasants had used bells to induce rain; but when firearms came in, they used mortars, and these grew in size until some of them were 40 feet high and cost a great deal of money.[11] The result was indecisive; but it is easy to see how imitative magic would suggest to the mind of man that a great deal of noise might be a hint to the thunder to make a visit; and with the thunder might come the rain—in the same way that the feast of lights at the time of the winter solstice brought back the disappearing sun. The theory of the effectiveness of gunfire was bolstered by the generalization that "many battles have ended in, or been followed by, downpours of rain," but this brilliant invention is somewhat dulled by the observation that "historically, battles are summer phenomena, and doubtless many summer days of less momentous importance have closed with downpours of rain. . . . There is no ground *a priori* for supposing that concussion would have any effect at all upon the condensation of vapor and clouds."

THUNDER SOURS MILK?

This is an ancient folk belief that is still current in areas where efficient refrigeration is not in use—where people depend on wells, cellars, and other cool places for the preservation of milk; and there is even a "scientific" explanation—namely, that electricity in the atmosphere, increasing in abundance during a thunder storm, oxidizes the ammonia in the atmosphere and forms nitric acid. The acid sours the milk.

This sounds reasonable enough, perhaps, the only trouble with the explanation is that it is not true. "According to modern theory, it is not lightning that sours milk but the warm, humid weather which usually accompanies summer thunderstorms. Such sultry conditions promote rapid multiplication of lactic-acid bacteria."[12] Thunderstorms occurring in the winter do not seem to sour milk! Nor has milk in an electric refrigerator soured during a thunderstorm.

This nonsense is related to another bit of folklore, namely, that the abundance of the crops depends on the amount of milk that gets soured during the season. This time the myth is closer to the truth, it seems, since ammonia and nitrous oxides, produced by the passage of lightning through the air, become ammonium hydroxide and various nitrates, which are fertilizers. "Hence a thundery summer tends to favor crops."[13]

NATURE EXISTS ONLY TO SERVE MAN?

It's right in the Bible!

The Judeo-Christian tradition represents a Religion of the Book—a book which is the all-time best seller of Western civilization, the most influential book of that culture, and probably the least understood. This Bible is viewed by some as the literal word of God and by others as a collected library of history, poetry, drama, prophecy, and ethics. But nobody thinks it is unimportant.

On the sixth day of creation, according to Genesis, "God created man in his own image . . . and God said unto them, Be fruitful, and multiply, and replenish the earth, and subdue it; and have dominion over the fish of the sea, and over the fowl of the air, and over every living thing that moveth upon the earth . . ." (Gen. 1:28).

Those words supposedly supply the moral justification, as far as our ethical background is concerned, for all the mastery of earth which men have been able to accomplish; so that the Psalmist could celebrate the position of man in the words, "Thou hast made him a little lower than the angels" (Psalms 8:5).

A modern critical reading of the Bible, however, is quick to recognize that the original manuscripts are not available, that anything we have is a translation, and that all writing must be understood in the context of the culture in which it arose. And "the fact remains that the Bible is an ancient, oriental book."[14] When it was written (Old Testament by about 150 B.C., perhaps; the actual writing was in process for a thousand years, from about 1200 B.C.[15]) such a book as Genesis was a "rewriting of traditions and tales transmitted orally" and intended to hold a listening audience, not a critical, historically-minded sophisticated group of scholars. Hence the lines separating fact and fiction were likely to be fuzzy, since "what holds a folk audience spellbound is interest in the plot, romantic atmosphere, and not in the least historical accuracy."[16] In Bible days man was not sufficiently the master of nature to be able to place the ecology in a hazardous position. He did not disturb the balance of nature very much. He did not wipe out scores of species of birds for their feathers or for his shooting pleasure (the Massachusetts Audubon Society stated in 1966 that there "is only one bird today for each 30 birds 50 years ago," for instance); nor did he ruin the land by ripping down the forests for profit ("We are cutting timber from our 55,000 square miles of accessible softwood forests almost 24 percent faster than it is being replaced"[17]); nor did he fill the clean air with pollution from hundreds of industrial chimneys. (According to an item in the *New York Times* of Feb. 6, 1967, "A Public Health Service estimate last year showed that 85 tons of soot and dirt fell on each square mile of New York City in a month.")

In our day we are accustomed to think about man's mastery of nature in terms of the conquest of space; but a much more homely example is at hand in the simple facts of the lumbering industry: a water-power mill of 1630 at the top of its form could cut perhaps a thousand board feet in one day; by 1767 the gang saw could turn out five times as much lumber; the circular saw, put to use in 1820, could cut 40,000 board feet daily; ten years later the power of steam was added and the figure grew to 125,000 board feet per day. By the 1950's the total had climbed to a million. Even before the turn of the century (in 1899) in Wisconsin alone they were cutting 43 *billion* feet per year.[18]

Thus in our day has mankind responded to the words, "Behold, I have given you every herb bearing seed, which is upon the face of all the earth, and every tree, in the which is the fruit of a tree yielding seed" (Gen. 1:29). So energetically has man wielded ax and saw that, as the Milnes put it, "the remaining patches of virgin forest in the world can be counted. His plows ripped the native sod so thoroughly that in 1957 only one-fourth of a square mile of unplowed tall-grass plains could be found in America."[19]

The prime nonsense in the idea that "nature exists to serve man" is in making the dichotomy: man is himself a part of nature, not a creature apart. If he has the intelligence and the inventiveness to work out a method of clearing land for cultivation and then of opening up the soil to take the seed, he also has the intelligence to make a record of the fact that sloping land without roots to hold it washes away in the rainfloods and leaves the slopes without topsoil; and that if he allows cattle or sheep to overgraze a prairie to the point where the livestock nips grass roots, weeds and thorns will take the place of the grass—as happened within a single generation on the great plains of Texas. In short, it is a two-way thoroughfare that man travels; not all take and no give. Man has obligations as well as privileges, and one would think that such a fact would become apparent very early in human culture. Yet with a cheerful shout of "Après moi le déluge," we seem intent on getting what we can for ourselves while the getting is good, letting others worry about the dust storms. Thus, as Governor Ronald Reagan has emphasized in connection with the assault on California's remaining redwoods, when you've seen one tree you've seen them all, so why not put the lumber to use?

Some commentators lay the blame on the so-called Protestant Ethic: if one works unceasingly for the glory of God one is entitled to whatever riches one can accumulate; some have placed the blame on Social Darwinism, the doctrine that the strong get what they want and the weak disappear from the scene, as nature intended that they should; and others have placed the blame on our money economy, which permits a man to stack away more wealth than he can possibly use. But if Moses wrote the Pentateuch, as some say, he also presented his people with a set of commandments which included the exhortation, "Thou shalt not covet."

Primitive man knew better than to consider himself apart from nature. He went so far as to identify himself with various animals and plants. This was true for every member of the tribe; and one did not disturb or eat one's totem. Moreover, nonliterate people never kill either plant or animal except to satisfy hunger; and therefore they do not exploit natural resources irresponsibly. The primitive is a conservationist.

Outwardly our Western civilization makes a semigod out of Albert Schweitzer and widely acclaims his "reverence for life" doctrine; but on weekdays our industrialists poison the rivers, pollute the air, devastate the landscape, and exterminate marine life while testing for offshore oil. At the moment we are doing our best to wipe out the whale for immediate commercial profits, using floating butchering and rendering factories and explosive projectiles against which the greatest mammal remaining has no defense; and our irresponsible use of insecticides is producing ever-more-silent springtimes.

Perhaps it should not be surprising that a civilization that permits these things should not balk at the ultimate crime of genocide—nor should we permit ourselves to believe that this is something new and unheard of: our Belsens, Buchenwalds, and Dachaus were possibly more efficient and more effectively organized; but by 1873 the British had succeeded in exterminating all the aboriginal inhabitants of Tasmania, and in Australia and Africa they were responsible for the destruction of whole societies.[20]

That the exploding world population will require greater output of food and thus perhaps strain our natural resources is not the point here: we are discussing irresponsible, laissez-faire destruction for profit, not controlled, scientifically planned extraction of food. Yet even while experts are assuring us in the journals and books that we have now the power to "free us from the tyranny of physical nature that has plagued Man since his beginning" and that "the ancient tyranny of matter has been broken"[21] by invention and technology because we can now change the world and shape it to our needs—even while we hear this in one ear the other ear hears such voices as that of the Agricultural Organization of the UN saying that "between one billion and a billion and a half persons suffer from varying degrees of malnutrition, from chronic hunger to starvation" (Boston *Traveler,* Jan. 5, 1967).

With an estimated world population of 3.593 billion for 1970 and of 6.129 billion for A.D. 2000,[22] together with a life expectancy increase (in the United States, from age 35 in 1760 to age 70.2 in 1964),[23] it is obvious that the future welfare of our species is in a very sharp way connected to our treatment of the balance of nature on this planet. If mankind is to be free of hunger and of infectious diseases, with most people leading vigorous physical and mental existences up to the age of 90 or 100 by the year 2000, as the geneticist and biologist Dr. H. Bentley Glass has optimistically predicted, then our values must be overhauled—and Dr. Glass, along with most other writers on technological advance, concedes this point. We are not winning the war against hunger *yet.* According to Secretary Freeman, the world output of food in 1965 was not appreciably increased over that of the previous year, and thus "the grim apocalyptic figure of famine gallops across the earth, casting an ominous shadow over the immediate years ahead."[24]

In short, if we have no respect for our natural resources, for our animals, birds, fishes, perhaps we should learn to have some for ourselves. Ecology binds us to them all, and not to act accordingly could be man's final flaming nonsense.

10

More Nonsense—About Other Animals

Our language indicates, and our legends illustrate, how superior mankind considers itself to the rest of the animal world. Atrocities committed by the Germans in two World Wars were *bestial*. A wife beater is *beastly*. "And God said, Let us make man in our image, after our likeness: and let them have dominion . . . over every creeping thing that creepeth upon the earth" (Gen. 1:26). There's the denigration of the quadruped in the language; there's mastery of all the natural world in the legend. Man is supreme. And why not? Who made the language? Who wrote the legends?

Man is haughtily superior; but at the same time he is indefatigably curious about other living things, and for the most part woefully ignorant and credulous without limit. Hence even the grayest and soberest newspapers give important placement and all the needed space to any animal story with a twist—such as that of the lad who went hunting and got shot by his dog. It turned out to be a simple enough story: the boy stopped to rest, snoozed off with his gun leaning against him in some way so that the dog, pawing at his master to get some action, accidentally hit the trigger. The story made the wires from coast to coast.

Ordinarily a piece of nonsense from the animal world is accepted without question. Thus we find Sam Johnson's famous dictionary defining *ichneumon* as "a small animal that breaks the eggs of the crocodile." It was believed that the mongoose tracked the crocodile (*ichnos* is *track*). Hence ichneumon, literally "tracker," now *means* mongoose. It is true that the mongoose is an egg eater, but so is a dog if you give him a chance, and beat the egg up for him.

It is through the same uncritical acceptance and ignorance that we take for truth the symbol of the bloody-fanged gorilla dragging off the woman—and transfer it to the Nazis in a newspaper cartoon to show the immeasurable depths of depravity to which so-called humans can sink. The gorilla does not rape his mates; he is pre-eminently a peace-loving creature, will never attack without provocation, stays within his own territory, and does not invade that of other animals. Being a vegetarian, he does not hunt meat for food. It would be quite reasonable to use the gorilla as a symbol for peaceful living.[1] But, in accordance with the kingdom that is within us, he doesn't *look* peaceful: he looks terribly dangerous and fearful. So sculpture, Hollywood, and *Horror Story Magazine* build on the fear and we get King Kong or some incredible monstrosity never seen on earth or sea, and we pay admission fees for the beautiful shudders.

In much the same tradition we read about some deranged criminal who has dismembered or mutilated a child, and we call him a throwback to the Neanderthal or the supposedly tooth-gnashing troglodyte. Our newspapers frequently commit this solecism. The results of research, however, indicate that Neanderthal man was a peaceful creature: he did not invent weapons of war, and clearly had strong religious feelings, as the ceremonial materials and objects in graves have shown. He certainly never thought of bombing anybody.

But the Myth of the Beast dies hard; indeed, it dies not. Man's characterization of the brute (there it is again—*Brute* is pejorative) as indecent, murderous, and deadly is actually a psychological projection: a projection of what man senses in himself. To the drunk, everybody around him is drunk. Projection. What beast ever organized deliberate total-liquidation assaults upon other beasts with the intention of wiping a whole population from the face of the earth? For that matter, what beast ever treated his neighbors to the slaughter practiced by innumerable peoples past and present, such as killing all the men in a conquered town and taking all the women as slaves, while the priests chant hymns of praise to their gods? Without getting at all bitter about it, we can safely say that there is no jungle creature that even faintly approaches the behavior of man at his worst; nor, to turn the coin over, is there any jungle creature more benign than man at his best.

The fact is that the variations permitted through the mammalian type of sexual reproduction are so enormous that we and other animals can hit the highs and the lows to extremes paralleled only by the most exquisite high-fidelity sound systems: way up; and way down. In addition, the potentialities of the complex mind possessed by man have endowed him with the capacity to develop the most destructively evil as well as the most constructively beneficial traits in the natural world.

However, man's interest in the so-called lower orders has been exceeded by almost nothing save his ignorance of them. Only the Bible can compete with the Bestiary as a world best seller in terms of both circulation and influence—the difference being that one has a canon of acceptable and apocryphal writings while the other remains incomplete but growing. The Bestiary as a single volume does not exist, although many examples of bestiaries exist; we are using the term to include all the lore of the beasts that has been collected, copied, translated, borrowed, or observed and related by mankind, from the oral tradition to the written records. Probably it can never be complete, since new items are being added all the time, as anybody knows who keeps his eyes on the newspapers, and they range all the way from the Alsatian bitch recently enrolled on the staff of the West Bohemian gas works to the creator of the "most efficient" light production known. Not to keep you in suspense, the dog was Ajka, employed as a leak detector. She had 800 miles of gaslines to inspect, and the reason for her breaking into the news via an Associated Press wire was because she had detected 52 leaks and was being credited with a sense of smell sixty times as sharp as that of a man. How they got the figure of 60 is an interesting point; but ours is not to wonder why, ours not to make reply, ours but to certify: AP wire from Prague in the *New York Times* (Jan. 5, 1955). The source of the "most efficient form of light production known" is the glowworm, according to the distinguished marine biologist, Alister Hardy. The glowworm, he reports, gives "the coldest light, i.e., that produced with the minimum amount of energy lost as heat; in the glowworm and the ostracod only about one percent is so lost."[2]

When an item is added to mankind's Bestiary that is based on scientific observation or even on eyewitness reports, we tend to accept it without question; but the truth is that we also accept the nonsense items with an equally hospitable mind unless we just happen to know better as the result of more accurate information. It is a weakness so human, at least, that we share it with Aristotle and Pliny, who reported some of the weirdest natural history on record.

In the Middle Ages, for instance, it was generally understood—and believed—that a lion is frightened by the creaking of wheels; that he prefers living on top of a mountain so that the scent of hunters is wafted upward to him, whereupon he rubs out his tracks with his tail; that he sleeps with his eyes open; that the cubs are born dead and stay that way for three days, at which point their father finds them and breathes in their faces—and they live. (The religious symbolism is plain.) Lions, it was known, eat only on alternate days (this was before we had zoos); a lioness has five kittens at her first accouchement, four at the next, and so on down to one, after which she is sterile. When a lion is sick, eating a monkey will cure him; but he is scared stiff of a white rooster. And so forth. Perhaps one of the cheeriest associations with the King of Beasts is the etymology of *dandelion*: dents de lion. Nice?

JUNGLE GRAVEYARD—A FAMILY PLOT?

There is a persistent inanity which seriously asserts that when jungle animals know that their death is upon them (it is not explained by what mechanism they are made more aware of this than is mankind) they make a trek for one of the secret graveyards trampled out by the elephant herds; and there they lie down and die.

Greed may well be the original source of this myth: what ivory trader could not dream of a windfall like finding the animal graveyard where, in addition to the bones of the lion and the fox, the final remains of the great tuskers would lie heaped up and ready for the taking?

Well-a-day, no such graveyard has ever been discovered; but the minds of men are easily captured by legends of waters that restore youth; by stories of the Golden One, El Dorado; by whispers about buried treasure and chests of doubloons and pieces of eight from the Spanish galleons (just to keep the interest sharp, someone actually salvages a few hundred thousand dollars' worth off the Florida coast every once in a while). But no one ever shows up with news about the animal graveyards.

The Tiger's Eyes Blaze in the Dark?

Anyone who drives a car very much at night is sure, sooner or later, to scare up some animal whose eyes, in the headlights, have what some of us see as a malevolent and devilish glow. But the lights have to strike at just the right angle; if the animal turns its head a little, the fire goes out. The point is, there would be no glow of any kind if there were not some light coming at the animal from an outside source which his eyes can reflect: it isn't our four-footed cousin who is emitting the light.

The source of light which the eyes reflect may be very small in candle power—it doesn't have to be headlights; a lantern or a candle will do, and either one would make the situation more mysterious than the powerful mazdas. The reason it works is that animals who do reflect light in this way (many do, but not all) have a structure within the eye known as the tapetum. The eyes glare because of the refraction of light by the particles in the tapetum.

Once in a while a human being turns up whose eyes possess a tapetum—you meet them in fiction occasionally, and they are not imaginary but based on actual recorded specimens. In such cases, of course, all the neighbors are properly awed and attribute to the person all kinds of special instinctual powers and so forth.

In short, the tiger's eyes will not blaze in the dark unless there is a light of some kind in that darkness which his eyes can reflect. The belief that such animals as the tiger do actually emit light from their eyes is very old. Polyak explained that the ancient Greeks thought that the act of vision was "accomplished by very slender 'visual rays'— comparable to the rays of sunlight or to very thin spider-web threads believed to be emitted from the eyes like long, delicate rods or tentacles—that touched the objects which then became visible." This was the "emanation hypothesis" which was not doubted by the best of the philosophers and naturalists, except for a few—Aristotle among them. Plato supported the theory. The Arabs believed it right down to the Middle Ages.[3] The Elizabethan zoologist Topsell[4] states positively: "The eies of Panthers and cats cast forth beames in the shaddow and darknes." Even the almost-contemporary William Blake (d. 1827), singing about "The Tiger," gave us the couplet:

> In what distant deeps or skies
> Burnt the fire of thine eyes?

One has to admit, it *does* look that way. But any panther or cat will tell you it's a canard.

KEEP SNAKES AWAY WITH A CIRCLE OF ROPE?

Of course there's no truth in the familiar lunacy that if you make a complete circle with a rope and place yourself in the middle of it, you're safe against snakes; but if there were, the efficacy would be in the *circle,* not in the rope. The circle is the magic symbol; it has been potent for thousands of years. The circle stands for many things— eternity, because it has no beginning and no end; completeness, whole- ness. The great snake who lives in the sea and surrounds the earth lies there with his tail is his mouth—a circle. When he shudders, sailors beware! The circle also stands for perfection. Whether the Round Table unconsciously followed this symbolism or not, we cannot know; we like to think it did. The circle is also the sun, and Stonehenge was a circle. Somehow or other the idea took root that if you're inside a circle you're safe. Children's games reflect this, reaching back into the dim memories of mankind. But rattlesnakes don't know anything about this, so don't trust the magic. Rattlesnakes aren't going to sneak up on a person asleep and give him the tooth number without provoca- tion, anyhow. The whole thing is silly.

THE TOAD CAN LIVE SEALED UP IN CEMENT?

All kinds of shuddering fears that mankind has had for toads show up in the popular beliefs about the harmless—indeed, useful—little fellows. God knows they are not handsome, from the human point of view, which is perhaps why the enchanted princess has to perform the herculean task of kissing the toad in the fairy story. He then, of course, on cue, turns into a handsome prince. *That* old thing. But if humanity deems the toad ugly, we want to know if anybody has asked a toad lately whom he considers the handsomest female creature in all the world? Point of view makes all the difference.

In any event, mankind's revulsion to the toad creates all sorts of impressions: that the toad is slimy; he is certainly not. That the toad will make warts come out on your hands if you touch him; he will not—we took that up earlier. That he is in some way a creature of the Devil rather than of God, and that therefore the Devil aids him in supernatural ways—e.g., helps him to live if you seal him up in a wall or in cement or something. He will not: the poor toad breathes air, and if you cut off his oxygen he'll die as will the rest of us. But you will remember that in the opening scene of *Macbeth* the witches are called away from their meeting in the storm by their familiar spirits, and the first says, "I come, Graymalkin," the latter being a fiend in the shape of a cat; and then the second says, "Paddock calls." This fiend is in the shape of a toad. Toads and frogs got mixed up a good deal in the natural histories of those days; but perhaps you have heard of a bull-paddy, meaning a bullfrog, which is cognate with paddock. Shakespeare played on the popular beliefs of his own day—and here he was suggesting that toads are indeed creatures of hell. In another mood, however, he could be kinder; and one of the nobles who had retreated to the forests in *As You Like It* opens Act II with a speech in praise of country living in which the lines occur:

> Which, like the toad ugly and venomous,
> Bears yet a precious jewel in his head.

Both pieces of nonsense were familiar: that the toad is venomous—which you can disprove any time you conquer that distaste for handling toads and give them a chance—if you can catch a few; and that the toad has a jewel in his head. If that were the case, one would think the Elizabethans who happened to be out of funds would catch a few toads and cash in.

One twelfth-century writer reports that if a dog swallows a toad he will never bark again. That theory will have to go without proof as far as we are concerned: no dog we ever knew had been *able* to swallow a toad. We have seen large dogs playfully snap up a toad and very promptly snap him out again—apparently the toad shoots out something in the dog's mouth that the canine dislikes: he spits and foams quite a while until he can get a long cool drink. But poisoned he is not.

In American slang, for some reason, a toad is an iron bar to derail trains; toad-hide is (rare) a dollar bill, as is frogskin (not so rare: it appears in S. J. Perelman's *Listen to the Mocking Bird*); and a toady is an obsequious lackey, a term of contempt.

We'd like to bring back the toad as a friend to man. He eats mosquitoes, minds his own business, and is a prince of fellows.

Ethics from Nature . . .

Many of the bestiaries of the Middle Ages were intended to do two jobs: instill ethical principles in the reader or reinforce those supposedly already instilled; and to give factual information about the natural world and its inhabitants. If anything were needed to show the folly of mixing this kind of science with religion, here are brilliant tutors.

For example, we are told that the stork is monogamous and returns always to the same nest; that the parents pad the nest with the feathers off their own breasts for the sake of the babies; and later, when the babies are full grown, they put in the same amount of time caring for the old folks that was spent on them in babyhood. This is reminiscent of the hoopoe bird, which in adulthood cares for the parents, preening their feathers, keeping them warm, and licking their eyes clean. The parents are thereby much encouraged. This is a lesson for us to speak well of our fathers and mothers and to treat them tenderly.

The pelican gets much closer to dogmatic niceties: pelicans live along the Nile. When the babies are large enough, they come up and flap their wings in the faces of their parents until the old folks get tired of it and strike back, killing them. Three days later the mother gives herself a wound in the side, and with the blood pouring out of her, lies upon the dead children. This of course brings them back to life. It may seem something like a roundabout way; but the point is the parallel between the pelican and Christ, who gave his blood before rising from the dead—for the salvation of mankind. This proves that God created all things and that he made us out of nothing; that we strike him in the face; and that after just punishment, he forgives us.

Beheaded Turtle Lives Until Sundown?

When our cheeks were tan and our feet were bare there were many things we were sure of that now have to be entered in the nonsense file. We knew that if you killed a snake, it would wiggle all the rest of the day; and that until the tail ceased all movement, at sundown, the snake was not really dead. Likewise a turtle with his head cut off was known to continue living until sundown. Possibly it was a fear of the reptile as a class that made us endow him with supernatural powers.

Certain it is that any vertebrate whose head has been removed is dead. Muscle spasms may occur after the removal of the head; but the snake *as a snake,* or the turtle *as a turtle,* is dead.

Death, however, can be a very tricky word to define. Not long ago the medical profession was having a serious controversy over the meaning; a patient's heart had stopped in the course of an operation and remained unbeating for some seconds until massage prompted the pumping to resume. Had the patient died?

The dictionary calls death "the permanent ending of all life in a person, animal or plant"; or "the ending of all vital functions without possibility of recovery" (Webster III). Yet in the "dead" turtle there are living cells still present for some time after the loss of the head. Which is why we said that *as a turtle* the animal existed no more. It is, after all, not a matter calling for the hairsplitting skills of a Duns Scotus; and let us wind the matter up by reminding the reader that the word *dunce* is derived ironically from "a *Duns* man"—referring to the great medieval scholar.

THE OSTRICH—EATER OF IRON?

An ostrich is an extremely muscular and very tough bird at the height of his powers; a blow from his beak or a kick from one of those ironclad feet could be serious.

Perhaps it is from narratives of early explorers that the idea became current that the ostrich is so rugged that he chews iron. It is a legitimate hyperbole as a figure of speech and no damage is done unless one begins to take it literally. But when you read of an ostrich killed at some zoo because somebody fed him razor blades, small scissors, jackknives, or assorted nuts and bolts, you realize that nonsense has contributed a most inhumane act. The esophagus of this bird giant is just as tender as that of a human heavyweight champion fighter: both are tough characters in action but both are as easily hurt in the alimentary canal as you or I would be.

This particular nonsense is cognate with the half-jocose notion that goats have a voracious appetite for old tin cans—as is true inevitably in the comic strips. It is true that goats can find something to eat where a cow would starve; and one may say in jest that a goat will eat "anything." But tin cans are no more use to him—excuse me, madam; to her—than they would be to your kitten.

MAN BITES DOG

Despite the cynical remark of a city editor who jeered at the cub reporter for turning in a story of a dog biting a man ("You call that news? It would be news if the man bit the dog; but a dog biting a man is no news—it happens every hour!"), there are few subjects more certain of getting generous attention than tales of animals. The human is fascinated by the animal and always has been from Pliny to the present. Stories of animals have been used to illuminate morals, ethics, wisdom, subconscious wishes, symbolic yearnings—and as propaganda. Since our knowledge is so limited, almost anything can be told about animals with a straight face, especially by a traveler returned from some fabulous country so distant that the chances of his story's being checked for accuracy are negligible. The sky is the limit, and the nonsense, accumulating from the very first book on natural history and adding new material as it is copied and repeated, is unbounded. That the tradition continues into the last third of the twentieth century will be apparent to anyone with scissors and paste who examines the newspapers for ten consecutive days. Of course not all of it is nonsense, but one discovers that almost any sort of animal story with any interest at all is worthy of space.

For example, man is not the only animal to be right-handed or left-handed. Cats are, too. Dr. J. Michael Warren, director of the Animal Behavior Laboratory at Penn State, spent more than a year testing cats, and he found them almost evenly divided in preference for the right forepaw or the left forepaw in delicate food-snatching assignments. Indeed, the proportion of right to left was nine to eight. Somehow this strikes us as being extraordinary, because it never occurred to us that anybody outside of the human circle was important enough to be right-handed or left-handed.

Again, we are aware that certain lighting conditions have their effect upon human amorous behavior. What said the old song? "Give me the moonlight, give me the girl, and leave the rest to me." Or "For a bright and shining quarter you can make the Pullman porter turn the lights down low." Or "You can spoon right any old June night but if there's moonlight better work's done." But has any one of us considered the thought that lighting conditions may also affect the amorous behavior of others than ourselves? Or anything, for instance, as humble as the lowly glowworm? It appears to be a fact, however, that the female glowworm gives off a feeble light to attract the male; and that in areas where the bright lights of towns fight back the night—East Anglia is mentioned in particular in our source—and where there are frequent passings of automobile headlights, there is, according to a *New York Times* item dated June 19, 1966, "sex starvation in glowworms . . . and a slump in the glowworm population."

Cats Have Nine Lives?

We would not accuse the folk of any culture of having the naïveté to believe soberly that in the real world any cat experiences death more than once. Yet the phrase maintains its place among our idioms: Cats have nine lives.

All of us know perfectly well that when, as it must to all things, death comes to Graymalkin, that quadruped lies as still as any other. Perhaps what we are trying to convey is that the cat is wily, wary, and wiry; that it always lands on its feet; that it is a beautifully balanced engine of destruction; that it can never really be tamed; and that it never dies until it has to. But we know that when the animal turns in its portfolio as the family cat it has no more conscious business with life on this planet.

Where the idea of nine came from is hard to say. Gillian Tindall suggests that the number 9 was one of the sacred numbers of Egypt; and the daughter of Isis and Osiris was a cat by the name of Pasht—which is supposedly the root of our word puss.[5] The suggestion is ingenious enough to be memorable. To the editors of Webster II the origin runs back into onamatopoeia, *puss* being an imitation of a cat's spitting. But Webster III more cautiously refuses to guess. Chacun à son goût.

Mankind, at any event, appears to have looked at the cat with some awe through the ages—she has been everything from a virgin hearth-goddess or fertility symbol to the familiar spirit of witches and the incarnation of the devil, under which rubric cats were burned alive on Good Friday. The cat, somehow, has seemed to be more than an ordinary quadruped; to partake of something mysterious and beyond human knowledge. Kittredge gives more than a score of citations of witches wounded or killed in cat shape.[6] Nor do we have to return to the Elizabethans to find people imagining queer goings-on in this department: as late as 1911 a witch-cat was the cause of intense excitement in Pottsville, Pennsylvania, occupying the headlines of the Philadelphia *Public Ledger* for four days.

Pigs—Filthy Gluttons?

When Mrs. Trollope visited America in the early 1830's, one of the conventions which pained her more than almost any other (except that of tobacco chewing and the omnipresent spitting which accompanied it) was the way of the Americans at table. People silently bolted their food with all the dispatch of which they were capable, men, women, and children. There was no conversation. One reached for the butter on the other side of the table, or for anything else one wanted, with an animal intentness on being fully fed which revolted the tastes of this cultivated English observer. In fact it was not until the new leisure began to be available to the growing middle-class citizen after World War I that the problem of good manners became a matter of widespread interest—and then it was a matter of correct etiquette rather than one of urbane, sophisticated behavior that was at issue. One remembers books of etiquette promoted by the fear advertisements: "What is wrong with this picture?" and so forth. The sophisticated hid their smiles behind their handkerchiefs, but Lillian Eichler and Emily Post had the final chuckle when they deposited royalties from the sales of more than a million copies each of their etiquette books sold between 1920 and 1945.[7]

In short, it is only recently that the man in the street (that nonexistent, figurative, but powerful creature) had any care for polite manners—in eating or in anything else. Today we are fairly conscious on this subject and would not hesitate to label a pig anybody who wolfed his food at the table, if one may be forgiven for combining a lupine with a porcine metaphor. Yet a very few years ago we were doing the same thing, most of us.

Pigs and hogs *do* grunt and snuffle and squeal and push each other around and walk over each other's backs and root their way into the trough, no question about that. Not one of them would waste ten seconds listening to the admonitions of an arbiter elegantiarum. But this is true also of an unsupervised group at a boys' camp composed of scions of the proudest houses in the nation.

Pigs are gluttons. That is no popular fallacy. The nonsense comes into the picture at the point where the hogs are thought of as the only, or supreme, exemplars of gluttony. How about your own Fido? Does he stop and groom himself between the first bite and the last? Or, to reach higher into elegance, how about Felix? Both cat and dog will either finish the dish or satisfy himself under normal conditions.

As for being filthy, it is certainly true that mankind has forced the pig to live, in many instances, in foul surroundings and has fed him on garbage. The pig can live in such muck. Also the pig loves to wallow in mud—he finds it cooling and comfortable. But if you have ever seen pigs running free in the fields or owned one as a pet you know that this much-maligned animal is teachable, intelligent, and not necessarily dirty. The nose was made for rooting, let's concede that; it will never be as spotless as that of the dog or cat. But to call the animal filthy because we require him to live in filth seems less than equitable. Sheep are just as dirty—dirtier, actually, with all that wool. Some cows and horses will eat themselves to death if given unlimited quantities of grain. But the pig stops when he's full. Do you?

BEAR CUBS ARE SHAPELESS UNTIL LICKED?

The truth in so many instances is stranger than any fiction a minstrel can devise. Someone passes along the story of the phoenix rising from its own ashes; and while the instructed are seen to smile behind their hands, the man from the laboratory explains that the lowly amoeba is immortal, physically and chemically immortal, as humans use that term. So what to believe? The answer, in general, is Keep an open mind, but not so open that your brains catch cold. All of nature is so incredibly wonderful that the unbelievable may very well be true.

In the case of the bears, however, No. The story that the she-bear (the dam) licks the young cubs until they change from a shapeless ball of fur into a true-blue bear, and that if she stops halfway through the youngster will grow up deformed or perhaps even die—this is not true. It is not hard to see how such a legend could arise, however; bear cubs are extremely tiny for such large mothers, and at first glance they do appear quite formless. No doubt hunters returned from the woods asserting that the cubs have no discernible shape without the licking; and the authors of bestiaries, to whom nothing was more succulent than a good moral for an animal yarn, seized upon the opportunity to develop the virtues of maternal sacrifice and mother love. Patiently and ceaselessly the bear mother licks and laps, never caring for her own comfort, until the tiny spark of life beside her has assumed the noble shape of a bear. One could almost write a popular song about this; Irving Berlin on his day off, perhaps.

The fact is, the legend was accepted almost everywhere as gospel, despite the fact that Aristotle, himself the occasional perpetuator of mythical natural history, rejected this particular one for reasons best known to himself.[8]

Probably the best-known literary use of the myth is in *Henry VI, Part II* (Act III, scene 2), in the speech in which the Duke of Gloucester (Richard Crook-Back) permits the audience to share his dreams of kingship in a terrifying soliloquy that used to roll off the tongue of John Barrymore like an incantation to all the powers of hell:

> She did corrupt frail nature with some bribe,
> To shrink mine arm up like a wither'd shrub;
> To make an envious mountain on my back,
> Where sits deformity to mock my body;
> To shape my legs of an unequal size;
> To disproportion me in every part,
> Like to a chaos, on an unlick'd bear-whelp,
> That carries no impression like the dam.

According to the twelfth-century Latin Bestiary that T. H. White (author of *The Once and Future King* trilogy) translated, one reason put forward for the "fact" that bear cubs are formless is that "the period of gestation is short, since the thirtieth day relieves the womb," and the prematurity of the birth is the cause "from whence it comes that a hasty, unformed creation is brought forth." In fact, this particular Latin author holds that the etymology of *bear*, from *Ursus*, akin to *orsus*, a beginning, points to the fact that the mother bear "sculptures her brood with her mouth (*ore*)."[9] This is ingenious enough to be true, but early etymologies must be suspect, and Eric Partridge shows this one to be erroneous, unfortunately. Like *beaver*, the word *bear* is ultimately the word *brown*, with family representatives in Sanskrit, Indo-European, Lithuanian (*beras*, brown), Old English, and Dutch (*bruin*, brown).

The bear is not the only large animal bearing tiny progeny: the kangaroo, which stands almost as tall as a man, gives birth to wee little things less than half an inch long.[10]

The size of the baby kangaroo is dramatically highlighted by Gerald Durrell, who observed the birth process in detail. He reports that the first sight of the baby is as a pink blob about the size of the first joint on a man's little finger and that it is placed on the tail of the mother, almost an embryo. The youngster has to pull its way up the fur of the maternal abdomen and find its way blindly into the marsupial pouch, getting not the slightest help from the parent; and if it is not up to this herculean task, that's the end of it.[11]

Incidentally, speaking of tiny babies, the offspring of the *American* marsupial the common opossum (*Didelphis marsupialis*), is incredibly small, although the contrast between parent and child is not perhaps as dramatic as with the kangaroo because the parent opossum is not so big. The baby possum, after a gestation period of only 13 days, is born weighing only 1/200 of an ounce or 2 grams, and is smaller than a bee. Then the baby uses his large forepaws and claws to climb up the furry abdomen to the pouch, which he does in about 16 seconds without any help from mamma, except, apparently, that during the birth she has licked a straight path with her tongue "in a line between the cloaca and her pouch," and the baby follows this damp path. Finally at "home," it attaches to one of the teats and stays put. After 100 days it emerges from the pouch and clings to the mother's back.[12]

MOLES HAVE NO EYES?

That any animal who lives underground and burrows his way through the earth whenever he wants to travel—that such an animal can have eyesight seems impossible. For one thing, he'd have dirt in his eyeballs all the time. For another, what is there to see in the blackness of the tunnel? And anyone who has ever seen the ridges on his once-smooth lawn, going here and there but accomplishing nothing except the undermining of the sod, must assume that the mole is heading this way and that at random, without any sense of direction such as would be supplied by sight. It is not hard to see how the legend of the mole's blindness arose.

A Latin bestiary translated by T. H. White says, "The mole is called Talpa because it is condemned to perpetual blindness in dark places. It is without eyes." (*Talpa* comes from a Greek root meaning "to dig.")[13]

Shakespeare, who knew something of nature from firsthand experience, apparently did not accept such nonsense. At least young Hotspur, in the roaring scene in which the great Glendower, Mortimer, and Hotspur divide up the kingdom, with the last-named taunting Glendower at every conceivable point, explains to his friends after Glendower's departure why he cannot help sneering at him: Glendower lectures to him all the time, showing off his court knowledge:

> With telling me of the moldwarp and the ant,
> And of the dreamer Merlin and his prophecies,
> . . . .
> And such a deal of skimble-skamble stuff . . .[14]

Moldwarp and *moldiwarp* were old-time variants of *mole.*

A generation later Sir Thomas Browne in his *Pseudodoxia Epidemica* (1646) said that the fact that moles do have eyes in their heads must be "manifest unto any that wants them not in his own."

Even so, the myth remains, and many people today who have never held a mole in their hands—and there must be quite a few of these people, come to think of it—still believe that there are no eyes in the animal's head. They're *there,* all right.

The Porcupine Shoots His Quills?

If the mistakes in substantive fact perpetuated in the verse of a much-loved and most kindly Harvard professor named Henry Wadsworth Longfellow were placed end to end, it would probably serve no appreciably useful purpose and could not dim his triumph as the first American to be given a place in the Poets' Corner at Westminster Abbey. Most notable among them, perhaps, would be Paul Revere telling his friend to place "one if by land and two if by sea," referring to lanterns in the church tower, when Revere himself ordered two lanterns, knowing in advance that the British would come by sea, but only fearful that he would never make the Charlestown shore himself, undetected. Then there is the porcupine in *Hiawatha* who "shot his shining quills like arrows." That he never did. The cute little thing has no machinery for doing so. The quills can be raised up by muscular action; but they sit loosely in their little pouches and come out only when they get too loose or become attached to the roof of some dog's mouth: a fearful thing to experience.

This is not to say that in slapping with his tail the porcupine could not flip an occasional loose quill off through the air; but his purpose in slapping is to hit his enemy and thus implant the fierce little barbs. Shoot them he cannot, so there is not the faintest reason why you should be afraid to come close if you want to. Lots of times he won't move a muscle even if you prod him with a stick.

The name has some interest. Latin *porcus*, pig, combines with *spina*, thorn, and we get Italian *porcospino* and Middle English *porke despyne* and *porkepin*. The Ghost in *Hamlet*, as you remember, could, if he were not forbidden, have told tales of hell so harrowing as to make "each separate hair to stand on end/Like quills upon the fretful porpentine." That may be what the animal was called down in the country at Stratford; etymologically it makes no sense. But the form crept into the language for a time, and others besides Shakespeare used it, so we mustn't blame him specifically. *Porcupine* is cognate with words one might never guess to be associated with "quill pig" in any way: *porcelain*, *purslane* (the plant), and *porpoise*, for instance— the last being a contraction of *porcus pisces*, pig fish, a fish with a pig's snout.[15] Porpoise lovers may object, but it's too late now.

As a neighbor, the porcupine can be both helpful and harmful to man. In his helpful role he is a slow-moving, careless, and easily overtaken source of food for a hunter lost in the wilderness, perhaps starving and out of ammunition. The old-time woodsmen will tell you that you must never kill them for that very reason. Furthermore, as scavengers they are part of Mother Nature's cleanup squad.

In his maleficent character, however, the porcupine chews holes in cabins, strips trees and kills them, and in the tiger country helps to create man-killers. This last item is explained by Roger Caras: it seems that a healthy tiger in good condition is not likely ever to harass the villages as a man-eater. But "tigers that are injured while killing porcupines, and end up crippled by quills and festering sores, have often become man-eaters due to their no longer being capable of taking swifter prey."[16]

To the North American Indian fraternity brothers of Aesop, especially among the Plains and Plateau Indians, the porcupine, the beaver, and the coyote were favorite animal personalities in the folk stories. Where Aesop had the fox as the wily trickster, the Indian had the coyote, who was forever taking advantage of the good nature of the porcupine and the beaver, his close associates. But apparently the porcupine is the most stupid of all, since the beaver also selects him for practical jokes—as in the tale in which he offers old porky a free ride on his back out across the lake to the island, and then sneaks off and leaves him stranded there. But we are happy to report that the porcupine had an answer to *that*. You'll never guess. He sang a song which caused the ice to form on the lake, and then he walked home leisurely on its shining surface.[17]

In the Micmac folk stories the porcupine has control of the cold weather, which accounts for the ice.

In the Hausa Negro tales, he has special powers over man and particularly over witches.

But never, neither in fable nor in real life, does he throw a single quill.

Incidental intelligence about porcupine quills: it has been "determined" that a porcupine comes equipped with about 18,100 quills. Who made the observation is not known. He is welcome to the job, and we, for one, are not going to dispute his estimate. Even a score of quills would be enough to create real respect for the porcupine in us. Again: ". . . a single quill driven deeply into his forearm. He let it stay, and within less than two days was able to remove it easily from the opposite side."[18] All we can say to this is, "he" was lucky. Porcupine quills usually cause infection, so that it is not merely the discomfort of the needle but the much worse pain of pus-laden flesh. In fact, the Massachusetts Audubon Society has stated that the fisher alone among animals is immune to such infection. The fisher is a member of the weasel family, does no fishing, but loves porcupine meat.

Dogs Are Clairvoyant?

Since dogs are more frequently in human company than any other animal with the possible exception of cats, and since they are adapted to being companions in adventure to the extent that no other animal can approach—as playmates, hunting partners, bodyguards, police agents, seeing eyes, and even trencher mates—man sees in the dog more potential abilities than he sees in any other creature, and it is very easy to become slobberingly sentimental about one's dog, after the manner of that otherwise rather tough hombre, Jack London. Readers will remember the association of Buck with John Thornton in *The Call of the Wild*, for instance, where man and dog stop just short of actual osculation. Albert Payson Terhune, too, and many others could make the old viol throb in these matters.

Far be it from us to sneer at the love of dog for man or vice versa; it can be a deeply involving emotion and a very real one: but it can also lead to exaggerated claims, and this is where the nonsense creeps in.

We now enter an area where fact and argument count for very little: it resembles religious fanaticism in that respect. If I tell you that we had a dog who could foretell a death in the family, or who could find his way home from the suburbs of Oscaloosa, Iowa, to the old barn at West Harwich, Massachusetts, then you might as well put it down as an oddity of my mental processes and let it go at that—because you can never convince me to the contrary. That your dog can identify an honest man and differentiate him from a crook, after all, is not much more miraculous than that by scent alone, and not by the appearance of the track, a dog can tell which direction the rabbit took by the increasing intensity of the scent or its opposite.

In short, what is *naturally* within the dog's abilities is so wonderful that we keep getting it mixed up with what we call the supernatural.

You can read in cold print the "historical" incident relating to the Abraham Lincoln funeral cortege passing Chambers Street in its journey through New York City: a large St. Bernard slipped through the crowd and trotted to the hearse bearing Lincoln's body. Here it took up its steady tread as part of the honor guard, precisely underneath the dead President's body. The dog's owner, Mr. Ed Morton, explained afterwards that he had taken the dog with him to Washington, and Lincoln had patted its head. The papers solemnly printed the acknowledgment that the dog "recognized Lincoln's hearse" through some peculiar instinct at the later occasion.[19] To such a tale as this one can only say that it is impossible to explain the facts with the evidence so far on the table: maybe the dog had some special reason for wanting to walk under the hearse for a while; maybe it was a sunny day and he wanted to be in the shade; maybe he liked accompanying the horses in this way; but that he spotted the funeral wagon and identified it as Lincoln's on the basis of having once been stroked on the head by the great man—this can be called nonsense with impunity.

Even so, the bizarre does occur sometimes, and we have an instance of a dog who rattled every time he moved. Dog's name was Jason; and he was owned by an Ilford man named James Gerard, who found himself becoming more and more unnerved by the rattling of his dog, a Doberman. Gerard finally took Jason to the vet who X-rayed the dog. Gerard is a scrap-metal dealer and it developed that the dog had been snatching up bits of these scraps and, for various undoubtedly supernatural reasons, swallowing them. At any rate, the vet removed by surgery seven ball bearings and a curtain rail fixture. Each of the ball bearings was an inch in diameter.

Perhaps the closest dogs have come to partaking of the supernatural was in the days when they were the familiar spirits of witches and various demons. "Didn't witch folks have partner animals? . . . Mostly they were cats or black dogs or such matter at that, but sometimes they were birds."[20]

There is no denying, of course, that dogs have shown an almost human intelligence at times—in fact, there is on record at least one instance in which a dog was carried on the rolls by name, as if he were a human being, along with the rest of the soldiers on the paymaster's lists; this was Becerrillo, the great war dog in the company of Don Juan Ponce de León, and he had the official rank of crossbowman. The Indians feared him more than any ten Spaniards, it is related.[21] But being "human" does not confer clairvoyance; and the proposition with which we opened this article was the question of dogs having second sight. Actually, dogs are handicapped by being color-blind and usually nearsighted; but they can perceive motion seven times better than a human.[22] They can be fooled by appearances just as readily as any of the rest of us—as a possum near Burton, Kansas, proved to his own great satisfaction in the spring of 1966. In that country Pete Base had trained his dog to hunt rabbits, which it would catch and shake to death. The dog cornered a possum and gave him the rabbit treatment, but not very thoroughly because the catch appeared to die immediately. So the dog buried his prey and trotted off. Base, who happened to be watching, reported that the dog had hardly gone away when the possum pulled himself out of the shallow burial and took off in the opposite direction. What true clairvoyant would permit such subterfuge?

Perhaps the ability to see through the veil comes late in life, when a dog gets to be past 25 or so. As we all know, 12 is a long life for a dog; a 20-year-old is a Methuselah; and yet 34 has been accepted by some authorities as "possible" for a dog. The oldest dog reliably reported was the black Labrador Adjutant belonging to James Hawkes of Lincolnshire, who lived 27 years and 3 months.[23] Adjutant was clever, but not clairvoyant.

The Lion Is the King?

In respect to his position in folklore and literature, there is no argument: "Leo the Lion, mightiest of beasts, will stand up to anybody." He is the symbol of ferocity, courage, royalty. To which, almost worshipfully, is added the characteristic and heroic trait of compassion: ". . . for they spare the prostrate . . . they prey on men rather than on women."[24] This reputation has not dimmed with the years. Samuel Johnson's Dictionary (1755) said succinctly: "lion. The fiercest and most magnanimous of fourfooted beasts."[25] But it is the ferocity, the courage, which has dominated our respect and awe: we speak of "the lion's share"; we face our deepest peril when we put our hand—or head—into "the lion's mouth"; and if there is "a lion in the path," then we could not choose a riskier road. Hence it is not strange that in heraldry we find the lion appearing so frequently—often in threes—to represent the spirit of some proud and noble family.

Now we are not out to laugh the lion out of court or to try to disparage him in any way; some of our best friends are lions. On the other hand, our subject is the nonsense of popular error, and we would be derelict in our stern duty if we coughed politely into our handkerchiefs at this point, out of respect for a noble creature, and failed to point out at least the most obvious lunacies which popular hero worship of the lion has produced.

Perhaps the greatest piece of nonsense—and the most typical—is the assumption that one lion is necessarily similar in character to another lion: that they are all the same. Quite to the contrary, they don't even *look* the same. "Faces vary tremendously and individuals can be as readily distinguished by observers as can people. . . . They differ as much in disposition as they do in appearance. It is not only in children's books that we can find 'lazy' lions, 'happy' lions, 'timid' lions, and 'brave' lions."

Another error is the assumption that the lion is a creature of the jungle. He is not: he is a creature of the open country.

Another is that he is the largest of the cats. He is not, although he can measure 11 feet, tip to tip, stand 42 inches at the shoulder, and weigh 400 pounds. But the Siberian tiger, from whom, O God, deliver us, is longer, higher, heavier, and hungrier.

Another is that he is a ferocious killer. And here, dear children, we will solicit your closest attention, because a tiny moral makes its appearance at this juncture. The ferocious killer is that sweet flower of leonine womanhood whom he won as his mate. He goes along on the hunt, all right, but "almost all killing is done by the female. The lion roars, the lioness kills."[26]

Envoi

The greatest of all nonsense, we have maintained, occurs when we believe that we have now at last settled upon the final truth of anything. Yet we are so hot for certainty in this our life that we will continue to content ourselves with dusty answers and confirm their truth by the sheer force of our numbers: surely it remains incredible that fifty million Frenchmen can be wrong. . . .

Yet new research reveals new facts that change old truths; photographs taken by Ranger and Orbiter spacecraft, and especially by Surveyor 3 in the spring of 1967, on the moon's surface itself, show us that the green-cheese theory has to go. With a cry of triumph we leap to the new certainties exhibited in the moon-probe photos. After all, we have to believe *something*—we can't go on holding our loyalties in abeyance pending better evidence, forever!

Well, then, so be it. As long as we are mentally prepared for the shock when some old, beloved, and much-cuddled truth is exposed as cherished nonsense, we are none the worse for being shaken up. We may not like it particularly; but if we are prepared, it does us no harm. For years, everyone believed, and especially doctors, that if you burnt your finger or any other part of your body the very best thing to do was to bathe it immediately in hot water. This utterly mad practice should have been felt and experienced for the nonsense it is ages ago, for there was no relief to be had from such homeopathic magic. It only made the pain worse. But, somehow, that was considered to be good for you. During the last few years it has been established that the best thing to do on sustaining a burn is to plunge the injured part into as cold water as possible. The relief experienced is the best proof of the efficacy of this, one would have thought, obvious treatment. The rule appears to be: Treat heat with cold, treat cold with heat. Obvious as these rules may seem to us today, for centuries it was not they but their opposites that appeared obvious.

What is obvious, of course, is what we believe to be obvious, and most of us, as we have pointed out *ad nauseam* in the preceding pages, tend to identify our beliefs, our prejudices, with the laws of nature. By a sort of self-validating process the very fact that we believe a thing to be true tends to make that thing true in our eyes. The minds of some people are like the pupil of the eye: the more light you expose them to, the narrower they grow.

> Through the distorting glass of prejudice
> All nature seems awry, and but its own
> Wide-warped creations straight; but Reason's eye
> Beholds in every line of nature—truth,
> Immortal truth, and sees a God in all.

While the quest for certainty is both understandable and laudable, intelligence and humanity call for a tentative attitude, an attitude which is experimental, heuristic. The intelligent thrust of the mind is not toward belief or disbelief, toward proof or disproof, but simply toward the discovery of what is—discovery that must be constantly checked and verified. We all of us are prone to error, and all of us believe in some nonsense. Most of our beliefs are ours by faith alone. But man cannot live by faith alone, for faith is a poor substitute for thinking. However, there are many things that must be taken on faith. We cannot possibly prove everything for ourselves. In most matters of belief we must depend upon our other selves, our authorities, an authority being defined as one who *should* know. Authorities are not infallible and are therefore sometimes wrong. One of their most engaging qualities is their readiness to admit to error in the face of the necessary evidence. The nonsense that other people believe is exceeded only by the nonsense that we ourselves believe. The sensible thing is not to deny that a great many of our beliefs are nonsensical, but freely to admit the possibility and examine our beliefs from time to time by hanging large question marks upon them.

In these pages what we have attempted to demonstrate is not that man is a fool, but that he is achingly, agonizingly, and amusingly *human*. Man's immortal laughter is the brightest proof of his consciousness of the humanity that makes this heaven-storming creature reach for the stars.

Notes

1. Humans and Human Customs

1. N. R. F. Maier and T. C. Schneirla, *Principles of Animal Psychology* (New York: McGraw-Hill, Inc., 1935), pp. 164 ff.
2. Havelock Ellis, *The Philosophy of Conflict* (London: Constable, 1919), pp. 51-52.
3. Published by the National Council of Catholic Men, 1312 Massachusetts Avenue NW, Washington 5, D.C. Cited in Karl Sax, *Standing Room Only* (Boston: Beacon Press, 1955), p. 180.
4. Sir Arthur Keith, *The Place of Prejudice in Modern Civilization* (New York: John Day, 1931).
5. Both Lévy-Bruhl and Nilsson quotes cited by E. R. Dodds in *The Greeks and the Irrational* (Boston: Beacon Press, 1957).
6. See Konrad Lorenz, *On Aggression* (New York: Harcourt, Brace & World, 1966); Abraham Kardiner and John Preble, *Glencoe: The Story of the Massacre* (New York: Holt, Rinehart & Winston, 1966).
7. Irving, J. Lee, *Language Habits in Human Affairs* (New York: Harper & Brothers, 1941), p. 243.
8. Eric Partridge, *Origins: A Short Etymological Dictionary of Modern English* (New York: The Macmillan Co., 1959).
9. Alfred Korzybski, *Science and Sanity* (Lancaster, Pa.: Science Press, 1933), p. 384.
10. Richard Hofstadter, *Social Darwinism in American Thought: 1860-1915* (Boston: Beacon Press, paperback, 1958), p. 39.
11. William Appleman Williams, *The Contours of American History* (Cleveland: World Publishing Co., 1961), p. 439.
12. Voltaire, *L'Ingénu* (1767), chap. 10.
13. *Reader's Digest Almanac*, under "Social Security," "Medicare," "Education," "Industrial Employment," etc. (Pleasantville, N.Y., 1967).

14. From T. R. Ybarra's *Young Man of the World* (New York: Ives Washburn, Inc., 1942). Reprinted by permission.

15. Iona and Peter Opie (eds.), *The Oxford Dictionary of Nursery Rhymes* (New York: Oxford University Press, Inc., 1958), p. 435.

16. Charles Earle Funk, *A Hog on Ice and Other Curious Expressions* (New York: Harper & Brothers, 1948).

17. Burton Stevenson, *The Home Book of Proverbs, Maxims and Familiar Phrases* (New York: Dodd, Mead & Co., 1967).

18. James Montgomery, *Nothing but the Truth* (New York: Samuel French, Inc.), pp. 28, 29.

19. Wayland Young, *Eros Denied* (New York: Grove Press, Inc., 1966), p. 273.

20. J. B. S. Haldane, *Science and Human Life* (New York: Harper & Bros., 1933), p. 213.

21. Stanton A. Coblentz, *Avarice, A History* (Washington, D.C.: Public Affairs Press, 1965), p. 214.

22. Vergilius Ferm (ed.), *Encyclopedia of Religion* (New York: Philosophical Library, 1945); and Edgar Sheffield Brightman, *Atheism*.

23. Gillian Tindall, *A Handbook on Witches* (New York: Atheneum Publishers, 1966), p. 57.

24. Douglas Hill and Pat Williams, *The Supernatural* (New York: Hawthorn Books, 1966), p. 179.

25. *The Encyclopaedia Britannica* (11th edition) estimates from 100,000 to millions; Hill and Williams estimate at least 200,000 (*op. cit.*, p. 224).

26. Marion L. Starkey, *The Devil in Massachusetts* (New York: Alfred A. Knopf., 1950), p. 13.

27. George F. Weston, Jr., *Boston Ways* (Boston: Beacon Press, 1958), p. 216.

28. Starkey, *op. cit.*, p. 212.

29. Hill and Williams, *op. cit.*, p. 175.

30. *Ibid.*, p. 174.

31. *Ibid.*, p. 232 (with photograph).

32. Richard Calder, *Medicine and Man* (New York: Mentor Books, 1958), p. 30.

33. Leonard Louis Levinson, *The Left-Handed Dictionary* (New York: Collier Books, 1966), p. 112.

34. Calder, *op. cit.*, p. 13.

35. *Ibid.*, p. 79.

36. Harvey Einbinder, *The Myth of the Britannica* (New York: Grove Press, Inc., 1964), p. 24. The same author lists in an appendix 666 Britannica articles in the 1963 edition which are faulty, out of date, or inaccurate in one way or another. A work larger than the Britannica is the 700-volume encyclopedia commissioned by the first Manchu emperor, K'ang-hi, in 1726, which is still widely used. A copy is in the British Museum.

37. Earl Morse Wilbur, *Our Unitarian Heritage* (Boston: Beacon Press, 1963), p. 361.

38. Hannah Campbell, *Why Did They Name It . . . ?* (New York: Fleet Publishing Corp., 1964), p. 63.

39. Meredith F. Eller, *The Beginnings of the Christian Religion* (New York: Bookman Associates, 1958), pp. 236, 240, 243, 374. Also Roy B. Chamberlin and Herman Feldman (eds.), *The Dartmouth Bible*, revised edition (Boston: Houghton Mifflin Co., 1961), p. 860; Roland H. Bainton, *The Horizon History of Christianity* (New York: Harper & Row, 1964), pp.

49, 95; *The Interpreter's Bible,* Vol. VII (Nashville: Abingdon-Cokesbury, 1951), p. 73; Kenneth Scott Latourette, *Christianity Through the Ages* (New York: Harper Chapelbooks, 1965), p. 46; and Johannes Weiss, *Earliest Christianity,* Vol. I, (New York: Harper Torchbooks, 1959), pp. 4, 15.

40. Gordon W. Allport, "Mental Health: A Generic Attitude," *Journal of Religion and Health,* October, 1964: "It is a disturbing thing (but again confirmed by many researches) that, on the average, churchgoers are more bigoted toward minority groups than nonchurchgoers."

41. Charles Y. Glock and Rodney Stark, *Christian Beliefs and Anti-Semitism* (New York: Harper & Row, 1966), pp. 128, 137.

42. Gallup Poll figures in the Boston *Globe,* Dec. 26, 1966, show that 44 percent of the nation's adults were churchgoers in 1966; that the same figure was true for 1965; and that the peak of church attendance was 49 percent in 1958.

43. Albert Schweitzer, *The Quest of the Historical Jesus* (New York: The Macmillan Co.), p. 396.

44. Vilhjalmur Stefansson, *My Life with the Eskimo* (New York: The Macmillan Co., 1913), p. 255.

2. Persistent Notions About Food

1. Hannah Campbell, *Why Did They Name It. . . ?* (New York: Fleet Publishing Corp., 1964), p. 3.

2. T. K. Derry and Trevor I. Williams, *A Short History of Technology* (London: Oxford University Press, 1961), pp. 497, 695.

3. Irving S. and Nell M. Kull, *An Encyclopedia of American History* (New York: Popular Library, Inc., Eagle Books, 1965), p. 137.

4. *Encyclopædia Britannica,* 11th ed.

5. L. Jean Bogert, *Nutrition and Physical Fitness,* (8th ed., 1966; Philadelphia: W. B. Saunders Co.), p. 380.

6. For an account of this case see Frederic Wertham, *The Show of Violence* (New York: Doubleday & Co., Inc., 1949), pp. 65-94.

7. A. J. Clement, "Caries in the South African Ape-Men," *British Dental Journal,* vol. 101 (1956), pp. 4-7.

8. Weston A. Price, *Nutrition and Physical Degeneration* (New York: Harper & Brothers, Hoeber Medical Division, 1939).

9. V. Suk, "Eruption and Decay of Permanent Teeth in White and Negroes" (with comparative remarks on other races), *American Journal of Physical Anthropology,* vol. 2 (1919), pp. 351-388.

10. Bogert, *op. cit.,* p. 382.

11. *Ibid.,* p. 384.

12. *Ibid.,* p. 380.

13. *Consumers' Guide,* U. S. Government Publication, vol. 10, No. 9 (August, 1944); War Food Administration.

14. H. W. Haggard and E. M. Jellinek, *Alcohol Explored* (New York: Doubleday, Doran, 1942), p. 99. See also M. E. Chafetz, *Liquor: The Servant* (Boston: Little, Brown and Co., 1965).

15. Haggard and Jellinek, *op. cit.,* pp. 191-193.

16. *Works,* I, p. 264.

17. *Ibid.,* p. 196.

18. Charles J. Brim, *Medicine in the Bible* (New York: Froben Press, 1936).

19. Sir George James Frazer, *Folklore in the Old Testament*, 3 vols. (New York: The Macmillan Co., 1919).
20. Maria Leach and Jerome Fried (eds.), *Dictionary of Folklore* (New York: Funk and Wagnalls, 1950), vol. 2, p. 869.
21. Sir Thomas Browne, *Works* (London: Faber & Faber, 1964), vol. 2, p. 81.
22. Morris Fishbein (ed.), *Modern Home Medical Adviser* (Garden City: Doubleday & Co., 1949), p. 778.
23. L. Jean Bogert, *op. cit.*, p. 377.
24. Clifford C. Snyder, "Tissue Excision Urged for Snakebite," *Journal of the American Medical Association*, vol. 198, no. 13 (Dec. 26, 1966), pp. 35, 36.
25. Haggard and Jellinek, *op. cit.*, p. 99.
26. Mark Graubard, *Man's Food: Its Rhyme and Reason* (New York: The Macmillan Co., 1943), p. 5.
27. Redcliffe N. Salaman, *The History and Social Influence of the Potato* (New York: Cambridge University Press, 1949).
28. Frederick J. Simoons, *Eat Not This Flesh* (Madison: University of Wisconsin Press, 1961), p. 106.
29. *Ibid.*, p. 49.
30. *Ibid.*, p. 108.
31. Estes Kefauver, *In a Few Hands: Monopoly Power in America* (New York: Pantheon Books, 1965), p. 18.
32. Mark Graubard, *op. cit.*, p. 136.
33. James Bradstreet Greenough and George Lyman Kittredge, *Words and Their Ways in English Speech* (New York: The Macmillan Co., 1901; reprinted in Beacon Paperbacks, 1962), p. 331.
34. Roy H. Copperud, *A Dictionary of Usage and Style* (New York: Hawthorn Books, 1964).
35. H. W. Fowler, *Modern English Usage*, revised and edited by Sir Ernest Gower (New York: Oxford University Press, 1965), p. 651.
36. Bergen and Cornelia Evans, *A Dictionary of Contemporary American Usage* (New York: Random House, 1957), p. 551.
37. *Ibid.*
38. Mitford M. Mathews (ed.), *A Dictionary of Americanisms on Historical Principles* (Chicago: University of Chicago Press, 1951).
39. Harold Wentworth and Stuart Berg Flexner, *Dictionary of American Slang* (New York: Thomas Y. Crowell, 1960).
40. H. W. Fowler, *op. cit.*

3. Beliefs About the Human Body

1. Captain Marryat, *Peter Simple*. Everyman edition (New York: E. P. Dutton & Co., Inc., 1907), p. 264.
2. G. L. Walls, *The Vertebrate Eye* (Bloomfield Hills, Michigan: Cranbrook Institute of Science), pp. 16, 543.
3. Adolph H. Schultz, "On tool-use and crowded teeth," *Current Anthropology*, vol. 7 (1966), p. 356.
4. *Ibid.*
5. *Ibid.*
6. Ashley Montagu, "The Significance of the Variability of the Upper Lateral Incisor Teeth in Man," *Human Biology*, vol. 12 (1940), pp. 323-358. Frank Colyer, *Variations and Diseases of the Teeth in Animals* (London: John

Bale, Danielson & Sons, 1936). W. W. James, *The Jaws and Teeth of Primates* (London: Pitman Medical Publishing Co., 1960). Peter J. Brekhus, *Your Teeth* (Minneapolis: University of Minnesota Press, 1941).

7. R. M. and Ada W. Yerkes, *The Great Apes* (New Haven: Yale University Press, 1929), pp. 23, 421.

8. See H. H. Ploss, M. Bartels, and Paul Bartels, *Woman* (London: Heinemann, 1935, vol. 1), p. 82.

9. D. J. Morton, *The Human Foot* (New York: Columbia University Press, 1935), p. 46.

10. Lee McCarthy, *Diagnosis and Treatment of Diseases of the Hair* (St. Louis, Missouri: C. V. Mosby), p. 66. The reference to Simon indicates C. Simon, "Blanchement Rapide des Cheveux" in *Nouvelle Practique Dermatologique* (Paris: Masson & Cie., 1936, vol. 5), p. 840.

11. H. H. Newman, *Multiple Human Births* (New York: Doubleday, Doran, 1940), p. 55.

12. I. A. Rosanoff and A. J. Rosanoff, "A Study of Mental Disorders in Twins," *Journal of Juvenile Research*, vol. 15 (1931). A. J. Rosanoff, L. M. Handy, and I. R. Plesset, "The Etiology of Manic-Depressive Syndromes with Special Reference to Their Occurrence in Twins," *Psychological Monographs*, vol. 48 (4), No. 216 (1937). *Idem.*, "The Etiology of Child Behavior Difficulties, Juvenile Delinquency and Adult Criminality with Special Reference to Their Occurrence in Twins," *Psychological Monographs*, vol. 1 (1941).

13. Carl E. Akeley, *In Brightest Africa* (New York: Doubleday, 1920), pp. 99-103. Stewart Edward White, *Lions in the Path* (New York: Doubleday, 1926), pp. 84-90.

14. Mildred Trotter, "The Resistance of Hair to Certain Supposed Growth Stimulants," *Archives of Dermatology and Syphiology*, vol. 7 (1923), pp. 93ff.

15. Edith L. Potter and F. L. Adair, *Foetal and Neonatal Death* (Chicago: University of Chicago Press, 1940).

16. C. McNeil, in the *Edinburgh Medical Journal*, vol. 50 (1943), p. 491.

17. Beryl Corner, *Prematurity* (Springfield, Illinois: Charles C. Thomas, Publisher, 1960).

18. E. L. McAdam, Jr., and George Milne (eds.), *Johnson's Dictionary: A Modern Selection* (New York: Pantheon Books, 1963), p. 67.

19. Vilhjalmur Stefansson, *My Life with the Eskimo*, p. 155; *The Friendly Arctic* (New York: The Macmillan Co., 1915, new rev. ed. 1943), p. 455.

20. Fritz Kahn, *Our Sex Life* (New York: Alfred A. Knopf, Inc., 1939), p. 395.

21. August A. Thomen, *Doctors Don't Believe It, Why Should You?* (New York: Simon and Schuster, Inc., 1941), p. 86.

22. Viktor Frankl, *Man's Search for Meaning* (Boston: Beacon Press, 1962), p. 15.

23. Aleš Hrdlička, *Alaska Diary* (Lancaster, Pennsylvania: Jacques Cattell Press, 1943), p. 229: "The air here must be free from the microbes of 'cold.'"

24. W. H. Haggard, *The Human Body* (New York: Harper & Brothers, 1938), p. 220.

25. Logan Clendening, *The Human Body* (New York: Alfred A. Knopf, Inc., 1929), p. 42.

26. H. S. Jennings, "Eugenics" in *Encyclopedia of the Social Sciences* (New York: The Macmillan Co., 1937), vol. 5, p. 619.

27. J. B. S. Haldane, *Heredity and Politics* (New York: W. W. Norton, 1938), p. 89. See also, Ashley Montagu, *Human Heredity* (Cleveland: World Publishing Co., 1963).
28. V. V. Rozanov, *Solitaria* (London: Wishart, 1927), p. 96.
29. Julian Huxley (ed.), *Aldous Huxley 1894-1963* (New York: Harper & Row, 1965), p. 162.
30. Howard W. Haggard, *Man and His Body* (New York: Harper & Brothers, 1938), p. 293.
31. Logan Clendening, *op. cit.*, p. 35.
32. For the American usage, Webster III. For the Epigoni, Oskar Seiffert, *A Dictionary of Classical Antiquity* (the 1891 edition revised and edited by H. Nettleship and J. E. Sandys) (New York: Meridian Books, 1956).
33. Sir John Boyd Orr, *Food, Health and Income* (New York: Macmillan, 1936).
34. Vilhjalmur Stefansson, *My Life with the Eskimo* and *The Friendly Arctic*.
35. J. M. Tanner, *Education and Physical Growth* (London: University of London Press, 1961), p. 113.
36. J. M. Tanner and Gordon Rattray Taylor, *Growth* (New York: Time-Life Science Library, 1965), p. 186.
37. Howard W. Haggard, *Man and His Body* (New York: Harper & Brothers, 1938), p. 40.
38. Samuel Goodstone, *The Doctor Has a Heart Attack* (Boston: Beacon Press, 1964), p. 104.
39. Edward S. Gifford, Jr., *The Evil Eye* (New York: The Macmillan Co., 1958), p. 146.
40. Ashley Montagu, "The Concept of Atavism," *Science*, vol. 87 (1938), pp. 462, 463.
41. A. S. Parks (ed.), *Marshall's Physiology of Reproduction*, 3rd ed., vol. 2 (London and New York: Longmans, 1958), p. 822; and L. I. Dublin, *Factbook on Man* (New York: The Macmillan Co., 1965), p. 16.
42. For a detailed discussion of this subject see Ashley Montagu, *The Reproductive Development of the Female* (New York: Julian Press, Inc., 1957).
43. Ashley Montagu, *Life Before Birth* (New York: New American Library, 1964), pp. 24, 25; *idem., Prenatal Influences* (Springfield, Illinois: Charles C. Thomas, Publisher, 1962), pp. 32-50.

4. Misconceptions About the Human Mind

1. Earnest A. Hooton, *Why Men Behave like Apes and Vice Versa* (Princeton: Princeton University Press, 1940), p. 205.
2. For a detailed anatomy of Hooton's views see Robert K. Merton and Ashley Montagu, "Crime and the Anthropologist," *American Anthropologist*, vol. 42 (1940), pp. 384-408.
3. Clifford Beers, *A Mind That Found Itself* (New York: G. P. Putnam's Sons, 1935).
4. E. F. Daglish, *The Life Story of Beasts* (New York: William Morrow & Co., Inc., 1931), p. 206.
5. R. M. Yerkes, *Almost Human* (New York: Century, 1925), p. 121; R. M. and A. W. Yerkes, *The Great Apes* (New Haven: Yale University Press, 1929); Wolfgang Kohler, *The Mentality of the Apes* (New York: Harcourt, Brace & Co., 1925); Irven DeVore (ed.), *Primate Behavior* (New York: Holt, Rinehart & Winston, Inc., 1965); C. H. Southwick (ed.), *Primate Social Behavior* (Princeton: Van Nostrand, 1963); A. M. Schrier,

H. F. Harlow, and F. Stollnitz (eds.), *Behavior of Nonhuman Primates*, 2 vols. (New York: Academic Press, 1965); A. R. and G. G. Simpson (eds.), *Behavior and Evolution* (New Haven: Yale University Press, 1958).

6. Gertrude Davies Lintz, *Animals Are My Hobby* (New York: Robert McBride, 1942).

7. R. M. Yerkes, *Almost Human*, p. 240, and *The Great Apes*, p. 470.

8. J. A. Loeser, *Animal Behavior* (London: Macmillan & Co., 1940); E. S. Russell, *The Behavior of Animals* (London: Arnold, 1934); N. Tinbergen, *Social Behavior in Animals* (New York: John Wiley & Sons, Inc., 1953); W. H. Thorpe, *Learning and Instinct in Animals* (Cambridge: Harvard University Press, 1956); J. L. Cloudsley-Thompson, *Animal Behavior* (New York: The Macmillan Co., 1961); William Etkin (ed.), *Social Behavior and Organization Among Vertebrates* (Chicago: University of Chicago Press, 1964); Adolf Portmann, *Animals as Social Beings* (New York: Viking Press, Inc., 1961).

9. Loeser, *op. cit.*, pp. 64, 65.

10. H. S. Jennings, *Behavior of Lower Organisms* (New York: Columbia University Press, 1906; reprinted, Indiana University Press, 1962).

11. S. H. Kraines and E. S. Thetford, *Managing Your Mind* (New York: The Macmillan Co., 1944).

12. J. C. Eccles, "Hypotheses Relating to the Mind-Body Problem," *Nature*, vol. 168 (1951), p. 3.

13. Maria Leach and Jerome Fried (eds.), *Dictionary of Folklore, Mythology and Legend* (New York: Funk & Wagnalls, 1949, vol. 1), p. 526; Stith Thompson, *Motif-Index of Folk Literature* (Bloomington: Indiana University Press, 6 vols., 1932-1937).

14. Sigmund Freud, *The Interpretation of Dreams* (New York: Modern Library, 1938), p. 390.

15. Abraham Lincoln, "Response to a Serenade," Nov. 10, 1864.

16. Ashley Montagu, *The Humanization of Man* (Cleveland: World Publishing Co., 1962) and *The Human Revolution* (World, 1965); Weston La Barre, *The Human Animal* (Chicago: University of Chicago Press, 1954); Hugh Miller, *Progress and Decline* (Los Angeles: Ward Ritchie Press, 1963); Elsworth Faris, *The Nature of Human Nature* (New York: McGraw-Hill, 1937).

17. Ruth Benedict, *Patterns of Culture* (Boston: Little, Brown and Co., 1936).

18. A. Roe and G. G. Simpson (eds.), *Evolution and Behavior* (New Haven: Yale University Press, 1958); Ashley Montagu, *The Humanization of Man* (Cleveland: World Publishing Co., 1962); Theodosius Dobzhansky, *Mankind Evolving* (New Haven: Yale University Press, 1963).

19. T. R. Garth, "A Study of the Foster Indian Child in the White Home," *Psychological Bulletin*, vol. 32 (1935), pp. 708, 709.

20. J. H. Rohrer, "The Test Intelligence of Osage Indians," *Journal of Social Psychology*, vol. 16 (1942), pp. 99-105.

21. H. H. Newman, *Multiple Human Births* (New York: Doubleday & Co., Inc., 1940), p. 19; H. H. Newman, F. N. Freeman, and K. J. Holzinger, *Twins: A Study of Heredity and Environment* (Chicago: University of Chicago Press, 1937); J. Shields, *Monozygotic Twins: Brought Up Apart and Brought Up Together* (London and New York: Oxford University Press, 1962); H. L. Koch, *Twins and Twin Relations* (Chicago: University of Chicago Press, 1966); Amram Scheinfeld, *Twins* (Philadelphia: J. B. Lippincott Co., 1967).

22. W. Barclay Squire, "Music" in *Shakespeare's England*, vol. 2 (London and New York: Oxford University Press, 1926).
23. William L. Langer, *An Encyclopedia of World History* (Boston: Houghton Mifflin Co., 1952).
24. See Ashley Montagu, *The Idea of Race* (Lincoln, Nebraska: University of Nebraska Press, 1965), p. 19.
25. R. B. Cattell, *General Psychology* (Cambridge, Massachusetts: Sci-Art Publishers, 1941), p. 380.
26. Banesh Hoffman, *The Tyranny of Testing* (New York: Crowell-Collier Press, 1964), p. 110.

5. Absurdities About Race

1. That things are not always what they are named is a fact worthy of some concentrated study—or at least of stopping to clip news reports occasionally. On July 9, 1966, *The New Yorker* reported that in the Sheraton Motor Inn on 12th Avenue, neither the Riverview East nor the Riverview West has windows.
2. Joseph A. de Gobineau, *The Moral and Intellectual Diversity of Races* (Philadelphia: J. B. Lippincott Co., 1856).
3. Houston Stewart Chamberlain, *The Foundations of the Nineteenth Century*, translation by John Lees, with an Introduction by Lord Redesdale, 2 vols. (London and New York: John Lane, 1910).
4. John Stuart Mill, *Principles of Political Economy*, 2 vols. (London: Longmans, 1848).
5. Frederic E. Faverty, *Matthew Arnold: The Ethnologist* (Evanston, Illinois: Northwestern University Press, 1951).
6. Matthew Arnold, *Culture and Anarchy and Friendship's Garden* (New York: Macmillan & Co., 1883), pp. 124, 125.
7. From Goethe's *Wilhelm Meister*, quoted by Carlyle in *Past and Present*.
8. See John Oakesmith, *Race and Nationality* (New York: Stokes, 1919), p. 41.
9. Thomas Henry Huxley, "Emancipation—Black and White," in his *Science and Education* (New York: Collier, 1901), pp. 64, 65.
10. Karl Pearson, *National Life from the Standpoint of Science* (London: Black, 1901), p. 44.
11. Pearson, *The Grammar of Science*, 2nd ed. (London: Black, 1900); revised reprint, Everyman Edition (New York: Dutton, 1937), p. 310. For a devastating critique of Pearson's views see J. A. Hobson, *Imperialism* (London: Allen and Unwin, 1938, and Ann Arbor Paperbacks, University of Michigan Press, 1965), pp. 153ff.
12. Bernard Bosanquet, *The Philosophical Theory of the State* (London: Allen & Unwin, 1899).
13. J. A. Hobson, *Imperialism: A Study.* 2nd ed., (London: Allen & Unwin, 1905), p. 157.
14. Margaret Mead, *New Lives for Old: Cultural Transformation—Manus, 1928-53.* With a New Preface, 1965. (New York: William Morrow, 1966), pp. xiii-xvii.
15. Franz Boas, "Racial Purity," *Asia*, vol. 40 (1940), pp. 231-234.
16. Sir Arthur Keith, *The Place of Prejudice in Modern Civilization* (New York: John Day, 1931), p. 50.

17. Clark Wissler, *Indians of the United States* (New York: Doubleday, Doran, 1940), p. 241, and the 1967 World Almanac.

18. Computed from R. M. Yerkes, *Psychological Examining in the United States Army*, Memoirs of the National Academy of Sciences, Vol. 15, Tables 205, 206, pp. 689, 730 (Washington, D.C.: U.S. Government Printing Office, 1921). Reproduced from Frank Lorimer and Frederick Osborn, *The Dynamics of Population* (New York: The Macmillan Co., 1934), p. 140, Table 46.

19. Ashley Montagu, "Intelligence of Northern Negroes and Southern Whites in the First World War," *American Journal of Psychology*, vol. 48 (1945), pp. 161-188.

20. For a full account of this piece of history see Ashley Montagu, *Man's Most Dangerous Myth: The Fallacy of Race*, 4th ed. (Cleveland and New York: World Publishing Co., 1964), pp. 386-392.

21. Giorgio de Santillana, *The Crime of Galileo* (Chicago: University of Chicago Press, 1959), p. 329.

22. Frederick D. Grant, *Rome and Reunion* (New York: Oxford University Press, 1965), p. 185: ". . . as I discovered when the *Encyclopaedia Britannica* delayed and finally, after three years, rejected a few articles the editor had asked me to prepare: they were unacceptable to the Roman Catholic censor of educational books, since they represented a 'Protestant' view of the Bible."

23. Victor Heiser, *An American Doctor's Odyssey* (New York: W. W. Norton, 1936).

24. Max Müller, *Biographies of Words, and The Home of the Aryans* (London: 1888), p. 89.

25. H. H. Bender, *The Home of the Europeans* (Princeton: Princeton University Press, 1922), p. 322.

26. Louis L. Snyder, *Race: A History of Modern Ethnic Theories* (Chicago: Ziff-Davis Publishing Co., 1939), p. 86.

27. Eric Partridge, *Origins: A Short Etymological Dictionary of Modern English* (London: Routledge & Kegan Paul, 2nd ed., 1959).

28. John Smith, *A Map of Virginia with a Description of the Countrey* (Oxford: Joseph Barnes, 1612).

29. "Nobody knows what the phrase 'black power' really means, neither those who oppose it nor those who have given it currency. To Roy Wilkins it means 'anti-white power.' To Dr. Martin Luther King it means 'black supremacy.' To Vice-President Hubert Humphrey it means 'apartheid.' . . . Floyd B. McKissick, national director of CORE . . . describes it as a slogan to 'bring the black American into the covenant of brotherhood,' so that Negroes can achieve economic and political equality. . . ." (Editorial, *New York Times*, July 12, 1966).

30. T. Wingate Todd and D. W. Lyon, "Cranial Suture Closure: Its Progress and Age Relationship. Part IV. Ectocranial Closure in Adult Males of Negro Stock," *American Journal of Physical Anthropology*, vol. 8 (1925), pp. 149-168.

31. Miguel Leon-Portilla (ed.), *The Broken Spears: The Aztec Account of the Conquest of Mexico* (Boston: Beacon Press, 1962).

32. Frank Ford, *Diseases of the Nervous System in Infancy, Childhood and Adolescence*, 5th ed. (Springfield, Illinois: Charles C Thomas, 1966), p. 725.

33. Amram Scheinfeld, *Your Heredity and Environment* (Philadelphia: Lip-

pincott, 1965), p. 295. L. T. Hilliard and B. H. Kirman, *Mental Deficiency*, 2nd ed. (Boston: Little, Brown & Co., 1965).

34. T. Wingate Todd and Anna Lindala, "Dimensions of the Body, Whites and American Negroes of Both Sexes," *American Journal of Physical Anthropology*, vol. 12 (1928), p. 73.

35. Franklin P. Mall, "On Several Anatomical Characters Said to Vary According to Race and Sex," *American Journal of Anatomy*, vol. 9 (1909), pp. 1-33.

36. E.g., G. Levin, "Racial and 'Inferiority' Characters in the Human Brain," *American Journal of Physical Anthropology*, vol. 22 (1937), pp. 345-380.

37. Ashley Montagu, *An Introduction to Physical Anthropology*. 3rd ed. (Springfield, Illinois: C. C. Thomas, 1961), p. 199; and *The Science of Man* (New York: Odyssey Press, 1964), p. 53.

38. Vilhjalmur Stefansson, *My Life With the Eskimo* (New York: Collier, paper), p. 112. *The Friendly Arctic* (New York: Macmillan), p. 479.

39. Earnest A. Hooton, *Why Men Behave Like Apes* (Princeton: Princeton University Press, 1940), p. 60.

40. Tom Harrisson, *Savage Civilizations* (New York: Knopf, 1937), p. 265.

41. Katherine Mayo, *Mother India* (New York: Harcourt, Brace & Co., 1927), p. 22.

42. A. H. Clark, "Is India Dying? A Reply to 'Mother India,'" *Atlantic Monthly*, vol. 41 (1928), pp. 271-279.

43. Benjamin Kidd, *The Control of the Tropics* (New York: Macmillan Co., 1898), p. 53.

44. Maurice Fishberg, *The Jews* (New York: Scribner's Sons, 1911), p. 79ff.

45. See Karl Kautsky, *Are the Jews a Race?* (New York: International Publishers, 1926). Ashley Montagu, "Are the Jews a 'Race?'" in his *Man's Most Dangerous Myth: The Fallacy of Race*. 4th ed. (Cleveland and New York: World Publishing Co., 1964), pp. 317-338. H. L. Shapiro, *The Jewish People* (London and New York: UNESCO, 1963).

46. Shakespeare, *King Lear*, Act II, scene 2, line 21.

47. Romanzo Adams, *Interracial Marriage in Hawaii* (New York: The Macmillan Co., 1937); and M. J. Herskovits, *The American Negro* (New York: Alfred Knopf, 1927).

48. H. L. Shapiro, *Race Mixture* (New York and Paris: UNESCO, 1953). "The Creative Power of Race Mixture," in Ashley Montagu, *Man's Most Dangerous Myth: The Fallacy of Race*. 4th ed. (Cleveland and New York: World Publishing Co., 1964), pp. 185-223.

49. Edward L. Youmans (ed.), *Herbert Spencer on the Americans and the Americans on Herbert Spencer* (New York: D. Appleton & Co., 1883).

50. In *Globus*, vol. 83, pp. 14-15.

51. The newspaper *PM*, Oct. 8, 1942, cited in Carey Williams, *Brothers under the Skin* (Boston: Little, Brown & Co., 1943), p. 315.

52. A. McClung Lee, *Race Riot* (New York: Dryden Press, 1943), p. 110.

53. John Dollard, *Caste and Class in a Southern Town* (New Haven: Yale University Press, 1937), pp. 378-379.

54. Otto Klineberg, *Race Differences* (New York: Harper & Brothers, 1935), pp. 128-131.

55. W. B. Shelley, H. J. Hurley, and A. C. Nichols, "Axillary Odor," *Archives of Dermatology and Syphilology*, vol. 68 (1953), p. 430.

56. G. K. Morlan, "An Experiment on the Identification of Body Odor," *Journal of Genetic Psychology*, vol. 77 (1950), pp. 257-265.

57. Yas Kuno, *Human Perspiration* (Springfield, Illinois: C. C. Thomas, 1956), pp. 168-170.

58. Shelley, Hurley, and Nichols, *op. cit.*

59. Karl Pearson, "Relationship of Intelligence to Size and Shape of the Head and Other Mental and Physical Characters," *Biometrika*, 1906, pp. 5, 105-146. Also R. Pearl, "On the Correlation Between Intelligence and the Size of the Head," *Journal of Com. Neurology and Psychology*, 1906, pp. 189-199. Also K. Murdoch and L. R. Sullivan, "A Contribution to the Study of Mental and Physical Measurements in Normal Children," *American Phys. Educ. Review*, 1923, pp. 28, 209-215, 276-280, 328. D. G. Paterson, *Physique and Intellect* (New York: Century Co., 1930).

60. Harold Wentworth and Stuart Berg Flexner, *Dictionary of American Slang* (New York: Thomas Y. Crowell, 1960).

61. Joseph Laurent, *New Familiar Abenaki and English Dialogues* (Quebec: Leger Brousseau, 1884), pp. 136-161.

62. Esther Warner, *New Song in a Strange Land* (Boston: Houghton Mifflin, 1948), p. 7, footnote.

63. "Then said Harbonah, one of the chamberlains that were before the king, Behold also, the gallows fifty cubits high, which Haman hath made for Mordecai . . ." Book of Esther, 7:9.

64. Stephen Vincent Benét, *John Brown's Body* (Garden City: Doubleday, Doran, 1928), p. 157.

65. Vilhjalmur Stefansson, *My Life with the Eskimo*, p. 149.

66. Malinowski, *The Sexual Life of Savages*, vol. 2, pp. 303, 448 (New York: Liveright, 1929).

67. Stefansson, *The Friendly Arctic* (New York: Macmillan, 1924), p. 405; and *My Life with the Eskimo* (New York: The Macmillan Co., 1913), p. 375.

68. Saul K. Padover (ed.), *The Complete Jefferson* (New York: Tudor Publishing Co., 1943), p. 666.

69. Philip S. Foner (ed.), *Basic Writings of Thomas Jefferson* (New York: Halcyon House, Willey Book Co., 1950), p. 601.

70. *Ibid.*, p. 682.

71. Emil Ludwig, *Talks with Mussolini* (Boston: Little, Brown and Co., 1933), pp. 69-70.

72. Hermann Rauschning, *The Voice of Destruction* (New York: G. P. Putnam's Sons, 1940), p. 232.

73. R. D. G. Ph. Simons, *The Colour of the Skin in Human Relations* (Princeton, New Jersey: Elsevier Publishing Co., 1961).

74. Dwight L. Dumond, *America's Shame and Redemption* (Marquette, Michigan: Northern Michigan University Press, 1965). This is one of the most eloquent books ever written on the subject and should be required reading for every American.

6. Nonhistorical History, Heroes, and Hagiology

1. D. C. Somervell, abridgment of Toynbee's *A Study of History* (New York: Oxford University Press, 1947), p. 4.

2. Eric Partridge, *Origins* (London: Routledge & Kegan Paul, 1959), p. 70.

3. J. Boss, "Caesarean section with maternal survival among Jews in the Roman period," *Man*, vol. 61 (1961), pp. 18-19.

4. Logan Clendening, *Behind the Doctor* (New York: Alfred A. Knopf, 1933), p. 381 ff.

5. *Time*, March 3, 1967.
6. Duncan Hines, *Adventures in Good Eating* (New York, 1950), p. 268.
7. Elsdon C. Smith, *The Story of Our Names* (New York: Harper & Brothers, 1950), p. 94.
8. Richard D. Mallery, *Our American Language* (New York: Halcyon House, 1947), p. 130.
9. F. L. Cross (ed.), *The Oxford Dictionary of the Christian Church* (London: Oxford University Press, 1963).
10. Frank W. Wadsworth, *The Poacher from Stratford* (Berkeley and Los Angeles: University of California Press, 1958), pp. 58, 118, 132; and R. C. Churchill, *Shakespeare and His Betters* (Bloomington: Indiana University Press, 1959), p. 34, 37 ff.
11. Joseph Gaer, *The Lore of the Old Testament* (Boston: Little, Brown, 1951), p. 142.
12. *Ibid.*, p. 145.
13. Alister Kershaw, *A History of the Guillotine* (London: John Calder, Ltd., 1958), p. 20.
14. *Ibid.*, p. 21.
15. *Ibid.*, p. 7.
16. *Ibid.*, p. 17.
17. George F. Weston, Jr., *Boston Ways: High, By and Folk* (Boston: Beacon Press, 1957), p. 134.
18. René Vallery-Radot, *The Life of Pasteur* (Garden City: Garden City Publishing Co. [n.d]), p. xvi.
19. F. L. Cross, (ed.), *The Oxford Dictionary of the Christian Church* (London: Oxford University Press, 1963).
20. Roland Bainton, *The Horizon History of Christianity* (New York: Harper & Row, 1964), p. 47.
21. Vincent Taylor, "The Life and Ministry of Jesus," in *The Interpreter's Bible*, vol. 7 (Nashville: Abingdon-Cokesbury, 1951), p. 115.
22. Roy B. Chamberlin (ed.), *The Dartmouth Bible*, 2nd ed. (Boston: Houghton Mifflin Company, 1961), p. 968.
23. Sir Thomas Browne, *Pseudodoxia Epidemica*, vol. 1 (London, 1646), p. 134.
24. Donald C. Ringwald, *Hudson River Day Line* (Berkeley, California: Howell-North Books, 1965), pp. 1-5 and appendix p. 215.
25. Frank Donovan, *River Boats of America* (New York: Thomas Y. Crowell Co., 1966), p. 40.
26. Howard H. Quint and Robert H. Ferrell (eds.), *The Talkative President* (Amherst: University of Massachusetts Press, 1964), p. 4.
27. *Ibid.*, p. v.
28. *Ibid.*, p. 1.
29. Albert A. Trevor, *History of Ancient Civilization* (New York: Harcourt Brace & Co., 1937), p. 489. An ancient description of the ship is given in G. W. Botsford and E. G. Sihler, *Hellenic Civilization: Sources and Studies* (New York: Columbia University Press, 1915), pp. 641-646. Here the writer, Moschion the paradoxigraphist, gives "cistern" instead of "pool," and he is probably right.
30. Ruth Benedict, *Race, Science and Politics* (New York: Viking Press, 1943), p. 10.
31. E. Adamson Hoebel, *Anthropology: The Study of Man*, 3rd ed. (New York: McGraw-Hill, 1966), p. 230.

32. Marcus Tullius Cicero, *Letters to Atticus*, Loeb Classical Library, vol. 1 (London: Heinemann, 1920), p. 325.

33. Lawrence Wright, *Clean and Decent: The Unruffled History of the Bathroom and the W.C.* (New York: Viking Press, 1960), p. 14.

34. *Ibid.*

35. Philip L. Barbour, *The Three Worlds of Captain John Smith* (Boston: Houghton Mifflin Co., 1964), p. 168.

36. *Ibid.*, p. 84.

37. Paul Lewis, *The Great Rogue: A Biography of Captain John Smith* (New York: David McKay Co., 1966), p. 172.

38. Carl Sandburg, *Cool Tombs*. Quoted in Louis Untermeyer (ed.), *Modern American Poetry; Modern British Poetry* (New York: Harcourt, Brace & Co., 1950), p. 215.

39. Columbia Encyclopedia, 2nd ed. (New York: Columbia University Press, 1950).

40. Giorgio de Santillana, *The Crime of Galileo* (Chicago: University of Chicago Press, 1955), p. 5.

41. *Ibid.*, pp. xi, 290.

42. *Ibid.*, pp. 322, 323.

43. Harvey Einbinder, *The Myth of the Britannica*, pp. 1, 2, 256, 282.

44. The *New York Times Magazine*, Jan. 8, 1967: "The put-down of the year came from Cornell University. A team of experts there spent seven years and $100,000 to find out that the American bathroom . . . is 'minimal in terms of contemporary knowledge, technology, values and attitudes.'"

45. Lawrence Wright, *op. cit.*, p. 12.

46. *Ibid.*, p. 14.

47. *Ibid.*, p. 2.

48. *Ibid.*, p. 24.

49. William Graham Sumner, *Folkways* (Boston: Ginn & Co., 1906), p. 443.

50. Dr. Ralph V. Platou, Department of Pediatrics, Tulane Medical School, *New York Times*, Sept. 15, 1965.

51. FBI figures reported in *Reader's Digest Almanac* for 1967, p. 67.

52. John Bartlett, *Familiar Quotations* (Boston: Little, Brown & Co., 12th edition, 1949), p. 1168.

53. Paul F. Boller, Jr., *Quotemanship: The Use and Abuse of Quotations for Polemical and Other Purposes* (Dallas: Southern Methodist University Press, 1967), p. 324.

54. William S. Walsh, *Handy-Book of Literary Curiosities* (Detroit: Gale Research Co., 1966, reprinted from the Lippincott edition of 1892), p. 403.

55. Walsh, *op. cit.*, and J. G. Davies, *The Early Christian Church* (New York: Holt, Rinehart & Winston, 1965), p. 161.

7. Fallibilities of the Law

1. Irving and Nell Kull, *Encyclopedia of American History* (New York: Popular Library, 1965), p. 381.

2. Philip Appleman, *The Silent Explosion* (Boston: Beacon Press, 1966), p. 98.

3. Roy H. Cooperud, *Dictionary of Usage and Style* (New York: Hawthorn Books, 1964). Webster III agrees. Any crime has a *corpus delicti*, a body of substantial facts necessary to the commission of the crime.

4. Exod. 34:28; and for the Ten Commandments, Exod. 20:3 ff. and Deut. 5:7 ff.
5. Ernest P. Seelman, *The Law of Libel and Slander in the State of New York* (New York: Seelman, 1964), p. 210.
6. Eric Partridge, *Origins* (London: Routledge & Kegan Paul, 1959).
7. *Koniezny v. J. Kresseco,* New York Surrogate's Court, pp. 256, 275.
8. *In re Dougherty's Estate,* New York Surrogate's Court, Oct. 9, 1959, 194 New York Supplement, 2nd Ser., p. 50.

8. Literary and Language Legends

1. Roy H. Copperud, *A Dictionary of Usage and Style* (New York: Hawthorn Books, Inc., 1964).
2. Theodore M. Bernstein, *The Careful Writer* (New York: Atheneum, 1965).
3. Bergen and Cornelia Evans, *A Dictionary of Contemporary American Usage* (New York: Random House, 1957).
4. Robert G. Davis, School of General Studies, Columbia University, in private correspondence, 1966.
5. Marian Roalfe Cox, *Cinderella: 345 Variants* (Publications of the Folklore Society, 1892), vol. xxxi, p. 506. It is pointed out that "glass is an all but unknown material for shoe-making in the genuine folk-tales of any country except France," but in Perrault's time a *tissu en verre* did happen to be fashionable.
6. John Baker Opdycke, *Mark My Words: A Guide to Modern Usage and Expression* (New York: Harper & Brothers, 1949), p. 388.
7. *Miscegenation: The Theory of the Blending of the Races, Applied to the American White Man and the Negro.* The work is attributed to David Goodman Croly and George Wakeman by J. M. Bloch, *Miscegenation, Melaleukation and Mr. Lincoln's Dog* (New York: Schaum, 1958), and to David Goodman Croly by Mitford M. Mathews (ed.), *A Dictionary of Americanisms on Historical Principles* (Chicago: University of Chicago Press, 1951). It has been newspaper tradition for many years that these men were the authors and publishers of the pamphlet, and there has so far been no hint from any direction that such is not the case.
8. Cited in Mathews, *op. cit.*
9. Schele De Vere, *Americanisms: The English of the New World,* cited in Mathews, *op. cit.*
10. Mathews, *op. cit.*
11. In paperback reprints both by Macmillan, the original publisher, and by Beacon Press.
12. Ashley Montagu, *Man's Most Dangerous Myth,* 4th rev. ed. (New York: World Publishing Co., 1964), p. 400.
13. E. L. McAdam, Jr., and George Milne, *Johnson's Dictionary: A Modern Selection* (New York: Random House, 1963), p. 319.
14. Eric Partridge, *Origins: A Short Etymological Dictionary of Modern English* (New York: The Macmillan Co., 1959), p. 363.

9. The Mythical World of Nature

1. Special report to the *Christian Science Monitor,* March 14, 1966.
2. The facts about quicksand were developed by Lawrence Perez, Director

of the Soil Mechanics Laboratory at Cooper Union. His findings were
summarized in *Science Digest*, June, 1941, p. 16.

3. Vilhjalmur Stefansson, *The Friendly Arctic* (New York: The Macmillan Co.), pp. 14, 602.
4. Richard Hofstadter, *Social Darwinism in American Thought 1860-1915* (Boston: Beacon Press, 1955), p. 39.
5. Harris E. Starr, *William Graham Sumner* (New York: Henry Holt, 1925), p. 258.
6. Rand McNally World Guide, selected and adapted from the Columbia Lippincott Gazetteer of the World, Chicago, 1953, p. 256. The *Gazetteer* was published by Columbia University Press in 1952, and, according to Andrew McNally III's Preface, "This was the first major world gazetteer in English to appear in nearly half a century." The book, therefore, can be taken as a *contemporary* authority.
7. *Natural History Magazine*, January, 1951.
8. Maria Leach and Jerome Fried (eds.), *Standard Dictionary of Folklore, Mythology and Legend* (New York: Funk & Wagnalls, 1950), vol. 2, p. 62.
9. Frank H. Forrester, *1001 Questions Answered about the Weather* (New York: Dodd, Mead & Co., 1957), p. 156.
10. Richard Inwards (ed.), *Weather Lore* (London: Rider & Co., 1950), p. 171.
11. Sir Napier Shaw, "The Artificial Control of Weather," an abstract reprinted from the *Meteorological Magazine*, April, 1921, p. 60 f., in *Monthly Weather Review*, April, 1921, p. 244.
12. Richard Inwards, *op. cit.*, p. 170.
13. *Ibid.*
14. Fred Gladstone Bratton, *A History of the Bible* (Boston: Beacon Press, 1959), p. ix.
15. Robert H. Pfeiffer, *The Books of the Old Testament* (New York: Harper & Row, Chapelbook paperback, 1965), p. 5.
16. *Ibid.*, p. 8.
17. Lorus and Margery Milne, *The Balance of Nature* (New York: Alfred A. Knopf, 1960), p. 217.
18. John Stewart Collis, *The Triumph of the Tree* (New York: Viking Press, Inc., Explorer Books, 1960), p. 212.
19. Lorus and Margery Milne, *op. cit.*, p. 199. The tall-grass plain they refer to is "Tucker Prairie," 15 miles east of Columbia, Missouri, now a reservation.
20. Clive Turnbull, *Black War: The Extermination of the Tasmanian Aborigines* (Melbourne: Cheshire, 1948); Alan Morehead, *The Fatal Impact* (New York: Harper & Row, 1965); Ronald Segal, *The Race War* (New York: Viking Press, Inc., 1967).
21. Emmanuel G. Mesthene, "What Modern Science Offers the Church," *Saturday Review*, Nov. 19, 1966. Mesthene is executive director of Harvard University Program on Technology and Society.
22. Figures from the Population Division, UN, as reported in *Reader's Digest Almanac for 1967*, p. 177.
23. Figures from U.S. Public Health Service, *ibid.*, p. 606.
24. Orville L. Freeman, U.S. Secretary of Agriculture, speaking at St. Paul as reported in the *New York Times*, Oct. 24, 1966.

10. More Nonsense—About Other Animals

1. George Schaeffer, *The Mountain Gorilla* (Chicago: University of Chicago Press, 1963).
2. Alister C. Hardy, *The Open Sea* (Boston: Houghton Mifflin, 1956), p. 254.
3. Stephen Polyak, *The Retina* (Chicago: University of Chicago Press, 1941). Gordon L. Walls, *The Vertebrate Eye* (Bloomfield Hills, Michigan: Cranbrook Institute of Science, 1942), p. 228.
4. Edward Topsell, *The History of Four-Footed Beasts* (London: E. Cotes, 1658).
5. Gillian Tindall, *A Handbook of Witches* (New York: Atheneum, 1966), p. 99.
6. George Lyman Kittredge, *Witchcraft in Old and New England* (New York: Russell & Russell, 1956), p. 496.
7. Max Lerner, *America as a Civilization* (New York: Simon & Schuster, 1957), p. 640.
8. *Shakespeare's England* (Oxford: The Clarendon Press, 1926), Vol. 1, p. 485.
9. T. H. White, *The Bestiary: A Book of Beasts* (New York: G. P. Putnam's Sons, 1960, Capricorn paperback ed.), p. 45.
10. Chalmers Mitchell, *The Childhood of Animals* (New York: Stokes, 1913), p. 17.
11. Gerald Durrell, *Two in the Bush* (New York: Viking Press, 1966).
12. Desmond Morris, *The Mammals* (New York: Harper & Row, 1966), p. 50.
13. T. H. White, *op cit.*, p. 95.
14. *Henry IV, Part I*, Act III, scene 1, line 148.
15. Eric Partridge, *Origins* (London: Routledge & Kegan Paul, 1959).
16. Roger A. Caras, *Dangerous to Man* (Philadelphia: Chilton Books, 1964), p. 12.
17. Maria Leach and Jerome Fried (eds.), *Dictionary of Folklore* (New York: Funk & Wagnalls, 1949).
18. Lorus and Margery Milne, *The Balance of Nature* (New York: Alfred A. Knopf, 1960), p. 107.
19. Lloyd Lewis, *Myths after Lincoln* (Gloucester, Mass.: Peter Smith, n.d.).
20. Manly Wade Wellman, *Who Fears the Devil?* (New York: Ballantine Books).
21. George R. Stewart, *Names on the Land* (New York: Random House, 1945), p. 11.
22. Peter Putnam, *The Triumph of the Seeing Eye* (New York: Harper & Row, 1963), p. 103.
23. *Guiness Book of World Records*, 1966 ed., p. 29.
24. T. H. White, *op. cit.*, pp. 7, 9.
25. E. L. McAdam, Jr., and George Milne (eds.), *Johnson's Dictionary: A Modern Selection* (New York: Pantheon Books, 1963), p. 236.
26. Roger A. Caras, *op. cit.*, pp. 13-15.

Index